Selected Topics in the Classical Theory of Functions of a Complex Variable

Athena Series

SELECTED TOPICS IN MATHEMATICS

Edwin Hewitt, *Editor*

AMBROSE-LAZEROWITZ: Logic: The Theory of Formal Inference

BELLMAN: A Brief Introduction to Theta Functions

CARDANO: The Book on Games of Chance

ERDÉLYI: Operational Calculus and Generalized Functions

FICKEN: The Simplex Method of Linear Programming

HEINS: Selected Topics in the Classical Theory of Functions of a Complex Variable

HIRSCHMAN: Infinite Series

HOCHSTADT: Special Functions of Mathematical Physics

KAZARINOFF: Analytic Inequalities

WILLIAMSON: Lebesgue Integration

Maurice Heins
University of Illinois

Selected Topics in the Classical Theory of Functions of a Complex Variable

HOLT, RINEHART AND WINSTON
New York

Library of Congress Catalog Card Number: 61-7856

23548—0112

Printed in the United States of America

Preface

Maître de philosophie : ... et vous savez le latin, sans doute ?
Monsieur Jourdain : Oui; mais faites comme je ne le savais pas.

Molière, *Le Bourgeois Gentilhomme*,
Act 2, Scene 4.

This text is intended for mathematics students who have had or are completing a first course in the theory of functions of a complex variable. Its object is to present to such students a number of important topics from the theory of analytic functions which may be treated without erecting an elaborate superstructure. We have in mind such theorems as the big Picard theorem, the Riemann mapping theorem, and the Fatou radial-limit theorem. These are all results that, as the student must have heard, are among the most celebrated in the theory of analytic functions. Yet they do not generally find their way into a first course. As matters stand at the present time, it is an attractive assignment in mathematical exposition to give to such an audience an account of the theorems cited above and other results that meet the stipulations that the preliminaries should not be discouraging at this stage of the student's development and that, at the same time, the theorems brought forth should be consequential and worthy of the repertoire of the serious mathematics student.

The mathematical background (apart from the elements of the theory of functions of a complex variable) of the students to whom this book is directed varies greatly. It is reasonable to assume that they are well-acquainted with elementary real analysis and have some knowledge of general topology. In my experience, however, it is not reasonable to expect a knowledge of integration and measure theory, let alone even a modest introduction (of a nonformal kind) to the theory of Fourier series. Such material will not be presupposed. What is needed from real-variable theory will be developed in the book. Even from the elements of the theory of functions of a complex variable only a small amount will be required. A student conversant with the material of the first volume of Knopp's *Theory of Functions* should find that no excessive demands are made on his knowledge of complex-function theory.

We are by no means advocating that the student do without a solid grounding in Lebesgue theory. Far from it. Rather, our point is that he will benefit from encountering, prior to or at the inception of an intensive study of Lebesgue theory, areas of mathematical thought that add to the body of evidence that the Lebesgue theory plays an indispensable role in the study of many important classes of functions.

In my teaching I have found it desirable to present certain topics via (finite) sequences of exercises rendered accessible by adequate indications of the essential difficulties. The active participation of the student in developing the mathematics being studied is a very valuable part of the learning process. Of course, the use of such sequences of exercises is not new. The *Aufgaben und Lehrsätze* of Professors Pólya and Szegö remains a model for this method of exposition. In the present book certain topics will be so presented. For example, we introduce early via a problem set a minimal account of Fourier series and their connection with complex analysis. Another topic so treated is the proof of the Riemann mapping theorem using Koebe's method. Once the fundamentals are outlined, the elaboration of the details is well within the reach of the intended student. Professors Pólya and Szegö are my predecessors here.

The logarithm of the modulus of an analytic function is a subharmonic function; this fact subsumes a body of the theorems about the modulus of an analytic function under the theory of subharmonic functions. Because of this, the ideas of F. Riesz, to whom the theory of subharmonic functions is due, will be much in evidence—but not for this reason only. It is also thanks to Riesz that such fundamental results as Lebesgue's theorem on the derivative of a monotone function have been given proofs striking for both elegance and clarity. The Fatou theorem looks to Lebesgue's theorem in a natural way. The importance of the role of Riesz's proof of the Lebesgue theorem for our purposes is obvious. The work of F. Riesz will be seen to have contributed much to the special character of this book.

The theory of functions of a complex variable has been aptly called by Professor Ahlfors a mathematical microcosm organically interrelated with many branches of mathematics—certainly with real-function theory, topology, differential geometry, and algebra. The historical result of these relations has been a cross fertilization of these several fields. The theory of functions of a complex variable has yielded interesting examples for the fields we have mentioned, and they in turn have furnished methods and milieux for new problems concerning analytic functions. In this book we seek to indicate something of the cohesion between the theory of functions of a complex variable and other branches of mathematics. Of course, we can do this only in an extremely limited way, given the level at which the present work is written. The point of view is important, however, and deserves emphasis as an idea to be planted.

Some of the material we treat is to be found in the standard treatises on the theory of functions of a complex variable, for example, Ahlfors's *Complex Analysis*, Saks-Zygmund's *Analytic Functions*, Carathéodory's *Funktionentheorie* (also in English translation), and the monographs of Landau (*Neuere Ergebnisse der Funktionentheorie*) and of Julia (*Principes géométriques d'analyse*).

We have also found it possible to introduce some results obtained in the last few decades which we regard as thoroughly accessible to the student we have tried to describe in the early paragraphs of this preface. In this category we mention a method of Carleman (see Chap. 5, § 11) an account of which has not hitherto been given in monographic form.

For suggested reading, we have given references at various places to papers in mathematics journals. These papers, readily available in American college libraries, are mathematically accessible to our student.

Note to second corrected printing: It was possible to incorporate all corrections and additions save two in the body of the text. In these two cases (pages 50 and 82) the reader is referred by numerical superscripts to the notes on page 156.

Contents

[1]

Preliminaries

1. Terminology, Notation, Chordal Metric, and Topology of the Extended Plane. It will be convenient to list here for future reference some notation and terminology that will be constantly used throughout the present work.

Notation.

$$\begin{aligned} N &= \text{set of nonnegative integers,} \\ I &= \text{set of integers,} \\ R &= \text{set of real numbers,} \\ K &= \text{set of complex numbers,} \\ \hat{K} &= \text{extended complex plane, that is, } K \text{ with the element } \infty \text{ adjoined.} \end{aligned} \tag{1.1}$$

Given a set A and $E \subset A$, the complement of E with respect to A will be denoted by $A - E$.

Given $a \in \hat{K}$ and r a positive real number or $+\infty$, $\Delta(a; r)$ denotes

$$\{z \mid |z - a| < r\} \tag{1.2}$$

when $a \in K$, and

$$\{z \mid |z| > r^{-1}\} \tag{1.3}$$

when $a = \infty$. We write (1.2) and (1.3) more briefly as $\{|z - a| < r\}$ and $\{|z| > r^{-1}\}$ respectively and shall follow this practice in describing sets when there is no likelihood of confusion. Similarly, $C(a; r)$ denotes

$$\{|z - a| = r\} \tag{1.4}$$

or

$$\{|z| = r^{-1}\}, \tag{1.5}$$

according as $a \neq \infty$ or $a = \infty$. That is, $\Delta(a; r)$ is the open circular disk with center a (respectively, ∞) and radius r (respectively, r^{-1}), and, similarly, $C(a; r)$ is the corresponding circumference.

Chordal Metric. In the study of meromorphic functions, whose definition we shall recall explicitly later, it is very convenient for many purposes to employ the chordal metric which was introduced in the theory of functions of a complex variable by Carathéodory (cf. C. Carathéodory, *Theory of Functions*, chap. 3, vol. 1. *New York*: Chelsea Publishing Company). We define this as follows. Let S denote the spherical surface in (x_1, x_2, x_3) space with center $(0, 0, \frac{1}{2})$ and radius $\frac{1}{2}$, and let π denote the *stereographic projection* of S onto $\hat{K}$, that is, the map that carries the north pole of S into ∞ and a point $(x_1, x_2, x_3) \in S$ not the north pole into $\xi_1 + i\xi_2$, where $(\xi_1, \xi_2, 0)$ is the point of intersection of the plane $\{x_3 = 0\}$ with the line through the north pole of S and (x_1, x_2, x_3). The *chordal distance* between points a and b of $\hat{K}$, denoted by $[a, b]$, is simply the euclidean distance between $\pi^{-1}(a)$ and $\pi^{-1}(b)$, π^{-1} being the inverse of the map π. It is a matter of straightforward computation using the explicit formula for π^{-1} to verify that

$$[a,b] = \frac{|a - b|}{\sqrt{1 + |a|^2}\sqrt{1 + |b|^2}} \tag{1.6}$$

when a and b both belong to K, and that

$$[a,\infty] = \frac{1}{\sqrt{1 + |a|^2}} . \tag{1.7}$$

EXERCISE

1. Verify formulas (1.6) and (1.7).

Topology of $\hat{K}$. A subset O of $\hat{K}$ will be termed *open* provided that for each point z belonging to O there exists a disk $\Delta(z; r)$ contained in O. The family of open subsets of $\hat{K}$ so defined endows $\hat{K}$ with a Hausdorff topology, which we shall term the *topology of the extended plane*. The open sets of the finite plane in the sense of the topology of the extended plane are precisely the open sets in the sense of the standard topology of the finite plane.

$\hat{K}$ is *compact* in the sense of the topology of the extended plane. That is, if $(O_\lambda)_{\lambda \in \Lambda}$ is a family of open sets of $\hat{K}$ whose union is $\hat{K}$, then there exists a finite subfamily $(O_{\lambda_k})_{k=1,2,\cdots,n}$ whose union is already $\hat{K}$. It suffices to consider a member O_μ of the family $(O_\lambda)_{\lambda \in \Lambda}$ such that O_μ contains ∞ and to observe that $\hat{K} - O_\mu$ is bounded and closed in the topology of K. Hence, applying the Heine-Borel-Lebesgue theorem to the open covering of $\hat{K} - O_\mu$ obtained by replacing the O_λ by $O_\lambda \cap K$, we see that the compactness of $\hat{K}$ follows at once.

It is essential to distinguish clearly between the subsets of K closed in the sense of the topology of K and those subsets closed in the sense of the topology of $\hat{K}$. Every subset F of K closed in the second sense is closed in the first sense. However, the converse is not true. It is easily seen that a subset E of K is closed in the sense of the $\hat{K}$ topology if, and only if, it is bounded and closed (in the sense of the K topology).

EXERCISE

2. The chordal distance $[a, b]$ endows $\hat{K}$ with a metric space structure. Show that the topology we have introduced on $\hat{K}$ is the same as that induced by the chordal metric. In other words, a set $E \subset \hat{K}$ is open in the sense given in the text if, and only if, for each $a \in E$ there exists $r > 0$ such that whenever $[a, z] < r$, $z \in E$. The set $\{[a, z] < r\}$ is readily interpreted in terms of the stereographic projection.

Region. This term will be reserved for a nonempty open connected subset of $\hat{K}$. We recall that a subset E of a topological space X is termed *connected* provided that there do not exist open subsets O_1, O_2 of X satisfying: $O_k \cap E \neq \emptyset$, $k = 1,2$; $O_1 \cap O_2 \cap E = \emptyset$; $E \subset O_1 \cup O_2$. A *path* in X is a continuous map P of the closed unit interval $\{0 \leqslant t \leqslant 1\}$ into X. Given $E \subset X$, we say that P *lies in* E provided that $P(t) \in E$, $0 \leqslant t \leqslant 1$. The subset E is termed *arcwise connected* provided that whenever $a,b \in E$, there exists a path P lying in E such that $P(0) = a$, $P(1) = b$. It is easy to show that if E is arcwise connected, then E is connected. The standard argument is based on observing that $\{0 \leqslant t \leqslant 1\}$ is connected and that if E were not connected and O_1, O_2 satisfied the stated conditions, then a path P lying in E satisfying $P(0) \in O_1$, $P(1) \in O_2$ would be such that $P^{-1}(O_1)$ and $P^{-1}(O_2)$ would be open (in the topology of the closed unit interval) nonempty disjoint subsets of the closed unit interval and would have as their union the closed unit interval. The connectedness of $\{0 \leqslant t \leqslant 1\}$ would be violated.

The converse is not true. For example, the closure (in the sense of the topology of K) of

$$\left\{x + iy \mid y = \sin \frac{1}{x}, \quad x \in R - \{0\}\right\}$$

is connected but not arcwise connected. However, it is the case that a region Ω in $\hat{K}$ is arcwise connected. This fact is readily established as follows. Let $a \in \Omega$, let O_1 denote the set of points $z \in \Omega$ such that there exists a path P lying in Ω with $P(0) = a$ and $P(1) = z$, and let $O_2 = \Omega - O_1$. Then it is easily verified that O_1 and O_2 are open. For example, if $b \in O_1$ and $\Delta(b; r) \subset \Omega$ and if P is a path lying in Ω such that $P(0) = a$ and $P(1) = b$, then Q defined by $Q(t) = P(2t)$ for $0 \leqslant t \leqslant \frac{1}{2}$ and $Q(t) = (2t - 1)z + (2 - 2t)b$ for $\frac{1}{2} \leqslant t \leqslant 1$, where $z \in \Delta(b; r)$, is a path of the desired type when $b \in K$. This construction is readily modified when $b = \infty$. An analogous argument shows that O_2 is open. Hence $O_2 = \emptyset$. Since a is arbitrary, it follows that Ω is arcwise connected.

2. The Cauchy-Goursat Theorem. We recall some essential facts concerning the Cauchy-Goursat theorem (there will be no question of treating refined formulations of this theorem until the last part of the book). In classical function theory we may go quite far with very simple versions of the Cauchy-Goursat theorem.

In order to have a standard terminology, we shall agree to the following usage. We say that a complex-valued function f is *analytic* at $a \in \hat{K}$ provided the domain of f is a neighborhood of a and that if a is finite, f possesses a derivative at each point of some neighborhood of a, while if $a = \infty$, $z \to f(1/z)$ possesses a derivative at each point of some neighborhood of 0. [The notation

"$z \to f(1/z)$" is used here to indicate a function satisfying the following conditions: (a) its domain is a neighborhood of 0 such that $1/z$ is in the domain of f for z in this neighborhood; (b) it assigns to z the value $f(1/z)$. In general the arrow will be used to indicate, as in this special case, ordered pairs of a function whose domain is clear from context, the "element" preceding the arrow being in the domain of the function.] We say that f is *analytic in* an open set $O \subset \hat{K}$ provided that f is analytic at each point of O, and finally we say that f is *analytic on* O provided that the domain of f is O and f is analytic in O.

The Cauchy-Goursat Theorem for a Triangle. Let $z_1,z_2,z_3 \in K$, let T denote the convex hull of $\{z_1,z_2,z_3\}$, and let f denote a function analytic at each point of T. The Cauchy-Goursat theorem for a triangle asserts that

$$\int_\gamma f(z)\, dz = 0 \tag{2.1}$$

where γ is the path satisfying the conditions: $\gamma(0) = \gamma(1) = z_1$, $\gamma(1/3) = z_2$, $\gamma(2/3) = z_3$, and γ is linear on each of the closed intervals $\{k/3 \leqslant t \leqslant (k+1)/3\}$, $k = 0,1,2$. We recall that a *convex set* $C \subset K$ is a set having the property that whenever a, $b \in C$, the segment $\overline{ab} = \{(1-\lambda)a + \lambda b \mid 0 \leqslant \lambda \leqslant 1\}$ is contained in C. Further, if $E \subset K$, then by the *convex hull* of E is meant the smallest convex subset of K containing E. If $E = \{z_1,z_2,z_3\}$, then the convex hull of E is

$$\left\{\sum_1^3 \lambda_k z_k \mid \lambda_k \geqslant 0\,, \sum \lambda_k = 1\right\}.$$

From this starting point a large number of basic theorems can be obtained. An immediate application is to the problem of determining the *primitives* of an analytic function locally. We recall that if f is an analytic function on an open set $O \subset K$, a function g with domain O is termed a *primitive* of f provided that

$$g' = f. \tag{2.2}$$

If f does possess a primitive g, then the primitives of f are the functions of the form

$$g + k\,,$$

where k is constant on each component of O. Now if f is analytic on $\Delta(a; r)$ where a is finite, then it is easily verified that g, defined by

$$g(z) = \int_{\overrightarrow{az}} f(\zeta)\, d\zeta\,, \quad z \in \Delta(a; r)\,, \tag{2.3}$$

where $\overrightarrow{az}$ is the path $(1-t)a + tz$, $0 \leqslant t \leqslant 1$, is a primitive of f. Further, if γ is a rectifiable path lying in $\Delta(a; r)$, then

$$\int_\gamma f(z)\, dz = g(\gamma(1)) - g(\gamma(0))\,. \tag{2.4}$$

This tells us that locally the integral of f depends only on the initial and terminal points of the path. The proof of (2.4) hinges on the uniform continuity of f on a compact subset of $\Delta(a; r)$ and the rectifiability of γ. We introduce a finite sequence $(t_k)_0^n$, where $0 = t_0 < t_1 < \cdots < t_n = 1$, and let $z_k = \gamma(t_k)$. From

$$\int_\gamma f(z)\,dz - \Big[g(\gamma(1)) - g(\gamma(0))\Big]$$

$$= \int_\gamma f(z)\,dz - \sum_{k=0}^{n-1} \Big[g(z_{k+1}) - g(z_k)\Big]$$

$$= \int_\gamma f(z)\,dz - \sum_{k=0}^{n-1} \int_{\Gamma_k} f(z)\,dz$$

$$= \Big\{\int_\gamma f(z)\,dz - \sum_{k=0}^{n-1} f(z_k)\,(z_{k+1} - z_k)\Big\} + \sum_{k=0}^{n-1} \int_{\Gamma_k} [f(z_k) - f(z)]\,dz\,,$$

where $\Gamma_k(t) = (1-t)z_k + tz_{k+1}$, $0 \leqslant t \leqslant 1$, it is easy to conclude (2.4) on considering partitions $(t_k)_0^n$ for which $\max_k |t_{k+1} - t_k|$ is sufficiently small.

An important step in the further development of the Cauchy theory consists in establishing a theorem of the following type:

THEOREM 2.1. *Let f be analytic on a region $\Omega \subset K$. Let φ denote a continuous map of the closed unit square $\sigma = \{0 \leqslant s,\ t \leqslant 1\}$ into Ω. Let γ be the path defined by*

$$\gamma(t) = \varphi(4t,0),\ 0 \leqslant t \leqslant \tfrac{1}{4};$$

$$\gamma(t) = \varphi(3-4t,1),\ \tfrac{1}{2} < t \leqslant \tfrac{3}{4};$$

$$\gamma(t) = \varphi(1,4t-1),\ \tfrac{1}{4} < t \leqslant \tfrac{1}{2};$$

$$\gamma(t) = \varphi(0,4-4t),\ \tfrac{3}{4} < t \leqslant 1.$$

It is assumed that γ is rectifiable. Then

$$\int_\gamma f(z)\,dz = 0. \tag{2.5}$$

Of course, γ is the path obtained by composition with φ from the peripheral path of the unit square taken in standard form.

We indicate a proof of this theorem given by F. M. Stewart. Use is made of the fact that f has a primitive locally. Let n denote a positive integer. Let

$$z_{i,j}^n = \varphi\Big(\frac{i}{n}, \frac{j}{n}\Big), \quad i,j = 0, \cdots, n.$$

Let m denote the distance between $\varphi(\sigma)$ and $K - \Omega$. Clearly, $m > 0\,(= +\infty$ if $\Omega = K)$. We fix n so that whenever (s_1,t_1) and (s_2,t_2) are two points of σ whose distance is at most $\sqrt{2}/n$, then

$$| \varphi(s_2,t_2) - \varphi(s_1,t_1) | < m\,,$$

which is possible thanks to the uniform continuity of φ. Now let $g_{i,j}$ denote a primitive of the restriction of f to $\Delta(z^n_{i,j};\, m)$. It is obvious that

$$0 = [g_{i,j}(z^n_{i+1,j}) - g_{i,j}(z^n_{i,j})] + [g_{i,j}(z^n_{i+1,j+1}) - g_{i,j}(z^n_{i+1,j})]$$
$$+ [g_{i,j}(z^n_{i,j+1}) - g_{i,j}(z^n_{i+1,j+1})] + [g_{i,j}(z^n_{i,j}) - g_{i,j}(z^n_{i,j+1})]\,. \tag{2.6}$$

We note that $g_{i,j}$ and $g_{i+1,j}$ differ by a constant on the intersection of their domains, since this intersection is a region. A corresponding remark holds for $g_{i,j}$ and $g_{i,j+1}$. We sum both sides of (2.6) for $i,j = 0,\cdots,n-1$, taking into account the cancellations that result thanks to the facts just stated. Applying (2.4) to the remaining contributions to the sum on the right, we obtain (2.5).

Theorem 2.1 admits a large number of applications. For example, it may be used to give a homology-theoretic formulation of the Cauchy theory (cf. L. V. Ahlfors, *Complex Analysis. New York*: McGraw-Hill Book Company, 1953). We shall not be concerned with this question in the present monograph, but the importance of Theorem 2.1 in this connection is worth mention. If we take φ such that $t \to \varphi(0,t)$ and $t \to \varphi(1,t)$ are both constant, we are led to the *homotopic* version of the Cauchy integral theorem:

THEOREM 2.2. *Let f be analytic on a region $\Omega \subset K$. Let γ_1 and γ_2 be rectifiable paths lying in Ω such that there exists a continuous map φ of $\{0 \leqslant t,\ \tau \leqslant 1\}$ into Ω satisfying:*

$$\varphi(t,0) = \gamma_1(t),\ \varphi(t,1) = \gamma_2(t), \qquad 0 \leqslant t \leqslant 1;$$
$$\varphi(0,\tau) = \gamma_1(0),\ \varphi(1,\tau) = \gamma_1(1), \qquad 0 \leqslant \tau \leqslant 1.$$

Then
$$\int_{\gamma_1} f(z)\,dz = \int_{\gamma_2} f(z)\,dz. \tag{2.7}$$

The notion of *simple connectivity* may be given any of a number of formulations. We shall say that a region $\subset \hat{K}$ is *homotopically simply-connected* provided that for every path γ lying in Ω and having the same initial and terminal point, i.e., for which $\gamma(0) = \gamma(1)$, there exists a continuous map of $\{0 \leqslant t,\ \tau \leqslant 1\}$ into Ω satisfying $\varphi(t,0) = \gamma(t)$, $0 \leqslant t \leqslant 1$; $\varphi(t,1) = \gamma(0)$, $0 \leqslant t \leqslant 1$; $\varphi(0,\tau) = \varphi(1,\tau) = \gamma(0)$, $0 \leqslant \tau \leqslant 1$. It is now easily verified that if, in the homotopic version of the Cauchy integral theorem, Ω is taken to be homotopically simply-connected, then (2.7) holds for all admitted f and γ_1 and γ_2.

We shall say that a region $\subset K$ is *holomorphically simply-connected* provided that (2.7) holds for f analytic on Ω and γ_1 and γ_2 rectifiable paths in Ω satisfying $\gamma_1(0) = \gamma_2(0)$, $\gamma_1(1) = \gamma_2(1)$. Thus we see that a homotopically simply-connected region $\subset K$ is holomorphically simply-connected. We shall see that the converse is true, and even more, thanks to the Riemann mapping theorem. Indeed, a holomorphically simply-connected region will be seen to admit a univalent conformal map onto $\Delta(0;1)$ or $\Delta(0;\infty)$.

Primitives. If $\Omega \subset K$ is such that every analytic function on Ω admits a primitive, then Ω is holomorphically simply-connected. For suppose that f, γ_1, γ_2 are given as in the definition of holomorphic simple connectivity. Let g denote a primitive of f and let $\gamma_1(0) = a$, $\gamma_1(1) = b$. Then

$$\int_{\gamma_k} f(z)\, dz = g(b) - g(a), \qquad k = 1,2. \tag{2.8}$$

[The proof is an immediate consequence of the local version (2.4).]

Conversely, suppose that Ω is holomorphically simply-connected and let f be analytic on Ω. We may construct a primitive of f as follows. Fix a point $a \in \Omega$. Let Γ denote the class of rectifiable paths γ lying in Ω that satisfy $\gamma(0) = a$. We introduce

$$g = \left\{(\gamma(1), \textstyle\int_\gamma f(z)\, dz) \mid \gamma \in \Gamma\right\}. \tag{2.9}$$

Thanks to the fact that Ω is holomorphically simply-connected, it is easily seen that g is a function with domain Ω. The verification that $g' = f$ is routine. Thus we see that holomorphic simple connectivity of a region $\subset K$ is equivalent to the existence of a primitive for each analytic function on the region.

EXERCISE

1. Suppose that $\Omega \subset K$ is a region and that for some $a \in \Omega$, each path γ lying in Ω and satisfying $\gamma(0) = \gamma(1) = a$ has the property that there exists a continuous map φ of $\{0 \leqslant t, \tau \leqslant 1\}$ into Ω satisfying: $\varphi(t,0) = \gamma(t)$, $0 \leqslant t \leqslant 1$; $\varphi(t,1) \equiv$ const.; $\varphi(0,\tau) = \varphi(1,\tau)$, $0 \leqslant \tau \leqslant 1$. Show that Ω is holomorphically simply-connected.

Analytic Logarithm of a Nonvanishing Analytic Function. Given f analytic on a region Ω and vanishing at no point of Ω. We are led to inquire whether there exists a function g *analytic* on Ω and satisfying

$$f = \exp \circ g. \tag{2.10}$$

Such a function g is called an *analytic* logarithm of f, for obvious reasons. Clearly, if such a g exists, the totality of analytic logarithms of f consists precisely of the functions $g_n = g + 2\pi i n$, $n \in I$ (for the purist, here $2\pi i n$ stands for the constant function on Ω taking the value $2\pi in$). Under what circumstances does such a g exist? If g exists, by (2.10) we have

$$\frac{f'(z)}{f(z)} = g'(z), \qquad z \in \Omega \cap K. \tag{2.11}$$

That is, the logarithmic derivative of the restriction of f to $\Omega \cap K$ has a primitive.

The converse is also true. Let g denote a function analytic on $\Omega \cap K$ satisfying (2.11) and $e^{g(z_0)} = f(z_0)$ for some $z_0 \in \Omega \cap K$. If $\infty \in \Omega$, g has a removable singularity at ∞, because of the fact that the logarithmic derivative of f vanishes to at least the second order at ∞. Noting that

$$(fe^{-g})' = 0\,,$$

we conclude that $f(z) = e^{g(z)}$, $z \in \Omega \cap K$. Hence g is an analytic logarithm of f when $\Omega \subset K$, and the analytic prolongation of g to Ω is an analytic logarithm of f when $\infty \in \Omega$. To sum up, we have

Theorem 2.3. *A function f analytic on a region Ω and vanishing nowhere admits an analytic logarithm if and only if the logarithmic derivative of the restriction of f to $\Omega \cap K$ has a primitive. If Ω is holomorphically simply-connected, every f analytic on Ω and vanishing nowhere has an analytic logarithm.*

In the following chapter the importance of Theorem 2.3 will become abundantly clear. For the present we give some exercises based on this theorem.

EXERCISES

2. Let ι denote the identity map of $\{\operatorname{Re} z > 0\}$ onto itself; that is, $\iota(z) = z$, $\operatorname{Re} z > 0$. Then the analytic logarithm L of ι normalized by $L(1) = 0$ is given by

$$L(z) = \int_1^z t^{-1}\, dt\,.$$

3. Given f analytic on a region Ω and vanishing nowhere. Suppose that f possesses an analytic logarithm g. Let n denote a positive integer. Then the analytic functions h on Ω satisfying $h^n = f$ are precisely the functions

$$\omega^k \exp \circ (g/n), \; k = 0,1,\cdots,n-1,$$

where $\omega = e^{2\pi i/n}$. We term the h the *analytic* nth *roots* of f.

4. Given a finite complex-valued continuous function f on a topological space X. It is assumed that f vanishes nowhere. By a *continuous logarithm* of f is meant a continuous complex-valued function g on X satisfying $f = \exp \circ g$. If such a function exists, it is determined additively up to a function that is constant on each component of X and takes values of the form $2\pi in$, $n \in I$.

The notion of the continuous logarithm is important in certain topological investigations (cf. Eilenberg, *Thesis*, and Kuratowski, *Topologie* II).

Suppose that f is analytic on a region Ω and that f vanishes nowhere. Show that if g is a continuous logarithm of f, then g is in fact analytic on Ω.

The notion of a continuous nth root of a continuous function (not necessarily nonvanishing) is analogously defined. The formulation is left to the reader. Suppose that f is analytic on a region Ω and that n is a positive integer. Show that if h is a continuous nth root of f, then h is analytic on Ω. Note that the nonvanishing of f is not assumed.

5. Binomial series. (This exercise finds its historical roots in the investigations of Abel concerning the binomial series.) Let $\alpha \in K$ and let $\binom{\alpha}{k}$ denote the kth binomial coefficient, which is defined recursively by

$$\binom{\alpha}{0} = 1, \qquad \binom{\alpha}{k+1} = \binom{\alpha}{k}\frac{\alpha - k}{k+1}, \qquad k \in N$$

The series

$$\sum_{k=0}^{\infty} \binom{\alpha}{k} z^k \tag{a}$$

converges for $|z| < 1$ when $\alpha \in K - N$ and trivially for all z otherwise. Let $A(z;\alpha)$ denote the sum of the series (a). Then

$$A(z;\alpha) = \exp\,[\alpha L(1+z)], \qquad |z| < 1,$$

where L is the function defined in Ex. 2 of this set.

---

3. Meromorphic Functions. It will be convenient to assemble in this section some of the basic facts concerning meromorphic functions. We are concerned with functions whose domain and range both lie in $\hat{K}$. A function f is said to be *meromorphic at* a provided that the domain of f is a neighborhood of a, that there exists $r > 0$ such that $\Delta(a;r)$ is contained in the domain of f and f is analytic in $\Delta(a;r) - \{a\}$, and finally that f is continuous (in the $\hat{K}$ sense) at a. A function f is *meromorphic in* a region (or open set) Ω provided that f is meromorphic at each point of Ω. Finally, a function f is said to be *meromorphic on* a region (or open set) Ω provided that it is meromorphic in Ω and that its domain is Ω.

If f is meromorphic in a region Ω and is not constant, then the set $\{z \mid f(z) = a\}$ clusters at no point of Ω. This is obvious for $a = \infty$. For $a \neq \infty$, it suffices to consider f on Ω less the poles of f.

Given f meromorphic at a, the *multiplicity of* f *at* a, denoted $n(a;f)$, is defined as follows: If $a \neq \infty$ and

$$\sum_{-\infty}^{+\infty} A_k(z-a)^k$$

is the Laurent expansion of f about a, then $n(a;f)$ is the absolute value of $\inf\{k \mid k \neq 0,\ A_k \neq 0\}$. If $a = \infty$ and

$$\sum_{-\infty}^{+\infty} A_k z^k$$

is the Laurent expansion of f about ∞, then $n(\infty;f)$ is the absolute value of $\sup\{k \mid k \neq 0,\ A_k \neq 0\}$. Clearly, $n(a;f) = +\infty$ if, and only if, f is constant in some neighborhood of a. The multiplicity plays a very essential role in the description of the local "covering" behavior of a meromorphic function. This matter will be discussed at length in Chap. 2. We note for the present that, if f is meromorphic on Ω and not constant, then $n(z;f) = 1$ save for a set of z not clustering at any point of Ω.

The Divisor of a Meromorphic Function. This is a convenient means for cataloguing the zeros and poles of a meromorphic function together with their multiplicities. The notion of a divisor permeates the theory of algebraic functions (in both its concrete and its abstract algebraic forms) and number theory. Given f meromorphic on a region Ω, by the *divisor* ∂_f of f is meant the function with domain Ω given by

$$\partial_f(z) = \begin{cases} 0, & f(z) \neq 0, \infty; \\ n(z;f), & f(z) = 0; \\ -\,n(z;f), & f(z) = \infty. \end{cases} \tag{3.1}$$

Algebraic Structure. Given f and g meromorphic on Ω, let E denote the union of the sets of poles of f and g. The analytic function

$$z \to f(z) + g(z), \qquad z \in \Omega - E \tag{3.2}$$

admits a unique meromorphic extension to Ω. This extension is termed the *sum of f and g*, denoted by $f + g$. Similarly, the *product* of f and g, denoted by fg, is defined as the unique meromorphic extension to Ω of

$$z \to f(z)g(z), \qquad z \in \Omega - E\,. \tag{3.3}$$

EXERCISES

1. Show that the family of functions meromorphic on Ω together with addition and multiplication given by the above definitions constitutes a field $M(\Omega)$. If $f,g \in M(\Omega)$,

$$\partial_{f+g} \geqslant \min\{\partial_f, \partial_g\} \qquad \text{and} \qquad \partial_{fg} = \partial_f + \partial_g\,.$$

2. Let f denote a meromorphic function on a region $\Omega_1 \subset \hat{K}$ that maps Ω_1 into a region Ω_2. Let g denote a meromorphic function on Ω_2. Let $h = g \circ f$.

Show that h is either the constant infinity or is meromorphic. When is h the constant infinity? If h is meromorphic, show that

$$n(a; h) = n(a; f)\, n[f(a); g]\,.$$

Although we shall not undertake to study either the connection between the algebraic structure of $M(\Omega)$ and the conformal structure of Ω or the connection between the algebraic structure of certain subrings of $M(\Omega)$ and the conformal structure of Ω, we do wish to point out that such relations exist. Historically, they may be traced back to the theory of algebraic functions. The original investigations for plane regions are due to Kakutani and Chevalley (cf. Kakutani, "Rings of Analytic Functions," *Lectures on Functions of a Complex Variable*, University of Michigan, 1955). For the reader with algebraic interests we recommend the paper of Kakutani, *op. cit.*, and a paper by L. Bers ("On Rings of Analytic Functions," *Bull. Amer. Math. Soc.*, **54**: 1948), which shows that if Ω_1 and Ω_2 are two regions $\subset K$ and if φ is an isomorphism of the ring $A(\Omega_1)$, of analytic functions on Ω_1 onto the ring $A(\Omega_2)$, of analytic functions on Ω_2, then either there exists a univalent analytic function ψ_1 mapping Ω_2 onto Ω_1 such that

$$\varphi(f) = f \circ \psi_1, \qquad f \in A(\Omega_1)\,, \tag{3.4}$$

or else there exists a univalent function ψ_2 mapping Ω_2 onto Ω_1 whose conjugate is analytic and which satisfies

$$\overline{\varphi(f)} = f \circ \psi_2\,, \qquad f \in A(\Omega_1)\,. \tag{3.5}$$

The function-theoretic requirements of these two papers are modest. There are open questions in this field which are worthy of investigation. For example, it is not known whether an analogue of Bers's theorem holds for field isomorphisms: If φ is an isomorphic map of $M(\Omega_1)$ onto $M(\Omega_2)$, does there exist ψ_1 or ψ_2 satisfying (3.4) or (3.5) with $M(\Omega_k)$ replacing $A(\Omega_k)$, $k = 1,2$?

Sequences of Meromorphic Functions. Let f, f_n, $n \in N$, be functions having a common domain D and taking values in $\hat{K}$. Then (f_n) is said to *tend uniformly* to f *on* D in the sense of the chordal metric, provided that

$$\lim_{n\to\infty} \{\sup_{p\in D} [f(p),f_n(p)]\} = 0\,.$$

The notion of a uniform Cauchy sequence in the sense of the chordal metric is correspondingly defined. Suppose that D is, in particular, an open set in $\hat{K}$. Then (f_n) is said to tend uniformly to f *in* D in the sense of the chordal metric provided that, for each compact $C(\neq \emptyset) \subset D$,

$$\lim_{n\to\infty} \{\sup_{z\in C} [f(z),f_n(z)]\} = 0\,. \tag{3.7}$$

Suppose now that D is a region, that each f_n is meromorphic on D, and that (f_n) tends uniformly to f in D (in the sense of the chordal metric). Then we may conclude that *f is meromorphic on D* or else is the infinite constant. It is of course clear that f is continuous since $f_n \to f$ uniformly in D. Now, if $f(a) \neq \infty$, there exist: A, $0 < A < 1$; $\Delta(a;r) \subset D$; and $m \in N$ such that

$$[0,f_n(z)] \leqslant A, \quad [0,f(z)] \leqslant A \qquad \text{for } z \in \Delta(a;r),\ n \geqslant m\,.$$

Since the condition

$$[0,w] \leqslant A$$

implies that

$$|\,w\,|^2 \leqslant \frac{A^2}{1 - A^2}$$

and, hence, that

$$\sqrt{1 + |\,w\,|^2} \leqslant \frac{1}{\sqrt{1 - A^2}}\,,$$

we conclude that

$$|\,f(z) - f_n(z)\,| \leqslant \frac{[f(z),f_n(z)]}{1 - A^2}\,, \qquad z \in \Delta(a;r),\quad n \geqslant m\,.$$

It follows that f is analytic at a. On the other hand, if $f(a) = \infty$, from the fact that

$$[w_1^{-1},w_2^{-1}] = [w_1,w_2]$$

it follows that $1/f$ is analytic at a. Now $E = \operatorname{int}\{z \mid f(z) = \infty\}$ is open and is closed relative to D. Hence f is either the constant ∞ $(E = D)$ or else is meromorphic in D $(E = \emptyset)$.

Remark: In this book in the case of finite-valued functions the term "uniformly" unqualified will always be taken in the sense of the metric of K.

4. The Mittag-Leffler and Weierstrass Theorems. The results developed in the following exercise set round out our picture of meromorphic functions in that they show that there exists a meromorphic function f on a region Ω having prescribed initial sections of its Laurent expansion at each point of a set in Ω clustering at no point of Ω. Further, if $\Omega \neq \hat{K}$, there exists $f \in M(\Omega)$ such that $\partial_f = \partial$ where ∂ is an arbitrary map of Ω into I subject to the sole condition that $\{z \mid \partial(z) \neq 0\}$ clusters at no point of Ω. Exercise 6 shows that if $\Omega \neq \hat{K}$, then $M(\Omega)$ is generated out of $A(\Omega)$. It is suggested that the reader review the basic facts concerning infinite products. For the proofs outlined in Exs. 2 and 3, compare Osgood, *Funktionentheorie* I.

We say that a sequence of functions (f_n) each with domain a region Ω and taking finite complex values *converges uniformly in* Ω provided that for each compact $C \subset \Omega$, (f_n) converges uniformly on C ("$f_n \to f$ uniformly in Ω" is similarly defined).

EXERCISES

1. Given a, b finite. Let $r = |a - b| > 0$. Show (a) that

$$(z - b)^{-1} = [(z - a) - (b - a)]^{-1}$$

$$= \sum_{k=0}^{\infty} \frac{(b - a)^k}{(z - a)^{k+1}} \qquad \text{for} \quad |z - a| > r$$

and that the series converges uniformly in $\{|z - a| > r\}$; (b) that the function $z \to (z - b)/(z - a)$ possesses an analytic logarithm $\lambda_{a,b}$ in $\{|z - a| > r\}$. In fact, if $\lambda_{a,b}$ is the analytic logarithm normalized to vanish at ∞,

$$\lambda_{a,b}(z) = -\sum_{k=1}^{\infty} \frac{(b - a)^k}{k(z - a)^k},$$

the convergence being uniform in $\{|z - a| > r\}$.

2. MITTAG-LEFFLER THEOREM: Let Ω denote a region satisfying $\infty \in \Omega \neq \hat{K}$. Let B denote an infinite set of points of $\Omega \cap K$ clustering at no point of Ω; let (b_n) denote a univalent enumeration of B. For each n, let P_n denote a polynomial of positive degree with no constant term. Then there exists a meromorphic function f on Ω such that the poles of f are the b_n and the principal part of f at b_n is $P_n[(z - b_n)^{-1}]$.

PROOF: Let a_n denote a point of $c(\Omega) = \hat{K} - \Omega$ nearest b_n. Let

$$r_n = \text{dist}\,\{b_n, c(\Omega)\} = \inf_{z \in c(\Omega)} |z - b_n|.$$

Verify that $\lim r_n = 0$. By Ex. 1(a), for each n there exists a polynomial Q_n such that

$$|P_n[(z - b_n)^{-1}] - Q_n[(z - a_n)^{-1}]| < 2^{-n}, \qquad |z - a_n| \geqslant 2r_n.$$

Verify that

$$f(z) = \sum_{n=1}^{\infty} \{P_n[(z - b_n)^{-1}] - Q_n[(z - a_n)^{-1}]\}, \qquad z \in \Omega,$$

has the stated properties and that the series converges uniformly in Ω. Consider the question of uniform convergence both in the sense of the chordal metric and in the sense defined at the beginning of this set of exercises.

Under the stated assumptions on Ω and B, show that there exists f analytic on $\Omega - B$ having an assigned principal part to its Laurent expansion about each b_n. The possibility of essential singularities is allowed.

3. Is the requirement that Ω be a region essential? Conclude from Ex. 2 the corresponding theorem (which is to be stated) for the situation where $\infty \notin \Omega$. What is the situation when we are concerned with functions in the extended plane?

4. WEIERSTRASS THEOREM. Let Ω denote a region satisfying $\infty \in \Omega \neq \hat{K}$. Let B be as in Ex. 2. Let (m_n) denote a sequence of positive integers. Then there exists an analytic function f on Ω such that the zeros of f are the b_n and the multiplicity of f at b_n is m_n.

PROOF: a_n, r_n as in Ex. 2. Using 1(b), infer that there exists μ_n such that

$$m_n \left| \lambda_{a_n, b_n}(z) + \sum_{k=1}^{\mu_n} \frac{(b_n - a_n)^k}{k(z - a_n)^k} \right| < 2^{-n}, \qquad | z - a_n | \geqslant 2r_n .$$

Now show that

$$g(z) = \prod_{n=1}^{\infty} \left(\frac{z - b_n}{z - a_n} \right)^{m_n} \exp \left\{ m_n \sum_{k=1}^{\mu_n} \frac{(b_n - a_n)^k}{k(z - a_n)^k} \right\}$$

has the asserted properties and that the product converges uniformly in Ω.

5. Do Ex. 3 (as far as it makes sense) for the Weierstrass theorem.

6. If f is meromorphic on a region Ω, not the extended plane, there exist analytic functions g_1, g_2 ($g_2 \not\equiv 0$) on Ω such that $f = g_1 g_2^{-1}$.

7. SCHMIEGUNGSSATZ. Given a region Ω and $B \subset \Omega$ not clustering at any point of Ω. Let (b_n) be a univalent enumeration of B. Suppose

$$g_n(z) = \sum_{j=0}^{m_n} A_j^{(n)}(z - b_n)^j, \text{ (resp., } \sum_{j=0}^{m_n} A_j^{(n)} z^{-j} \text{ if } b_n = \infty), \; n = 1,2,\cdots .$$

ASSERTION: There exists f analytic on Ω such that for each n,

$$\lim_{b_n} \frac{f(z) - g_n(z)}{(z - b_n)^{m_n+1}} \left[\text{resp., } \lim_{\infty} \, (f(z) - g_n(z)) z^{m_n+1} \right]$$

exists and is finite.

HINT: Let φ denote an analytic function on Ω whose zeros are the b_n, the multiplicity of φ at b_n being $m_n + 1$. Let ψ be meromorphic on Ω, the poles of ψ lying in B, and let ψ satisfy

$$\text{Principal part of } \psi \text{ at } b_n = \text{principal part of } \frac{g_n}{\varphi} \text{ at } b_n, \; n = 1,2,\cdots .$$

Verify that $f = \varphi\psi$ satisfies the stipulated conditions.

8. Suppose that in Ex. 7, g_n is replaced by

$$\sum_{j=l_n}^{m_n} A_j^{(n)}(z - b_n)^j,\ l_n < 0,\ m_n \geqslant 0 \text{ (resp., } \sum_{j=l_n}^{m_n} A_j^{(n)} z^{-j} \text{ for } b_n = \infty).$$

Then there exists f meromorphic on Ω with poles at most at the b_n, such that

$$\lim_{b_n} \frac{f(z) - g_n(z)}{(z - b_n)^{m_n+1}} \left[\text{resp., } \lim_{\infty} z^{m_n+1}(f(z) - g_n(z))\right]$$

exists and is finite.

9. Let g_n be as given in Ex. 7, $n = 1,\cdots,s$. All b_n are supposed finite. Show that there is a unique polynomial P of degree $\leqslant -1 + \sum_{n=1}^{s}(m_n + 1)$ such that $P^{(k)}(b_n) = g_n^{(k)}(b_n)$, $k = 0,\cdots,m_n$ for $n = 1,\cdots, s$.

HINT: Let $Q(z) = \prod_{n=1}^{s}(z - b_n)^{m_n+1}$ and let R denote the rational function that vanishes at ∞ and whose poles are among $b_1,\cdots,b_s$, the principal part of R at b_k being

$$\frac{\gamma_k(z)}{(z - b_k)^{m_k+1}},$$

where $\gamma_k =$ the m_kth section of the Taylor expansion of

$$\frac{g_k(z)}{\prod_{n\neq k}(z - b_n)^{m_n+1}}$$

about b_k. Then $P = QR$.

If each $m_n = 0$, we have the *Lagrange interpolation formula:*

$$P(z) = Q(z)\left[\sum_{n=1}^{s} \frac{g_n(b_n)}{Q'(b_n)} \frac{1}{z - b_n}\right].$$

---

5. Fourier Series and Analytic Functions, There are many interesting connections between the theory of Fourier series and analytic functions. Important ones are to be found in certain problems concerning the boundary behavior of analytic functions. To pursue these questions in a suitable manner one would be compelled to make use of the Lebesgue integral. Since we have not presupposed a knowledge of integration and measure theory, we can treat only limited aspects of these problems.

However, it is possible to develop the first principles of the theory of

Fourier series under restrictive conditions with the equipment we have at hand and to see the intimate connection between Fourier series and analytic functions as far as "internal problems" are concerned, where no reference is made to the behavior of an analytic function near the frontier of its domain. Thus we shall see that with no equipment other than the Cauchy-Goursat theorem for a triangle, the fundamental convergence theorem for Fourier series of continuously differentiable functions, and the theorem concerning term-by-term differentiation of power series, it is possible to arrive at the power-series representation of an analytic function (Ex. 15). The apparatus developed in the exercise set below permits us to treat the culminating exercise of the set—the problem of characterizing the continuous (finite-valued) functions on $C(0;1)$ that are the boundary functions of functions with domain $\overline{\Delta(0;1)}$ continuous on their domain and analytic in $\Delta(0;1)$. It is not possible to resist the temptation to insert two applications of elementary Fourier analysis, one to F. Riesz's proof of Weyl's "Gleichverteilungssatz" and the other to the Weierstrass approximation theorem (Exs. 5 and 6), although they do not belong to the theory of functions of a complex variable. The inequality of Ex. 11 will play a fundamental role in the study of Carleman's method (Chap. 5, § 12).

It will be convenient to introduce the notion of modulus of continuity (de la Vallée Poussin). Given a function f whose domain D is a part of R and which takes values in K, the *modulus of continuity of f*, denoted by ω_f, is the function with domain consisting of the nonnegative reals defined by

$$\omega_f(\delta) = \sup \{|f(x) - f(y)| \mid x,y \in D, |x - y| \leqslant \delta\}. \tag{5.1}$$

The modulus of continuity serves as a convenient method for revealing whether f is uniformly continuous. In fact, *f is uniformly continuous if, and only if, ω_f is continuous at* 0. Obviously, the notion of modulus of continuity applies to maps of metric spaces into metric spaces.

We shall be concerned with a continuous finite *complex-valued function f with domain R which is periodic with period* 2π; that is, $f(x + 2\pi) = f(x)$, $x \in R$. By the kth *Fourier coefficient* of f is meant

$$C_k(f) = (2\pi)^{-1} \int_{-\pi}^{\pi} f(x)e^{-kix}\, dx , \qquad k \in I . \tag{5.2}$$

By the *Fourier series* of f is meant

$$\sum_{-\infty}^{+\infty} C_k(f)e^{kix} . \tag{5.3}$$

(We are operating with the so-called *complex form* of the Fourier series of a function.) We introduce

$$K_n(x) = \sum_{k=-n}^{n} e^{kix} , \qquad n \in N , \tag{5.4}$$

and

$$K_n^*(x) = \frac{1}{n+1} \sum_{m=0}^{n} K_m(x), \qquad n \in N. \tag{5.5}$$

The function K_n^* is the arithmetic mean of $K_0, \cdots, K_n$; it plays an essential role in Fejér's theorem (Ex. 3). We also introduce the symmetric sections of the Fourier series of f and their arithmetic means. Specifically, let

$$S_n(x) = \sum_{k=-n}^{n} C_k(f) e^{kix}, \qquad n \in N, \tag{5.6}$$

and

$$\sigma_n(x) = \frac{1}{n+1} \sum_{k=0}^{n} S_k(x), \qquad n \in N. \tag{5.7}$$

EXERCISES

1. Establish the following formulas:

$$K_n(x) = \frac{\sin (n + \frac{1}{2})x}{\sin \frac{1}{2}x}; \tag{a}$$

$$K_n^*(x) = \frac{1}{n+1} \left[\frac{\sin \frac{1}{2}(n+1)x}{\sin \frac{1}{2}x}\right]^2 \geqslant 0; \tag{b}$$

$$(2\pi)^{-1} \int_{-\pi}^{\pi} K_n(x)\, dx = (2\pi)^{-1} \int_{-\pi}^{\pi} K_n^*(x)\, dx = 1. \tag{c}$$

In formulas (a) and (b) the obvious gloss is to be made for x an integral multiple of 2π.

2. Establish

$$S_n(x) = (2\pi)^{-1} \int_{-\pi}^{\pi} f(y)\, K_n(x-y)\, dy$$

$$= (2\pi)^{-1} \int_{-\pi}^{\pi} f(x+y)\, K_n(y)\, dy; \tag{a}$$

$$\sigma_n(x) = (2\pi)^{-1} \int_{-\pi}^{\pi} f(x+y)\, K_n^*(y)\, dy. \tag{b}$$

3. Theorem (Fejér): σ_n tends uniformly to f.
This may be proved with the aid of the following observations. First,

$$\sigma_n(x) - f(x) = (2\pi)^{-1} \int_{-\pi}^{\pi} [f(x+y) - f(x)]\, K_n^*(y)\, dy.$$

Second, if $0 < \delta < \pi$,

$$| \sigma_n(x) - f(x) | \leqslant (2\pi)^{-1} \int_{-\delta}^{\delta} | f(x+y) - f(x) | K_n^*(y)\, dy$$

$$+ \frac{2}{\pi} (\max | f |) \int_{\delta}^{\pi} K_n^*(y)\, dy$$

$$\leqslant \omega_f(\delta) + \frac{2}{\pi} (\max | f |) \frac{\pi}{n+1} \left(\sin \frac{\delta}{2}\right)^{-2}.$$

4. Theorem: If f' exists and is continuous on R, then S_n tends to f uniformly (uniform convergence of Fourier series under C' hypothesis).

Here we note that

$$S_n(x) - f(x) = (2\pi)^{-1} \int_{-\pi}^{\pi} [f(x+y) - f(x)]\, K_n(y)\, dy$$

and that, if $0 < \delta < \pi$,

$$| S_n(x) - f(x) | \leqslant (2\pi)^{-1} \int_{|y| \leqslant \delta} | f(x+y) - f(x) | \; | K_n(y) | \; dy$$

$$+ (2\pi)^{-1} \left| \int_{\delta \leqslant |y| \leqslant \pi} [f(x+y) - f(x)]\, K_n(y)\, dy \right| .$$

The first integral on the right is dominated by $(\max | f' |)\delta$. The second integral on the right may be controlled with the aid of the following:

(a) There exists $M > 0$ such that for y satisfying $\delta \leqslant | y | \leqslant \pi$ and for all x,

$$\left| \frac{f(x+y) - f(x)}{\sin \frac{1}{2} y} \right| , \qquad \left| \frac{\partial}{\partial y} \left[\frac{f(x+y) - f(x)}{\sin \frac{1}{2} y} \right] \right| \leqslant M .$$

(b) Lemma (Riemann): If g' exists and is continuous on $a \leqslant x \leqslant b$, then

$$\left| \int_a^b g(x) \sin \alpha x \, dx \right| \leqslant | \alpha |^{-1} \left[2 \max_{a \leqslant x \leqslant b} | g | + \max_{a \leqslant x \leqslant b} | g' | \, (b - a) \right] , \qquad \alpha \neq 0$$

(obvious use of integration by parts).

5. Theorem (Weyl): Let α denote a real irrational number. Let

$$\mu_n(x;f) = \frac{1}{n+1} \sum_{k=0}^{n} f(x + 2\pi\alpha k) .$$

Then μ_n tends uniformly to the constant $C_0(f)$ (Gleichverteilungssatz).

Outline of Proof, Following F. Riesz: (a) If $f(x) = e^{mix}$, where m is an integer $\neq 0$, then

$$\mu_n(x;f) = \frac{e^{mix}}{n+1} \frac{1 - e^{(2\pi\alpha mi)(n+1)}}{1 - e^{2\pi\alpha mi}} .$$

For this case the theorem is readily verified. (b) If $f(x) = \sum_{k=-m}^{m} A_k e^{kix}$, then

$\mu_n(x;f) = A_0 + r_n(x)$, where r_n tends uniformly to zero. (c) If g is a continuous function on R with period 2π, then

$$| \mu_n(x;f) - C_0(f) | \leqslant | \mu_n(x;f-g) | + | \mu_n(x;g) - C_0(g) | + | C_0(g-f) |$$
$$\leqslant \max |f-g| + | \mu_n(x;g) - C_0(g) | + \max |f-g|.$$

The proof is completed by taking $g = \sigma_m$ and applying Ex. 3.

6. THEOREM (WEIERSTRASS): Given a finite complex-valued function F with domain a bounded closed interval $\{a \leqslant x \leqslant b\}$, continuous on its domain. Then F admits uniform approximation by a polynomial.

It suffices to establish the theorem when $a = 0$ and $b = 1$. The general case can be reduced to this special one by considering $F(a + (b - a)t)$. In the special case, extend the definition of F to $\{-\pi \leqslant x \leqslant \pi\}$ so that the resulting function is continuous on its domain and vanishes at $-\pi$ and π. It now suffices to use Ex. 3 and to note that σ_n admits uniform approximation by a polynomial on $\{0 \leqslant x \leqslant 1\}$.

7. THEOREM (BESSEL):

$$\int_{-\pi}^{\pi} |f(x) - \sum_{k=1}^{n} a_{j_k} \exp(j_k ix)|^2 dx \geqslant \int_{-\pi}^{\pi} |f(x) - \sum_{k=1}^{n} C_{j_k}(f) \exp(j_k ix)|^2 dx$$
$$= \int_{-\pi}^{\pi} |f(x)|^2 dx - 2\pi \sum_{k=1}^{n} |C_{j_k}(f)|^2 .$$

Here $j_1, \cdots, j_n$ are distinct integers. Equality holds if and only if $a_{j_k} = C_{j_k}(f)$.

8. THEOREM (PARSEVAL):

$$\int_{-\pi}^{\pi} |f(x)|^2 dx = 2\pi \sum_{k=-\infty}^{+\infty} |C_k(f)|^2$$

(Exs. 3,7).

9. If $C_k(f) = 0$, $k \in I$, then f is identically zero.

10. If S_n converges uniformly, then $f = \lim S_n$.

11. THEOREM: Given g a finite complex-valued function with domain $\{0 \leqslant x \leqslant \pi\}$ satisfying $g(0) = g(\pi) = 0$ and such that g' exists and is continuous on $\{0 \leqslant x \leqslant \pi\}$. Then

$$\int_{0}^{\pi} |g'(x)|^2 dx \geqslant \int_{0}^{\pi} |g(x)|^2 dx .$$

Equality holds if and only if $g(x) \equiv a \sin x$.

This may be established by extending the definition of g to $\{-\pi \leqslant x \leqslant \pi\}$ as an odd function and applying the Parseval theorem (Ex. 8) to both g so extended and its derivative.

Analytic Functions and Fourier Series. Here we first treat internal problems. At this point we drop the notational agreement on f prevailing for Exs. 1 to 10. We suppose that

$$\sum_{k=0}^{\infty} a_k(z - z_0)^k$$

has a positive radius of convergence R and that $f(z)$ is the sum of the series for $z \in \Delta(z_0;R)$.

EXERCISES

12. Theorem: Given r, $0 \leqslant r < R$, $a_k r^k$ is the kth Fourier coefficient of $\theta \to f(z_0 + re^{i\theta})$ for $k \in N$; for k negative the Fourier coefficients vanish. Further,

$$\int_{-\pi}^{\pi} |f(z_0 + re^{i\theta})|^2 \, d\theta = 2\pi \sum_{k=0}^{\infty} |a_k|^2 r^{2k} . \tag{a}$$

13. Let $M(r) = \max |f(z_0 + re^{i\theta})|$. Then $|a_k| r^k \leqslant M(r)$, $k \in N$ (Cauchy inequalitites). Further, if $|a_l| \rho^l = M(\rho)$, $l \in N$, $0 < \rho < R$, then $f(z) \equiv a_l(z - z_0)^l$. Hence if $|f(z_0)| = |a_0| = M(\rho)$, $f(z) \equiv f(z_0)$.

This leads directly to the maximum (and the minimum) principle for the modulus of an analytic function: Given g analytic on a region Ω of the extended plane and $z_0 \in \Omega$. If $|g|$ has a relative maximum at z_0, then g is constant. If $g(z_0) \neq 0$ and $|g|$ has a relative minimum at z_0, then g is constant.

We may suppose z_0 finite. (Why?) If $|g|$ has a relative maximum at z_0, then for r sufficiently small, $M(r) \leqslant |g(z_0)|$. The remainder of this proof, as well as the proof of the minimum principle, is readily supplied.

14. Conclude directly from Ex. 12 that the Cauchy formula holds:

$$f(z) = \frac{1}{2\pi i} \oint_{C(z_0;r)} \frac{f(t)}{t - z} \, dt , \qquad z \in \Delta(z_0;r),\ 0 < r < R .$$

Remark: Of course, Exs. 12 to 14 can be established purely "function-theoretically" without appeal to results from the theory of Fourier series. However, the connection is worth pointing out. The next exercise shows how the Laurent expansion can be derived by Fourier methods.

15. Let f be analytic in $\mathcal{O} = \{r_1 < |z - z_0| < r_2\}$, where $0 \leqslant r_1 < r_2 \leqslant +\infty$. Let $c_k(r)$ denote the kth Fourier coefficient of $\theta \to f(z_0 + re^{i\theta})$, $r_1 < r < r_2$. Show that $c_k'(r) \equiv (k/r)c_k(r)$, and hence that $c_k(r) \equiv A_k r^k$. It follows that

$$f(z) = \sum_{-\infty}^{+\infty} A_k(z - z_0)^k , \qquad z \in \mathcal{O} .$$

This is the Laurent expansion for f in $\mathcal{O}$.

It is to be observed that if it is assumed merely that f' *exists and is continuous in* $\mathfrak{O}$, then the conclusion of the exercise holds, for this hypothesis is sufficient to permit the usual differentiation under the integral sign in calculating $c_k'(r)$. If we take f analytic on $\Delta(z_0;r)$ in the sense that $f'(z)$ exists for each z in $\Delta(z_0;r)$, then the Cauchy-Goursat theorem for a triangle assures the existence of a primitive F of f on $\Delta(z_0;r)$. Applying the results of Ex. 15 to F, we see that the Laurent coefficients A_k of F with $k < 0$ satisfy $|A_k| r^k \leqslant B$, r small. Hence, for such k, $A_k = 0$. Hence F admits an expansion in a power series in $z - z_0$ in $\Delta(z_0;r)$. Applying term-by-term differentiation, we see that f also admits such an expansion. This observation now assures us that if f possesses a derivative at each point of $\mathfrak{O}$, then f' is continuous in $\mathfrak{O}$.

We conclude this sequence of exercises with a more serious application of Fourier methods, namely, an application to an elementary problem concerning the *boundary values* of analytic functions. Suppose that f is a finite complex-valued function with domain $C(0;1)$, continuous on its domain. Under what circumstances does there exist a function F with domain $\overline{\Delta(0;1)}$, continuous on its domain, analytic in $\Delta(0;1)$, and satisfying

$$F(z) = f(z)\,, \qquad |z| = 1\,?$$

Clearly, there is at most one such function since the kth coefficient a_k of the power-series expansion of F in $\Delta(0;1)$ satisfies

$$a_k = \frac{1}{2\pi i}\oint_{C(0;r)} \frac{F(z)}{z^{k+1}}\,dz = \frac{1}{2\pi i}\oint_{C(0;1)} \frac{f(z)}{z^{k+1}}\,dz\,.$$

This assertion may also be established with the aid of the maximum principle. Further, if such an F exists, we have

$$\oint_{C(0;r)} F(z)z^k\,dz = 0, \qquad k \in N\,,$$

and hence

$$\oint_{C(0;1)} f(z)z^k\,dz = 0\,, \qquad k \in N\,. \tag{a}$$

EXERCISE

16. If condition (a) above is fulfilled, there exists a function F with the specified properties.

This may be shown as follows. By Ex. 3, the sequence of σ_n for $\theta \to f(e^{i\theta})$ tends uniformly to $\theta \to f(e^{i\theta})$. Further, $\sigma_n(\theta) = P_n(e^{i\theta})$, where P_n is a polynomial of degree $\leqslant n$. Verify that $(P_n)_0^\infty$ converges uniformly on $\overline{\Delta(0;1)}$ and that the limit function is the desired F.

There is an extensive literature on the boundary behavior of analytic functions. Important work is due to Fatou (see Chap. 4), the Riesz brothers, Lusin, and Privalov.

[2]

Covering Properties of Meromorphic Functions

1. Introductory Remarks. In this chapter we shall be concerned with the study of the "covering properties" of a nonconstant meromorphic function. This loose term is intended to convey descriptively the properties of a nonconstant meromorphic function f reflected in its *valence function* ν_f, which is defined by

$$\nu_f(w) = \sum_{f(z)=w} n(z;f)\,, \qquad w \in \hat{K}. \tag{1.1}$$

The valence function counts the number of times a given point is attained, multiplicity being taken into account.

An essential role in this study will be played by the notion of the order of a point with respect to a closed curve (*topological index* of a closed curve at a point). This notion has proved to be essential in studies devoted to the topological aspects of the theory of analytic functions (cf. M. Morse, *Topological Methods in the Theory of Functions of a Complex Variable*, and G. T. Whyburn, *Topological Analysis. Princeton*, Princeton University Press, 1958). F. Riesz (*Acta Szeged*, 1939) has given an elegant proof of the Jordan curve theorem, based on the topological index. An account of this proof will be found in the appendix, § 3 (b).

2. Continuous Logarithm of a Nonvanishing Continuous Function. We have already studied the question of analytic logarithms of nonvanishing analytic functions, and we have alluded to the notion of continuous logarithms and continuous powers of a nonvanishing finite complex-valued continuous function on a topological space X. Here we consider the existence question when X is a space of a very simple sort. We shall treat the cases of an interval and the real line. The cases of a rectangle and a strip are treated similarly and will be given in exercise form.

First, suppose that f is a nonvanishing finite complex-valued function whose domain is a bounded interval $\{a \leqslant t \leqslant b\}$, continuous on its domain and satisfying

$$|f(t) - f(a)| < |f(a)|\,, \quad a \leqslant t \leqslant b\,. \tag{2.1}$$

Let L denote an analytic logarithm of the identity in $\Delta(f(a);\ |f(a)|)$. Then $L \circ f$ is a continuous logarithm of f.

Suppose now that f is not necessarily subject to the condition (2.1). Let $m = \min |f| > 0$ and let n denote a positive integer satisfying

$$\omega_f\left(\frac{b-a}{n}\right) < m \,,$$

ω_f being the modulus of continuity of f. Then, with $t_k = a + k(b-a)/n$,

$$|f(t) - f(t_k)| < m \leqslant |f(t_k)|$$

for $t_k \leqslant t \leqslant t_{k+1}$, $k = 0,1,\cdots,n-1$. Hence the restriction of f to $\{t_k \leqslant t \leqslant t_{k+1}\}$ possesses a continuous logarithm g_k. We may choose the g_k in such a manner that $g_k(t_{k+1}) = g_{k+1}(t_{k+1})$, $k = 0,\cdots,n-2$. With this choice of the g_k,

$$g = \bigcup_0^{n-1} g_k$$

is a continuous logarithm of f.

We now turn to the case where f is a continuous map of R into $K - \{0\}$. Here it suffices to fix a logarithm α of $f(0)$ and to proceed as follows. Let g_n denote the continuous logarithm of the restriction of f to $\{-(n+1) \leqslant t \leqslant n+1\}$ that satisfies $g_n(0) = \alpha$. Then it is easily verified that

$$g = \bigcup_{n \in N} g_n$$

is a continuous logarithm of f.

EXERCISES

1. Establish the existence of a continuous logarithm for a continuous map f of a rectangle $\{a \leqslant t \leqslant b;\ c \leqslant \tau \leqslant d\}$ or of a strip $R \times \{a \leqslant \tau \leqslant b\}$ into $K - \{0\}$.

2. Suppose that Ω is a homotopically simply-connected region and that f is a continuous map of Ω into $K - \{0\}$. Show that f admits a continuous logarithm. [Consider the class Γ of paths in Ω issuing from a given point $a \in \Omega$, and let g_γ denote the continuous logarithm of $f \circ \gamma$ for which $g_\gamma(0)$ is a fixed logarithm of $f(a)$. Show that

$$F = \{(\gamma(1), g_\gamma(1)) \mid \gamma \in \Gamma\}$$

is a continuous logarithm of f.]

3. Continuous Argument. Given a continuous map f of a topological space X into $K - \{0\}$, by a *continuous argument* of f is meant a continuous real-valued function h on X such that $h(p)$ is an argument of $f(p)$ for each $p \in X$. If h_1 and h_2 are continuous arguments of f, $h_1 - h_2$ is constant on each component of X and takes values that are integral multiples of 2π.

Show that f possesses a continuous argument if and only if f possesses a continuous logarithm. Show further that in this case, the continuous arguments of f are precisely the imaginary parts of the continuous logarithms of f.

---

3. Closed Curve. It is convenient for our purposes to define a *closed curve* as a continuous map γ of R into $\hat{K}$ that is periodic with period 1. The advantages that accrue from this definition are (a) that a "sensing" is automatically built into the definition, and (b) that questions of "independence of initial point" recede into the background. It is sometimes convenient to use the not-strictly-correct term, "the closed curve γ," for the image of the map γ. The meaning intended in any given situation will be clear from context.

We say that γ is *rectifiable* provided that the restriction of γ to some interval $\{a \leqslant t \leqslant a + 1\}$ is rectifiable. In this case the restriction of γ to any closed interval of unit length is a curve whose length is independent of the interval. Further, if γ is rectifiable and if f is a function whose domain contains γ and whose restriction to γ is finite, complex-valued, and continuous, we define

$$\int_{\gamma} f\, dz$$

as the common value of

$$\int_{\gamma_a} f\, dz\,,$$

where γ_a is the restriction of γ to $\{a \leqslant t \leqslant a + 1\}$. (Note that we have just used γ in two senses in the preceding sentence.)

4. Order of a Point with Respect to a Closed Curve. Suppose that γ is a closed curve lying in K, and let $a \in K - \gamma$. Let θ denote a continuous argument of $\gamma - a$. Then

$$\frac{\theta(t + 1) - \theta(t)}{2\pi}$$

is an integer independent of $t \in R$ and admitted θ. This integer is termed *the order of a with respect to γ*. It is denoted by $O(a;\gamma)$. Intuitively speaking, it specifies the "number of times γ winds about a in a unit period."

The following lemma permits us to obtain the essential properties of the order of a point with respect to a curve.

LEMMA 4.1. *Let F be a continuous map of $R \times \{0 \leqslant \tau \leqslant 1\}$ into $K - \{0\}$ satisfying $F(t + 1, \tau) \equiv F(t, \tau)$, and let Θ be a continuous argument of F. Then*

$$\frac{\Theta(t + 1,\tau) - \Theta(t,\tau)}{2\pi}$$

is an integer independent of (t,τ) in the domain of F.

It suffices to note that

$$e^{i\Theta(t+1,\tau)} = \frac{F(t+1,\tau)}{|F(t+1,\tau)|} = \frac{F(t,\tau)}{|F(t,\tau)|} = e^{i\Theta(t,\tau)}.$$

We are now led to the following result: *$a \to O(a;\gamma)$ is constant on each component of $K - \gamma$; further, $O(a;\gamma) = 0$ for a in the unbounded component of $K - \gamma$.*

To see this, it suffices to show that $a \to O(a;\gamma)$ is locally constant and vanishes for a large. Given $a \in K - \gamma$, let $b \in \Delta(a;r) \subset K - \gamma$. Then

$$\gamma(t) - [a + (b - a)\tau]$$

is an F meeting the condition of the lemma. Further,

$$O(a;\gamma) = \frac{\Theta(1,0) - \Theta(0,0)}{2\pi}, \quad \text{and} \quad O(b;\gamma) = \frac{\Theta(1,1) - \Theta(0,1)}{2\pi}.$$

Clearly, $O(b;\gamma) = O(a;\gamma)$. If $|a| > \max|\gamma|$, then $|(\gamma(t) - a) + a| < |a|$, or, equivalently, $\gamma(t) - a \in \Delta(-a; |a|)$, and consequently $\gamma - a$ has a periodic continuous logarithm. Hence, $O(a;\gamma) = 0$. By convention we agree to set $O(\infty;\gamma) = 0$.

EXERCISES

1. Given closed curves γ_0 and γ_1 in K, neither containing a. We say that γ_0 is *a-deformable* into γ_1 provided that there exists F meeting the conditions of the lemma and such that

$$\gamma_0(t) \equiv a + F(t,0), \quad \gamma_1(t) \equiv a + F(t,1).$$

Show that a necessary and sufficient condition that γ_0 be a-deformable into γ_1 is that $O(a;\gamma_0) = O(a;\gamma_1)$. Show further that a-deformability is an equivalence relation in the set of closed curves in K not containing a. Let $\Gamma_n(t) = a + e^{2\pi int}$, $n \in I$. Then $O(a;\Gamma_n) = n$. Thus the classes containing the Γ_n exhaust all the equivalence classes.

2. Let f be a continuous map of $\{a \leqslant x \leqslant b\}$ into $K - \{0\}$, and let $(t_k)_0^n$ be a finite increasing sequence satisfying $t_0 = a, t_n = b$. Let h denote a continuous argument of f, and let h_k denote a continuous argument of the restriction of f to $\{t_k \leqslant t \leqslant t_{k+1}\}$. Then

$$h(b) - h(a) = \sum_{k=0}^{n-1} [h_k(t_{k+1}) - h_k(t_k)].$$

This result is particularly useful in the calculation of order.

---

5. Argument Principle. In treating the argument principle we want (in the first instance) to operate with a region $\subset K$ which has the property that the nonvanishing analytic functions on it possess analytic logarithms. We shall see, when we consider the Riemann mapping theorem, that this property is equivalent to the simple connectivity of the region in one of the senses laid down. However, there is no reason to anticipate this fact in the following statement of the *argument principle:*

THEOREM 5.1 (cf. Saks-Zygmund, *Analytic Functions*, p. 191). *Let Ω be a region $\subset K$ having the property that the nonvanishing analytic functions on it possess analytic logarithms. Let f be a meromorphic function on Ω having a finite number of zeros and poles. Let γ denote a closed curve in Ω containing no zeros or poles of f. Then*

$$O(0;f\circ\gamma) = \sum_{f(z)=0} n(z;f)\, O(z;\gamma) - \sum_{f(z)=\infty} n(z;f)\, O(z;\gamma)\,. \tag{5.1}$$

PROOF: Let $a_1,\cdots,a_\mu$ denote the distinct zeros of f, and let $b_1,\cdots,b_\nu$ denote the distinct poles of f. We have

$$f(z) = \frac{\prod_1^\mu (z - a_k)^{n(a_k;f)}}{\prod_1^\nu (z - b_k)^{n(b_k;f)}}\, g(z) \tag{5.2}$$

where g is a nonvanishing analytic function on Ω. Noting that if λ_c denotes a continuous logarithm of $\gamma - c$, $c \in K - \gamma$ and if L denotes an analytic logarithm of g, then

$$\sum n(a_k;f)\lambda_{a_k} - \sum n(b_k;f)\lambda_{b_k} + L\circ\gamma \tag{5.3}$$

is a continuous logarithm of $f\circ\gamma$, we conclude (5.1).

[If we wished to extend the argument principle to a multiply connected region, we should have to take into account the topological structure of the region and modify our hypothesis on γ so that the contribution to the change in a continuous argument of $f\circ\gamma$ corresponding to $g\circ\gamma$ would vanish. This could be done by using a homology approach and replacing γ by a bounding cycle. We shall not have occasion to consider this question further (cf. Ahlfors, *Complex Analysis*).]

EXERCISES

1. It is not necessary to require that f have only a finite number of zeros and poles. The argument principle holds if f is meromorphic in Ω and does not have a zero or pole on γ. This may be established as follows. First, show that the closure C of $\{a \mid O(a;\gamma) \neq 0\} \cap \Omega$ lies in Ω. This may be established by noting that otherwise there would exist a sequence (a_n): $a_n \in \Omega$, $a_n \to \alpha \in \text{fr}\,\Omega$, $O(a_n;\gamma) \geqslant 1$ for $n = 1,2,\cdots$ [or $O(a_n;\gamma) \leqslant -1$, all n]. Consider an analytic function g on Ω with simple zeros at the a_n and no others. By the Weierstrass product theorem, there would exist a sequence (g_n) of functions analytic in Ω, tending uniformly to g in Ω, the zeros of g_n being $a_1,\cdots,a_n$ and all simple. Conclude $O(0;g_n \circ \gamma) \to O(0;g \circ \gamma)$, and obtain a contradiction. Next, observe that f may be expressed in the form

$$\frac{\Pi_1}{\Pi_2} h$$

where Π_1 and Π_2 are Weierstrass products corresponding to the zeros and poles of f (possibly finite products), and h is a nonvanishing analytic function on Ω. This affords the possibility of approximating f by functions with a finite number of zeros and poles. The relation (5.1) is now readily established in its full generality since the orders with respect to γ of only a finite number of the zeros and poles are not zero.

2. Fundamental Theorem of Algebra: If P is a polynomial of positive degree n, then $\nu_P(0) = n$, ν_P being the valence of P. Consider $O(0;P \circ \gamma_r)$, where $\gamma_r(t) = re^{2\pi it}$ for r large, noting that $P(z) = az^n[1 + O(z^{-1})]$, $a \neq 0$, for z large.

3. Suppose that γ is rectifiable. Show that under the hypothesis that f is analytic at each point of γ and does not vanish at any point of γ,

$$O(0;f \circ \gamma) = (2\pi i)^{-1} \int_\gamma \frac{f'}{f}\, dz\,.$$

We now consider an application of the method employed in establishing the argument principle. Suppose that f is a continuous map of $\overline{\Delta(0;r)}$ into $\hat{K}$, meromorphic in $\Delta(0;r)$, and such that $|f(z)| < +\infty$ for $z \in C(0;r)$. (We take $r < +\infty$. The case $r = \infty$ is a trivial consequence of a property of rational functions.) Then

Theorem 5.2. *The valence of f_1, the restriction of f to $\Delta(0;r)$, is constant (finite) on each component of $\hat{K} - f[C(0;r)]$.*

It suffices to take $\gamma_\tau(t) = \tau re^{2\pi it}$ where τ is less than but sufficiently near 1, and to notice that (5.1) is replaced by

$$O(a;f \circ \gamma_\tau) = \nu_{f_1}(a) - \nu_{f_1}(\infty), \qquad a \in K - f[C(0;r)]\,. \tag{5.4}$$

But for such τ, we have $O(a;f \circ \gamma_\tau) = O(a;f \circ \gamma)$ where $\gamma(t) = re^{2\pi it}$.

Let us specialize further and suppose that f is univalent and also finite-valued. Let $\Gamma = f[C(0;r)]$. Here Γ is a closed Jordan curve [i.e., a homeomorph of $C(0;1)$]. From Theorem 5.2 we conclude that $f[\Delta(0;r)]$ is *a component of* $K - \Gamma$. Clearly, $f[\Delta(0;r)]$ cannot be the unbounded component of $K - \Gamma$. Further, $f'(z) \neq 0$ for $|z| < r$. In fact, if $f'(z_0) = 0$ for some z_0 satisfying $|z_0| < r$, then $\nu_f(a) > 1$ for each point a of $f[\Delta(0;r)]$. By the univalence of f, we should be forced to conclude that $f'(z) \equiv 0$. This is impossible. These observations lead to the fundamental conclusion:

If f is a univalent analytic function on a region $\Omega \subset K$, then (a) *for each open subset $O \subset \Omega$, $f(O)$ is open,* and (b) $f'(z) \neq 0$, $z \in \Omega$.

It suffices to consider $z \to f(z_0 + z)$, $|z| < r$ (r sufficiently small). We shall see that the first conclusion holds for an arbitrary nonconstant function meromorphic on a region. It expresses an essential topological property of a meromorphic function (open-mapping property).

EXERCISES

4. The properties just established for f univalent are useful in studying the analyticity of the inverse of f, which we shall denote by g. Property (a) shows that g is continuous since $g^{-1}(O) = f(O)$. Show that $g'(w_0)$ exists and is equal to $[f'(g(w_0))]^{-1}$, $w_0 \in f(\Omega)$, by observing that

$$f(z) = w_0 + (z - z_0)h(z), \qquad f(z_0) = w_0 ,$$

where h is analytic on Ω and nonvanishing, and that, therefore,

$$w = f(g(w)) = w_0 + [g(w) - g(w_0)]\, h(g(w)) .$$

5. Show that if $\overline{\Delta(a;r)} \subset \Omega$, then for each w in $f\,[\Delta(a;r)]$ we have

$$g(w) = (2\pi i)^{-1} \oint_{C(a;r)} \frac{zf'(z)}{f(z) - w}\, dz .$$

This affords a second proof of the analyticity of g.

6. THEOREM. Given f analytic at $a \in K$, $n(a;f) < +\infty$. If $n(a;f) = 1$, then f is univalent in some $\Delta(a;r)$. If $n(a;f) > 1$, then f is never univalent in any $\Delta(a;r)$.

Demonstrate this theorem by applying Theorem 5.2 to f on $\overline{\Delta(a;r)}$ for r sufficiently small. Remove the finiteness conditions on a and $f(a)$.

7. Formulate and prove a counterpart of Theorem 5.1 for the situation where $\Omega \subset \hat{K}$.

---

6. Local Analysis of an Analytic Function. We now turn to the local analysis of the covering properties of an analytic function. The object of this analysis is to render precise the loosely expressed dictum, "Locally an analytic function behaves topologically like a power of z."

LEMMA 6.1. *Suppose that f is analytic on $\Delta(0;R)$, is not constant, and satisfies $f(0) = 0$. Then there exists a function g whose domain is a region Ω, $0 \in \Omega \subset \Delta(0;R)$, satisfying the conditions:* (1) *g is analytic on Ω and univalent;* (2) *g maps Ω onto a disk centered at* 0; *and* (3):

$$f(z) = [g(z)]^{n(0;f)}, \qquad z \in \Omega . \tag{6.1}$$

PROOF: If $n(0;f) = 1$, then by Ex. 6 of § 5, this chapter, f is univalent in some $\Delta(0;r)$, $r < R$. Let f_r denote the restriction of f to $\Delta(0;r)$. Let δ denote an open disk centered at the origin, satisfying $\delta \subset f[\Delta(0;r)]$, and let $\Omega = f_r^{-1}(\delta)$. It suffices to take g as the restriction of f to Ω.

Suppose now that $n(0;f) > 1$. We have

$$f(z) = z^{n(0;f)}\, h(z), \qquad z \in \Delta(0;R)\,,$$

where h is analytic in $\Delta(0;R)$. We may take r satisfying $0 < r < R$ such that $h(z) \neq 0$, $z \in \Delta(0;r)$. Let h_1 denote a function analytic on $\Delta(0;r)$ satisfying

$$[h_1(z)]^{n(0;f)} = h(z), \qquad z \in \Delta(0;r)\,.$$

We note that $z \to zh_1(z)$ has multiplicity 1 at 0, and we apply to this function the result obtained in the preceding paragraph. If g now pertains to $z \to zh_1(z)$, it is immediate that (6.1) holds.

It is but one step to the case of a meromorphic function. Here we have the following theorem:

THEOREM 6.1. *If f is a function meromorphic on $\Delta(a;R)$ and is not constant, then there exists a function g whose domain is a region Ω, $a \in \Omega \subset \Delta(a;R)$, satisfying the conditions*: (1) *g is analytic on Ω and is univalent*; (2) *g maps Ω onto a disk centered at* 0; *and* (3):

$$f(z) = \begin{cases} f(a) + [g(z)]^{n(a;f)}, \; z \in \Omega, \textit{ when } f(a) \neq \infty; \\ [g(z)]^{-n(a;f)}, \; z \in \Omega, \textit{ when } f(a) = \infty. \end{cases} \tag{6.2}$$

It suffices to consider the functions: $f(a+z) - f(a)$ when a and $f(a)$ are both finite; $[f(a+z)]^{-1}$ when $a \neq \infty$, $f(a) = \infty$; $f(z^{-1}) - f(\infty)$ when $a = \infty$, $f(\infty) \neq \infty$; and $[f(z^{-1})]^{-1}$ when a and $f(a)$ are both ∞, and to apply Lemma 6.1 to the reduced function in question.

Theorem 6.1 leads to results of capital importance in the study of covering properties. We summarize them in the following corollary of Theorem 6.1:

COROLLARY 6.1. *If f is a function meromorphic on $\Delta(a;R)$ and is not constant, then* (1) *$\nu_f(w) \geqslant n(a;f)$ for w in some neighborhood of $f(a)$*; *and* (2) *there exists r, $0 < r < R$, such that the restriction h of f to $\Delta(a;r)$ satisfies* $\max \nu_h = n(a;f)$.

It is easy to see from the corollary that h has the further property that ν_h is constant on some neighborhood of $f(a)$.

The proof of the corollary is readily given. Let ρ denote the radius of $g(\Omega)$, and let $\delta = \Delta(f(a);\, \rho^{n(a;f)})$. We observe that (6.2) implies that $f(\Omega) = \delta$; that each point of δ, save $f(a)$, is attained by f at precisely $n(a;f)$ distinct points of Ω; and that the multiplicity of f at each of these points is 1. Further, $f(a)$ is attained by f in Ω precisely at a. Hence $\nu_f(w) \geqslant n(a;f)$, $w \in \delta$. On the other hand, if h is the restriction of f to $\Delta(a;r) \subset \Omega$, then $\nu_h \leqslant n(a;f)$. Assertion (2) of the corollary follows.

EXERCISES

1. Conclude from Corollary 6.1 that if f is a nonconstant meromorphic function on a region Ω, then for each open $O \subset \Omega$, $f(O)$ is open.

2. Conclude Corollary 6.1 using Theorem 5.2. Apply it to f of Lemma 6.1 restricted to $\overline{\Delta(0;r)}$, r sufficiently small, and thereupon choose r_1, $0 < r_1 < r$, so small that $f[\Delta(0;r_1)] \subset K - f[C(0;r)]$. Now pass to the general case. Note however that this approach does not bring to light the local structure of f in so striking a manner as does Theorem 6.1.

---

7. Lower Semicontinuity of the Valence Function. For many questions of analysis semicontinuity is an important concept. It pertains to real-valued functions on a topological space and may be defined as follows. Given a topological space X, $q \in X$, and a map φ of X into $\{-\infty < x \leqslant +\infty\}$. Then φ is said to be *lower semicontinuous* at q provided that for each real number $a < \varphi(q)$, the set $\{\varphi(p) > a\}$ is a neighborhood of q. Upper semicontinuity is defined analogously for a map φ of X into $\{-\infty \leqslant x < +\infty\}$: that is, φ is *upper semicontinuous* at q provided that for each real number $b > \varphi(q)$, the set $\{\varphi(p) < b\}$ is a neighborhood of q. Recalling the definition of continuity for a finite real-valued function, we see that lower semicontinuity replaces the usual requirement by that half of the requirement which says that the values attained by the function in a sufficiently small neighborhood of the point exceed any number less than the value of the function at the point; a corresponding statement holds for upper semicontinuity. A map φ of X into $\{-\infty < x \leqslant +\infty\}$ is termed *lower semicontinuous* provided that φ is lower semicontinuous at each point of X; similarly, a map φ of X into $\{-\infty \leqslant x < +\infty\}$ is termed upper semicontinuous provided that it is upper semicontinuous at each point of X. We shall see in Chap. 4 that upper semicontinuity is a natural concept in the study of subharmonic functions. For the present, the following exercises will serve to illuminate the role played by semicontinuity. However, the results of these exercises will not be needed in studying the lower semicontinuity of the valence function.

EXERCISES

1. If φ is a map of X into R, then φ is continuous at q if and only if φ is both lower and upper semicontinuous at q.

2. A map φ of X into $\{-\infty < x \leqslant +\infty\}$ is lower semicontinuous if, and only if, for each real a, $\varphi^{-1}\{a < x\}$ is open.

3. If X is compact and φ is a lower semicontinuous function on X, then φ attains a minimum (possibly $+\infty$). (Consider the open covering of X consisting of $\varphi^{-1}\{a < x\}$, $a > -\infty$, to conclude $\inf \varphi > -\infty$. If $\inf \varphi$ were not attained, the family of sets, $\varphi^{-1}\{a < x\}$, $a > \inf \varphi$, would be an open covering of X.

The contradiction is readily seen.) This is the Weierstrass theorem for the minimum of a continuous function, with the hypotheses "reduced by half."

This result, together with that of Ex. 4, permits us to anticipate the role played by semicontinuity in the calculus of variations and its generalizations.

4. Suppose that $(\varphi_\alpha)_{\alpha \in A}$ is a nonempty family of maps of X into R each of which is continuous at $q \in X$. Let φ denote the upper envelope of the family:

$$\varphi(p) = \sup_{\alpha \in A} \varphi_\alpha(p)\,.$$

Then φ is lower semicontinuous at q. In particular, if each φ_α is continuous on X, φ is lower semicontinuous on X.

We now turn to the study of the valence function and prove

THEOREM 7.1. *Given f meromorphic on a region Ω and not constant. The valence function ν_f is lower semicontinuous on $\hat{K}$.*

PROOF: If $\nu_f(a) = 0$, the assertion is trivial since $\nu_f \geqslant 0$. Suppose that $\nu_f(a) > 0$ and that $z_1,\cdots,z_m$ are m distinct points of $f^{-1}(\{a\})$. By Corollary 6.1, choosing R so that $\Delta(z_k;R)$, $k = 1,\cdots,m$, are mutually disjoint, we find that there exists $\rho > 0$ such that $\nu_f(w) \geqslant \Sigma\, n(z_k;f) \geqslant m$ on $\Delta(a;\rho)$. Hence, if $f^{-1}(\{a\})$ is infinite, $\nu_f(w)$ exceeds a given real number on some neighborhood of a; and if $f^{-1}(\{a\})$ is finite, $\nu_f(w) \geqslant \sum_{f(z)=a} n(z;f) = \nu_f(a)$ on some neighborhood of a. The assertion follows.

EXERCISE

5. Let $\Omega = \{\operatorname{Re} z > 0\} \subset K$. Let $\alpha > 0$. Let $f(z) = \exp[\alpha L(z)]$, where L is the analytic logarithm of the identity function on Ω satisfying $L(1) = 0$. Determine ν_f. Where is ν_f discontinuous?

---

8. Boundary Values of a Meromorphic Function. Given a function f meromorphic on a region Ω, the limiting values obtained from f at the points of the frontier of Ω play a role in the study of the continuity properties of ν_f. Let us formulate the notion of limiting values precisely. Given $\zeta \in \operatorname{fr} \Omega$, we say that $w \in \hat{K}$ is a *cluster value of f at ζ* or a *boundary value of f at ζ* (the latter is the designation used by Carathéodory) provided that there exists a sequence $(z_n){:}z_n \in \Omega$, $z_n \to \zeta$, $f(z_n) \to w$. We denote the set of boundary values of f at ζ by $B(f;\zeta)$. We say that $w \in \hat{K}$ is a *cluster value of f* or a *boundary value of f* provided that $w \in \bigcup_{\zeta \in \operatorname{fr}\Omega} B(f;\zeta)$. We denote the set of boundary values of f by $B(f)$. It is immediate that $B(f) = \bigcup_{\zeta \in \operatorname{fr}\Omega} B(f;\zeta)$. The following relation is worth noting:

$$B(f;\zeta) = \bigcap_{r>0} \overline{f[\Delta(\zeta;r) \cap \Omega]}\,. \tag{8.1}$$

The inclusion of $B(f;\zeta)$ in the set on the right side is readily verified from the definition of $B(f;\zeta)$. On the other hand, if w is a member of the right-hand side, for each $n \in N$, there exists $z_n \in \Delta[\zeta;1/(n+1)] \cap \Omega$ such that $f(z_n) \in \Delta[w;\ 1/(n+1)]$. Thanks to the properties of (z_n), $w \in B(f;\zeta)$.

We also note that $B(f)$ is empty if and only if $\Omega = \hat{K}$. Further, if f is the restriction to Ω of a function g continuous on $\overline{\Omega}$, then

$$B(f) = g[\text{fr}\ \Omega]. \tag{8.2}$$

We now consider the connection between $B(f)$ and the continuity properties of ν_f. The essential theorem here is

THEOREM 8.1. *Given f meromorphic on a region Ω and not constant. Then $\nu_f(w) < +\infty$, and ν_f is continuous at w if and only if $w \in \hat{K} - B(f)$.*

PROOF: If $\nu_f(a) = 0$ and ν_f is continuous at a, then $\nu_f(w) = 0$ in some neighborhood of a, and we see that a cannot be a point of $B(f)$. Hence $a \in \hat{K} - B(f)$. If $\nu_f(a)$ is finite and positive and ν_f is continuous at a, let $z_1,\cdots,z_m$ denote the distinct antecedents of a with respect to f. Let $\rho > 0$ be so chosen that $\Delta(z_k;\rho)$, $k = 1,\cdots,m$, are mutually disjoint and $\overline{\bigcup_1^m \Delta(z_k;\rho)} \subset \Omega$. By Corollary 6.1(1) and the fact that ν_f is constant in some neighborhood of a, we see that there exists $\Delta(a;r)$ such that $f^{-1}\left[\Delta(a;r)\right] \subset \bigcup_1^m \Delta(z_k;\rho)$. In fact, if r is taken sufficiently small, then $\nu_f(w) = \nu_f(a)$, $w \in \Delta(a;r)$, and each point of $\Delta(a;r)$ has at least $n(z_k;f)$ antecedents counted according to multiplicity in $\Delta(z_k;\rho)$. Hence each point of $\Delta(a;r)$ has no antecedents with respect to f outside $\bigcup_1^m \Delta(z_k;\rho)$, and the assertion follows. We conclude that a is not a boundary value of f.

Suppose that $a \in \hat{K} - B(f)$. Then clearly $\nu_f(a) < +\infty$. If $\nu_f(a) = 0$, then $a \in \hat{K} - \overline{f(\Omega)}$. For if $a \in \overline{f(\Omega)}$, we should have $a \in B(f)$. Hence, ν_f vanishes in some neighborhood of a. If $0 < \nu_f(a) < +\infty$, let $z_1,\cdots,z_m$ denote the distinct antecedents of a with respect to f, and let $\rho > 0$ be so chosen that $\Delta(z_k;\rho) \subset \Omega$ and the restriction of f to $\Delta(z_k;\rho)$ has a valence with maximum equal to $n(z_k;f)$, this choice of ρ being possible by Corollary 6.1(2). We see that

$$a \in \hat{K} - \overline{f[\Omega - \bigcup_1^m \Delta(z_k;\rho)]},$$

for otherwise $a \in B(f)$ or else f would attain a at a point distinct from the z_k. Hence, there exists $r > 0$ such that $f^{-1}\left[\Delta(a;r)\right] \subset \bigcup_1^m \Delta(z_k;\rho)$. Hence,

$$\nu_f(w) \leqslant \Sigma\, n(z_k;f) = \nu_f(a) \text{ in } \Delta(a;r).$$

It follows that $\nu_f(w) = \nu_f(a)$ in some neighborhood of a. The proof of Theorem 8.1 is complete.

It is now easy to see as a consequence of Theorem 8.1 that ν_f *is finite and constant on each component of* $\hat{K} - B(f)$. If $\Omega = \hat{K}$ so that f is a rational function, we have ν_f *constant*. This is, of course, a well-known property of the rational functions.

EXERCISES

1. Given f meromorphic in a region Ω. Show that $B(f)$ is closed.

2. Given f meromorphic on $\Delta(a;r) - \{a\}$. Show that $B(f;a)$ reduces to a point or $B(f;a) = \hat{K}$. Show that, in the former case, f possesses a limit at a, so that f admits meromorphic extension to $\Delta(a;r)$.

3. Suppose that f of Ex. 2 satisfies $B(f;a) = \hat{K}$. Show then that $\{\nu_f(w) = \infty\}$ is dense in $\hat{K}$. [This exercise is intended for readers familiar with category arguments. It is not needed in the sequel, and the result stated will be seen to be quite weak in comparison with the "big Picard theorem" (Chap. 3).]

HINT: Note that the lower semicontinuity of ν_f implies that $\{\nu_f(w) < +\infty\} = \bigcup_{n \in N} \{\nu_f(w) \leqslant n\}$ is the union of a countable family of closed sets (i.e., it is an F_σ).

4. SCHWARZ LEMMA: Given f analytic on $\Delta(0;1)$ and satisfying $f(0) = 0$, $|f| < 1$. Then $|f(z)| \leqslant |z|$, $|z| < 1$, and $|f'(0)| \leqslant 1$. Equality occurs in each of these assertions if for some η of modulus 1, $f(z) \equiv \eta z$. In the opposite direction, if $|f'(0)| = 1$ or $|f(z)| = |z|$ for some z satisfying $0 < |z| < 1$, then $f(z) \equiv \eta z$ for some η of modulus 1.

HINT: Consider $g{:}g(z) = f(z)/z$, $0 < |z| < 1$, $g(0) = f'(0)$; show that $B(g) \subset \overline{\Delta(0;1)}$, and note that $\nu_g(\infty) = 0$.

NOTE: Another proof of the Schwarz lemma may be given by showing first the following lemma: *If h is analytic on a region $\Omega \neq \hat{K}$, then*

$$\sup_{z \in \Omega} |h(z)| = \sup \{|w| \mid w \in B(h)\},$$

and then applying this lemma to g. We shall consider a closely related lemma in the context of the theory of subharmonic functions in Chap. 4 (see Theorem 8.2 of Chap. 4).

5. Apply Ex. 4 to establish the following theorem: If f is a univalent (that is, a one-to-one) analytic function mapping $\Delta(0;1)$ onto itself and satisfying $f(0) = 0$, then there exists η of modulus 1 such that $f(z) \equiv \eta z$.

HINT: Let g denote the inverse of f, and apply the Schwarz lemma to both f and g.

6. A Lemma of R. M. Robinson: Let f be meromorphic on

$$A = \{r_1 < |z| < r_2\},\ 0 < r_1 < r_2 < +\infty$$

and have a pole at $-\rho$, $r_1 < \rho < r_2$, and no other. Suppose further that $n(-\rho;f) = 1$, that $f(z)$ is real for z real, and that for each $\zeta \in \operatorname{fr} A$, $\overline{\lim_{z \to \zeta}} |f| \leqslant 1$. Then $|f(x)| < 1$ for $r_1 < x < r_2$. (*Duke Math. J.*, 10:341–354, 1943.)

7. Rouché Theorem: Given a region $\Omega \neq \hat{K}$. Let f_1 and f_2 denote functions that have domain $\bar{\Omega}$, are continuous maps of $\bar{\Omega}$ into $\hat{K}$, and are meromorphic in Ω. Suppose that $|f_2(z)| < |f_1(z)| < +\infty$ for $z \in \text{fr}\, \Omega$. Let g_k denote the restriction of f_k to Ω. Then

$$\nu_{g_1+g_2}(0) - \nu_{g_1+g_2}(\infty) = \nu_{g_1}(0) - \nu_{g_1}(\infty).$$

Hint: Consider $h = (g_1 + g_2)/g_1$, as in the classical case. Show that $B(h) \subset \Delta(1;1)$. The formula for the divisor of h in terms of the divisors of g_1 and $g_1 + g_2$ may be used advantageously.

---

9. Boundary-preserving Maps. Let f denote a meromorphic function on a region Ω_1 which maps Ω_1 into a region Ω_2. We say that f is a *boundary-preserving* map of Ω_1 into Ω_2 provided that $B(f) \subset \text{fr}\, \Omega_2$. This condition states that if a sequence $(z_n), z_n \in \Omega_1$, satisfies $z_n \to \zeta \in \text{fr}\, \Omega_1$, then every convergent subsequence of $(f(z_n))$ tends to a point of fr Ω_2. In case f is the restriction to Ω_1 of a continuous map g of $\bar{\Omega}_1$ onto $\bar{\Omega}_2$, then f is a boundary-preserving map of Ω_1 into Ω_2 if and only if $g(\text{fr}\, \Omega_1) \subset \text{fr}\, \Omega_2$. The designation "boundary-preserving" is drawn from this case. The boundary-preserving maps are distinguished by simple covering properties. They occur as extremal functions in a number of extremal problems. In special cases of Ω_1, Ω_2, the boundary-preserving maps admit simple representations.

[In the case where $\Omega_1 = \hat{K}$, f is always boundary-preserving, and if f is not constant, $\Omega_2 = \hat{K}$. In the case where $\Omega_2 = \hat{K}$, f is boundary-preserving if, and only if, $\Omega_1 = \hat{K}$.]

We first establish a characterization for a boundary-preserving map in terms of the valence function:

Theorem 9.1. *Given a meromorphic function f with domain a region $\Omega_1 \neq \hat{K}$ mapping Ω_1 into a region Ω_2. Then f is a boundary-preserving map of Ω_1 into Ω_2 if, and only if, ν_f is finite and constant on Ω_2.*

The proof of Theorem 9.1 is simple. If f is boundary-preserving,

$$\Omega_2 \subset \hat{K} - \text{fr}\, \Omega_2 \subset \hat{K} - B(f).$$

Hence, by the observation following Theorem 8.1, ν_f is finite and constant on Ω_2. Suppose conversely that ν_f is finite and constant on Ω_2. Since ν_f does not vanish on Ω_2 and does vanish on fr Ω_2, we see by Theorem 8.1 that $\text{fr}\, \Omega_2 \subset B(f) \subset (\hat{K} - \Omega_2) \cap \overline{\Omega_2}$; that is, $B(f) = \text{fr}\, \Omega_2$. We have incidentally shown that *if f is boundary-preserving, then* $B(f) = \text{fr}\, \Omega_2$.

An Example. Suppose that f is a nonconstant meromorphic function on a region Ω_1, and suppose that Ω_2 is a region for which $f^{-1}(\Omega_2) \neq \emptyset$. Let G denote a component of $f^{-1}(\Omega_2)$. Suppose that *the closure of G (relative to $\hat{K}$) lies in Ω_1*. Then the restriction of f to G is a boundary-preserving map of G into Ω_2. It suffices to note that $f(\text{fr}\, G) \subset \text{fr}\, \Omega_2$ since G is a component of $f^{-1}(\Omega_2)$.

The case: $\Omega_1 = \Omega_2 = \Delta(0;1)$. In the study of functions analytic in $\Delta(0;1)$, it is convenient to have available the totality of univalent analytic maps of $\Delta(0;1)$ onto itself (in other words, the conformal automorphisms of $\Delta(0;1)$). The reader conversant with a detailed study of rational functions of degree 1 (the so-called Möbius or linear fractional transformations) is familiar with these automorphisms. However, we do not presuppose such an acquaintance and shall proceed directly. For a full treatment of the rational functions of degree 1, see Carathéodory, *Theory of Functions*, part 1, Chap. 2. We introduce for $|a| < 1$, the rational function

$$z \rightarrow L_a(z) = \frac{z - a}{1 - \bar{a}z}. \tag{9.1}$$

This will be the only forced step in our considerations. We verify immediately that the inverse of L_a, which we shall denote by M_a, satisfies

$$M_a = L_{(-a)} \tag{9.2}$$

and that

$$|L_a(z)| = 1 \qquad \text{for} \qquad |z| = 1 \tag{9.3}$$

(consider $|zL_a(z)|$ for $|z| = 1$). Equation (9.3) assures us that L_a maps $\Delta(0;1)$ onto itself and $\Delta(\infty;1)$ onto itself, since the sole zero of L_a is a and the sole pole $\bar{a}^{-1}$. The verification of this assertion may be made as a simple application of Theorem 8.1 and naturally, by direct computation as well.

Suppose now that f is a boundary-preserving map of $\Delta(0;1)$ onto itself. Let $a_1, \cdots, a_m$ denote the distinct zeros of f. Let g be defined by

$$g = \frac{f}{\prod_1^m (L_{a_k})^{n(a_k;f)}}. \tag{9.4}$$

[Here we understand that L_{a_k} is also designating its restriction to $\Delta(0;1)$]. Now g is analytic and nonvanishing on $\Delta(0;1)$, and $B(g) \subset C(0;1)$. It follows that $|g| = 1$ and hence, that g is a constant η of modulus 1. Hence

$$f = \eta \prod_1^m (L_{a_k})^{n(a_k;f)}. \tag{9.5}$$

It is immediate that every function of the form

$$\eta \prod_1^m (L_{a_k})^{\mu_k}, \tag{9.6}$$

where μ_k is a positive integer, $k = 1, \cdots, m(> 0)$, is a boundary-preserving map of $\Delta(0;1)$ onto itself since the boundary set lies in $C(0;1)$. *Thus the functions* (9.6) *give the totality of boundary-preserving maps of* $\Delta(0;1)$ *onto itself.*

Conformal automorphisms of $\Delta(0;1)$. It is now clear, since the conformal automorphisms of $\Delta(0;1)$ are the boundary-preserving maps of $\Delta(0;1)$ onto itself of valence 1 on $\Delta(0;1)$, that they are the functions of the form

$$\eta L_a, \qquad |\eta| = 1, \ |a| < 1. \tag{9.7}$$

It is also useful to note that if f is a conformal automorphism of $\Delta(0;1)$ onto itself, then

$$f(z) = M_{f(0)}(\eta z), \qquad |z| < 1, \tag{9.8}$$

where η is a complex number of modulus 1.

We observe in passing the curious fact that the set of boundary-preserving maps of $\Delta(0;1)$ onto itself is the multiplicative semigroup generated out of the conformal automorphisms of $\Delta(0;1)$.

EXERCISES

1. Verify that the rational function of degree 1,

$$z \to \alpha(z) = \frac{z-1}{z+1},$$

maps $\{\operatorname{Re} z > 0\}$ onto $\Delta(0;1)$ and $\{\operatorname{Re} z < 0\}$ onto $\Delta(\infty;1)$. Show with the aid of α that a boundary-preserving map of $\{\operatorname{Re} z > 0\}$ onto itself is the restriction of a rational function to $\{\operatorname{Re} z > 0\}$.

2. Show that the conformal automorphisms of $\{\operatorname{Re} z > 0\}$ onto itself are the functions on $\{\operatorname{Re} z > 0\}$ of the form

$$f(z) = az + ib, \qquad a > 0, \quad b \text{ real}, \tag{a}$$

or the form

$$f(z) = a(z - ic)^{-1} + ib, \qquad a > 0, \quad b,c \text{ real}. \tag{b}$$

3. Show that the set of boundary-preserving maps of $\{\operatorname{Re} z > 0\}$ onto itself is the additive semigroup generated by the conformal automorphisms of $\{\operatorname{Re} z > 0\}$ onto itself.

4. Determine ν_f for the meromorphic function f on $\Delta(0;1)$, given by

$$f(z) = \frac{z^2}{M_{1/2}(z)}.$$

---

10. Two Theorems of Landau. In this section we shall study two theorems of Landau which pertain to the covering properties of functions of a certain class of bounded analytic functions. These theorems furnish excellent applications of the theorems developed in §§ 8 and 9.

Let a satisfy $0 < a < 1$. Let Φ_a denote the class of functions f analytic on $\Delta(0;1)$ satisfying: $f(0) = 0, f'(0) = a$, $|f(z)| < 1$ for $|z| < 1$. We introduce

$$r(f) = \sup \{r \mid f \text{ is univalent on } \Delta(0;r)\}$$

and let

$$\rho = \inf r(f). \tag{10.1}$$

The first theorem of Landau we shall establish is the following:

THEOREM 10.1. $\rho = a^{-1}(1 - \sqrt{1 - a^2})$. *There exist* $f \in \Phi_a$ *for which* $r(f) = \rho$. *They are the functions of the form* $F(\eta z)\eta^{-1}$, *where* η *is a complex number of modulus* 1 *and*

$$F(z) = z \frac{a - z}{1 - az}.$$

PROOF: It will be convenient to observe that the following elementary inequality holds:

$$|L_{|b|}(|z|)| \leqslant |M_b(z)| \leqslant M_{|b|}(|z|), \quad |z|, |b| < 1. \tag{10.2}$$

$|M_b(z)|$ is equal to one of the extreme members if, and only if, z and b are linearly dependent (relative to R). Also, it is convenient to observe that if $-1 < b < 1$, then $x \to M_b(x)$ is monotone-increasing on $\{-1 \leqslant x \leqslant 1\}$.

Suppose that $f \in \Phi_a$ and that $r(f) < 1$. Then either there exists ζ of modulus $r(f)$ for which $n(\zeta;f) > 1$ or else there exist $\zeta_1, \zeta_2 (\neq \zeta_1)$ of modulus $r(f)$ for which $f(\zeta_1) = f(\zeta_2)$. Let α denote respectively $f(\zeta)$ or the common value of $f(\zeta_1)$ and $f(\zeta_2)$. Then we have

$$|L_\alpha \circ f| \leqslant |L_\zeta|^2 \tag{10.3}$$

or

$$|L_\alpha \circ f| \leqslant |L_{\zeta_1}|\,|L_{\zeta_2}|$$

respectively. [Consider $L_\alpha \circ f/(L_\zeta)^2$ or $L_\alpha \circ f/L_{\zeta_1} L_{\zeta_2}$.]
On setting $z = 0$, we obtain in either case

$$|\alpha| \leqslant [r(f)]^2. \tag{10.4}$$

On the other hand, we have

$$f(z) = zg(z),$$

where g is analytic on $\Delta(0;1)$ and of modulus less than 1, and $g(0) = a$. From $L_a \circ g(z) = zh(z)$, where h is analytic on $\Delta(0;1)$ and of modulus at most 1, we have

$$f(z) = zM_a(zh(z)). \tag{10.5}$$

From (10.5) and (10.2), we conclude that

$$|f(z)| \geqslant |z| \frac{a - |zh(z)|}{1 - a|zh(z)|} \geqslant |z| \frac{a - |z|}{1 - a|z|}, \qquad |z| < 1. \tag{10.6}$$

Hence we have, setting $z = \zeta$ (resp., ζ_1),

$$|\alpha| \geqslant r(f) \frac{a - r(f)}{1 - ar(f)}. \tag{10.7}$$

It follows by (10.4), since $r(f) > 0$, that

$$r(f) \geqslant \frac{a - r(f)}{1 - ar(f)}.$$

Hence, for all $f \in \Phi_a$, $r(f)$ cannot be smaller than the smaller root σ of

$$x = \frac{a - x}{1 - ax}.$$

This root has the value given for ρ in the first sentence of the statement of the theorem. On the other hand, $F'(\sigma) = 0$; thus $r(F) = \sigma$. Hence $\sigma = \rho$. Clearly, every f of the form $F(\eta z)\eta^{-1}$ satisfies $r(f) = \rho$. Suppose that $f \in \Phi_a$ satisfies $r(f) = \rho$. It follows from (10.4) and (10.7) that $|\alpha| = [r(f)]^2$. Consequently, equality occurs in (10.3) for $z = 0$. Since $\alpha \neq 0$, it follows that $L_\alpha \circ f = \eta(L_\zeta)^2$ or $L_\alpha \circ f = \eta L_{\zeta_1} L_{\zeta_2}$, where η is a constant of modulus 1. Hence f is of degree 2, and we conclude that h of the representation (10.5) is a constant of modulus 1. The last assertion of the theorem follows.

EXERCISE

1. Amplify on the second sentence of the second paragraph of the proof, justifying the assertion made.

The second theorem of Landau that we shall treat here may be formulated as follows. Given $f \in \Phi_a$, let $E(f)$ denote the set of positive r for which there exists a region Ω_r, $0 \in \Omega_r \subset \Delta(0;1)$, such that f maps Ω_r univalently onto $\Delta(0;r)$. It is clear that for each $r \in E(f)$, Ω_r is the component of $f^{-1}[\Delta(0;r)]$ containing 0. Let $R(f) = \sup E(f)$ and let $P = \inf_{f \in \Phi_a} R(f)$. The theorem states

THEOREM 10.2. $P = \rho^2$. *Further,* $R(f) = P$ *if, and only if,* f *is one of the extremal functions of the form* $F(\eta z)\eta^{-1}$ *of Theorem* 10.1. *The number* ρ *is that of Theorem* 10.1.

PROOF: By (10.6) we have

$$\min_{|z|=r} |f(z)| \geqslant r \frac{a - r}{1 - ar}, \qquad 0 < r < 1. \tag{10.8}$$

The maximum value of the right-hand side of (10.8), subject to the restriction $0 < r < 1$, is attained for $r = \rho$; further, it is ρ^2. Now $\rho < a$. Hence, by (10.8) $f(z) \neq 0$ for $0 < |z| \leqslant \rho$. Let Ω denote the component of $f^{-1}[\Delta(0;\rho^2)]$ containing $z = 0$. Then $\Omega \subset \Delta(0;\rho)$. Hence the restriction of f to Ω is a boundary-preserving map of Ω onto $\Delta(0;\rho^2)$. Further, f vanishes in Ω only at $z = 0$, and $n(0;f) = 1$. Hence f maps Ω univalently onto $\Delta(0;\rho^2)$. It follows that $\rho^2 \leqslant P$. We observe that $R(F) = \rho^2$. In fact, $F'(\rho) = 0$, and since F is of degree 2, ρ^2 is attained by F only at $z = \rho$. Hence, $R(F) = \rho^2$, for otherwise we should be forced to conclude that $F'(\rho) \neq 0$. We conclude that $P = \rho^2$. Again we see that for each f of the form $F(\eta z)\eta^{-1}$, $R(f) = P$.

The converse remains to be shown. Again we turn to (10.6). If h is not a constant of modulus 1, we see from (10.6) that

$$\mu = \min_{|z|=\rho} |f(z)| > \rho \frac{a-\rho}{1-a\rho}. \tag{10.9}$$

Now the component of $f^{-1}[\Delta(0;\mu)]$ containing $z = 0$ lies in $\Delta(0;\rho)$. We have, by the same reasoning used above: $R(f) \geqslant \mu > P$. The proof of the theorem is readily completed.

EXERCISES

2. Show that for $f \in \Phi_a$, $R(f) \in E(f)$.

3. For $f \in \Phi_a$, let $R_1(f)$ denote the maximum positive number r such that

$$\Delta(0;r) \subset f[\Delta(0;1)].$$

Determine $P_1 = \inf R_1(f)$ and the associated extremal function(s) $F \in \Phi_a$ for which $P_1 = R_1(F)$.

HINT: Note that if b is a point of $\Delta(0;1)$ omitted by f, then

$$L_b \circ f = \exp \circ (-g)$$

where $\operatorname{Re} g > 0$. Further, $[g - g(0)]/[g + \overline{g(0)}]$ is controlled by the Schwarz Lemma.

---

11. Simple Connectivity.

We have already seen that the notion of simple connectivity may be approached in different ways. For example, we may focus attention on an internal topological property, as we did in the definition of homotopic simple connectivity. On the other hand, we may look to the function-theoretic behavior of a region, as we did in the case of holomorphic simple connectivity. The latter definition involves not only the region but also a concomitant entity, the family of analytic functions on the region. There are other possible definitions. One definition commonly used pertains to the way in which the region is imbedded in the extended plane. According to this, a region

$\Omega \subset \hat{K}$ is *simply-connected* provided that either $\Omega = \hat{K}$ or $\hat{K} - \Omega$ is connected. We shall return to the question of the equivalence of these definitions as well as to the question of other characterizations of simple connectivity in Appendix 3(c). For the present we note that the two definitions of simple connectivity, *homotopic* and *holomorphic*, are such that a region Ω in one of these senses has the following properties:

(l) Each f analytic on Ω that vanishes nowhere possesses an analytic logarithm.

(s) Each f analytic on Ω that vanishes nowhere possesses an analytic square root.

EXERCISE

1. If Ω has the property (l), then clearly it has the property (s). Show that if Ω has the property (s), it also has the property (l).

We shall see that in the proof of the Riemann mapping theorem, we shall be able to proceed with Ω satisfying merely the less stringent condition:

(s_1) Each f analytic on Ω that vanishes nowhere and is univalent possesses an analytic square root.

12. The Riemann Mapping Theorem. This theorem may be stated in terms of the (s_1) property as follows:

THEOREM 12.1. *Let Ω be a region having the property* (s_1) *and such that $\hat{K} - \Omega$ contains more than one point. Then there exists a univalent analytic function on Ω mapping Ω onto $\Delta(0;1)$.*

We say that a region Ω_2 is *conformally equivalent* to a region Ω_1 provided that there exists a univalent meromorphic function mapping Ω_1 onto Ω_2 (= one-to-one conformal map of Ω_1 onto Ω_2). A bona fide equivalence relation is thereby defined in the class of plane regions.

From the mapping theorem just stated and from elementary considerations we see:

$\Delta(0;1)$, K, and $\hat{K}$ are mutually conformally non equivalent regions having the property (s_1). *Every region having the property* (s_1) *is conformally equivalent to one of the regions $\Delta(0;1)$, K, $\hat{K}$.*

The first sentence may be established by noting that a non constant rational function attains all values and by the Liouville theorem. If Ω does not omit at least two points of $\hat{K}$, either it is $\hat{K}$ itself or it omits just one point. In the latter case, if this point, say a, is finite, then $z \to (z - a)^{-1}$ maps Ω onto K. The second sentence now follows from the Riemann mapping theorem.

We note that *if a region Ω_1 has the property* (s_1) *and if Ω_2 is conformally equivalent to Ω_1 then Ω_2 also has the property* (s_1). This remark permits us to reduce the proof of the mapping theorem as follows.

We may suppose that $\Omega \subset K$. Let $a \in K - \Omega$. By the (s_1) property, there exists an analytic function s on Ω satisfying

$$[s(z)]^2 = z - a, \qquad z \in \Omega.$$

Clearly s is univalent. Further, it is not possible for s to attain a complex value and its negative. Hence, if $z_0 \in \Omega$, $[s + s(z_0)]^{-1}$ is univalent and bounded. Hence we are assured that Ω is conformally equivalent to a region lying in $\Delta(0;1)$ and containing $z = 0$.

It is our object to develop the proof of the mapping theorem due to Carathéodory and Koebe. We shall want a preliminary auxiliary mapping used by Koebe (§ 13) and some simple results concerning compactness properties of bounded analytic functions (§ 14) before turning to the proof of the mapping theorem in § 15. Sections § 14 and § 15 will be presented in exercise form.

13. The Koebe Mapping. Suppose that Ω is a region having the (s_1) property and satisfying $0 \in \Omega \subset \Delta(0;1)$ as well as $\Omega \neq \Delta(0;1)$. Let ζ denote a point of fr Ω whose modulus is least. We may if we like fix ζ as that point of fr Ω with minimum modulus whose argument in the interval $\{-\pi \leqslant \theta < \pi\}$ is least. By the (s_1) property, there exists a unique function ψ analytic on Ω, satisfying $\psi(0) > 0$ and

$$\frac{\bar{\zeta}}{|\zeta|}\frac{\zeta - z}{1 - \bar{\zeta}z} = [\psi(z)]^2, \qquad z \in \Omega. \tag{13.1}$$

It is obvious that ψ is univalent. We now define φ by

$$\varphi(z) = \eta\,\frac{\psi(z) - \psi(0)}{1 - \psi(0)\psi(z)}, \qquad z \in \Omega, \tag{13.2}$$

where η is simply $\overline{\psi'(0)/|\psi'(0)|}$. Hence φ is an analytic univalent function on Ω of modulus less than 1 and satisfying: $\varphi(0) = 0$, $\varphi'(0) > 0$. The mapping φ so defined will be termed the *Koebe mapping associated with the reduced region* Ω. From (13.1) and (13.2) we see that φ satisfies

$$z = B \circ \varphi(z), \qquad z \in \Omega, \tag{13.3}$$

where B is a boundary-preserving map of $\Delta(0;1)$ onto itself of degree 2, and $B(0) = 0$. Hence we have the basic inequality

$$|z| \leqslant |\varphi(z)|, \qquad z \in \Omega. \tag{13.4}$$

We see from (13.3) that some frontier point of $\varphi(\Omega)$ lies in $\Delta(0;1)$ and that a frontier point of $\varphi(\Omega)$ nearest 0 has modulus greater than $|\zeta| = r$. We obtain from (13.1) and (13.2) the formula

$$\varphi'(0) = \frac{1 + r}{2\sqrt{r}}. \tag{13.5}$$

14. Compactness of a Family of Uniformly Bounded Analytic Functions. Let Ω denote a region $\subset K$. Let $B(\Omega)$ denote the set of functions analytic on Ω and satisfying $|f| \leqslant 1$. The following theorem is due to Montel.

THEOREM 14.1. *Given a sequence* $(f_n)_0^\infty$ *of members of* $B(\Omega)$. *Then there exists a subsequence* $(f_{m(n)})$ *that converges uniformly in* Ω.

EXERCISES

Establish the following lemmas and deduce Theorem 14.1.

1. Let a denote a map of $N \times N$ into $\hat{K}$. Then there exists a monotone-increasing map μ of N into itself such that for each $k \in N$, the sequence

$$j \to a(\mu(j),k)$$

possesses a limit (*selection principle*).

This may be established by use of the theorem: Given a sequence of elements of $\hat{K}$, there exists a subsequence possessing a limit; and the procedure of diagonalization. Thus, let $A^{(k)}$ denote the sequence $j \to a(j,k)$, $k = 0,1,\cdots$. Let $\mu^{(0)}$ denote an increasing map of N into itself such that $A^{(0)} \circ \mu^{(0)}$ possesses a limit. Let $\mu^{(1)}$ denote a subsequence of $\mu^{(0)}$ such that $A^{(1)} \circ \mu^{(1)}$ possesses a limit. Continuing recursively, we obtain a sequence $(\mu^{(j)})_0^\infty$ of maps of N into itself satisfying the conditions: (a) for each $j \in N$, $A^{(j)} \circ \mu^{(j)}$ possesses a limit; and (b) for each $j \in N$, $\mu^{(j+1)}$ is a subsequence of $\mu^{(j)}$. Let μ be defined by $\mu(j) = \mu^{(j)}(j)$. Verify that μ has the stated properties.

(To be specific, we term B a *subsequence* of a sequence A provided that there exists an increasing map ν of N into itself such that $B = A \circ \nu$.)

2. Let $(z_k)_0^\infty$ denote a univalent map of N onto the set of rational points of Ω. Then there exists a subsequence $(f_{m(n)})$ of (f_n) such that $\big(f_{m(n)}(z_k)\big)_{n=0}^\infty$ possesses a limit, $k \in N$. Let $a(j,k) = f_j(z_k)$, and apply the selection principle of Ex. 1.

3. Given $\overline{\Delta(a;2r)} \subset \Omega$. Let $\zeta_1, \zeta_2 \in \overline{\Delta(a;r)}$.
Then

$$|f(\zeta_2) - f(\zeta_1)| \leqslant \frac{2\,|\zeta_2 - \zeta_1|}{r}, \qquad f \in B(\Omega).$$

(Use the Cauchy integral formula.)

4. Let g_n denote $f_{m(n)}$. Then (g_n) converges uniformly on $\overline{\Delta(a;r)}$.
Use

$$|g_p(z) - g_q(z)| \leqslant |g_p(z) - g_p(z_k)| + |g_p(z_k) - g_q(z_k)| + |g_q(z_k) - g_q(z)|$$
$$\leqslant \frac{4}{r}|z - z_k| + |g_p(z_k) - g_q(z_k)|, \qquad z, z_k \in \overline{\Delta(a;r)}.$$

Given $\varepsilon > 0$, let $z_{k_1},\cdots,z_{k_l} \in \overline{\Delta(a;r)}$ be such that

$$\overline{\Delta(a;r)} \subset \bigcup_{j=1}^{l} \Delta\left(z_{k_j}; \frac{r\varepsilon}{8}\right).$$

5. $(f_{m(n)})$ converges uniformly on each compact subset of Ω.

---

15. Proof of the Mapping Theorem. Let Ω denote a reduced region (that is, $0 \in \Omega \subset \Delta(0;1)$) having the property ($s_1$). We may suppose that $\Omega \neq \Delta(0;1)$; otherwise we should have a trivial situation. There exists a sequence of reduced regions $(\Omega_n)_0^\infty$, $\Omega_n \neq \Delta(0;1)$, and a sequence of functions $(\varphi_n)_0^\infty$ satisfying the conditions: (1) $\Omega_0 = \Omega$; and (2) for each $n \in N$, φ_n is the Koebe mapping associated with Ω_n and $\Omega_{n+1} = \varphi_n(\Omega_n)$. Let $(f_n)_0^\infty$ be defined by the requirements that f_0 be the identity map of Ω onto itself and that $f_{n+1} = \varphi_n \circ f_n$, $n \in N$.

EXERCISE

1. Verify the following assertions:

(a) $|f_n| \leqslant |f_{n+1}|$, $n \in N$.

(b) The sequence (f_n) converges in Ω (use Theorem 14.1) and, in fact, uniformly in Ω (use Ex. 4, § 14, with $g_n = f_n$).

(c) Let r_n denote the distance from 0 to $\hat{K} - \Omega_n$. Then (r_n) is an increasing sequence with limit 1. [Use the fact that $(f_n'(0))_0^\infty$ possesses a finite positive limit and also Eq. (13.5).]

(d) f, the limit of the sequence (f_n), is a univalent map of Ω onto $\Delta(0;1)$. [From $|f_n| \leqslant |f|$, conclude $B(f) \subset C(0;1)$ and hence, since f has a simple zero at $z = 0$ and no other zero, the required assertion.]

REMARK: After we have introduced methods using harmonic functions in Chap. 4, we shall see that we can dispense with the use of Theorem 14.1. It is a very useful theorem, however, and of fundamental importance for many existence questions.

EXERCISES

2. Let Ω be a region $\subset K$ conformally equivalent to $\Delta(0;1)$. Let a denote a given point of Ω, and let f denote a univalent conformal map of Ω onto $\Delta(0;1)$ satisfying $f(a) = 0$. Show that

$$|g'(a)| \leqslant |f'(a)|, \qquad g \in B(\Omega),$$

and that equality occurs if and only if $g = \eta f$, where η is a constant of modulus 1.

3. Let Ω be a region $\subset K$ and $\neq K$ having the property (s_1). Let $a \in \Omega$, and let $\alpha = \sup | g'(a) |$, where $g(a) = 0$ and g is univalent and in $B(\Omega)$. Using Theorem 14.1, show that there exists a g meeting the stated conditions, say g_0, such that $\alpha = g_0'(a)$. Show with the aid of the Koebe mapping that g_0 maps Ω onto $\Delta(0;1)$. (This proof of the mapping theorem is due to Fejér and F. Riesz.)

4. A region having the property (s_1) is homotopically simply-connected.

[3]

The Picard Theorem

1. Statement of the Theorem. Our concern in this chapter will be to establish the so-called "*big Picard theorem*," which may be stated as follows:

Given f meromorphic on $\Delta(a;r) - \{a\}$. *If* ν_f *is finite at three distinct points, then* $\lim_a f$ *exists, and so f admits meromorphic extension to* $\Delta(a;r)$.

This theorem has been the impetus for a large number of investigations. The original proof involved the use of the modular function, which plays an important role in number theory and the theory of automorphic functions. Subsequently, so-called "elementary" proofs were given, based upon the theorem of Bloch. In the present chapter we shall follow this elementary approach in establishing the big Picard theorem. A deeper study of the Picard theorem involves in a natural way the use of the modular function or closely related apparatus (such as that employed in R. Nevanlinna's theory of meromorphic functions).

2. The Bloch Theorem. Suppose that f is a function analytic on a region Ω and not constant. By the *Bloch number* $b(f)$ of f is meant the supremum of the set of positive numbers r satisfying the condition: there exists a subregion $\Omega_1 \subset \Omega$ that f maps univalently onto a disk of radius r. By the *Landau number*, $l(f)$ of f is meant the supremum of the set of positive numbers r such that $f(\Omega)$ contains a disk of radius r. Let Φ denote the family of functions f analytic on $\Delta(0;1)$ and normalized by the condition

$$f'(0) = 1. \tag{2.1}$$

By the *Bloch constant* β is meant

$$\inf_{f \in \Phi} b(f),$$

and by the *Landau constant* λ is meant

$$\inf_{f \in \Phi} l(f).$$

Clearly, $b(f) \leqslant l(f)$ and $\beta \leqslant \lambda$. The theorem of Bloch is

THEOREM 2.1. $\beta > 0$.

The remarkable feature of the Bloch theorem is that despite the vastness of the class Φ, the Bloch constant β is positive. Let Φ_1 denote the subfamily of Φ

consisting of those members of Φ whose power-series expansions about $z = 0$ have a radius of convergence greater than 1. Clearly,

$$\beta \leqslant \inf_{f \in \Phi_1} b(f) .$$

On the other hand, given $f \in \Phi$, g given by $g(z) = f(rz)r^{-1}$, $0 < r < 1$, is a member of Φ_1, and $b(g) \leqslant b(f)r^{-1}$. Hence

$$\inf_{f \in \Phi_1} b(f) \leqslant \beta r^{-1} ,$$

and, consequently,

$$\inf_{f \in \Phi_1} b(f) = \beta . \tag{2.2}$$

This means that a lower bound for the $b(f)$, $f \in \Phi_1$, is no greater than β.

Suppose now that $f \in \Phi_1$. We note that each of the functions $g_a = f \circ M_a$, $|a| < 1$, satisfies $b(g_a) = b(f)$ and that $g_a'(0) = f'(a)(1 - |a|^2)$. Let a be so chosen that $|g_a'(0)|$ is maximized. Clearly, the maximum value, which is at least as large as 1, is attained for some a in $\Delta(0;1)$, say a_0. Let $g = g_{a_0}/|g_{a_0}'(0)|$. Then $b(g) \leqslant b(f)$, and g satisfies the inequality

$$(1 - |z|^2)\,|g'(z)| \leqslant 1. \tag{2.3}$$

Thanks to this inequality, we can obtain a lower bound for $b(f)$ that is independent of f. In fact, let $h = g - g(0)$ so that $b(h) = b(g)$. Then

$$|h(z)| \leqslant \frac{1}{2} \log \frac{1 + |z|}{1 - |z|} . \tag{2.4}$$

On applying Theorem 10.2, Chap. 2, to

$$z \to \frac{h(rz)}{\frac{1}{2}\log[(1 + r)/(1 - r)]}, \qquad |z| < 1 ,$$

where $0 < r < 1$, we find that

$$b(f) \geqslant b(h) \geqslant \frac{1}{2} \log \frac{1 + r}{1 - r}\, \delta \left\{ \frac{2r}{\log[(1 + r)/(1 - r)]} \right\}, \tag{2.5}$$

where

$$\delta(x) = \left(\frac{x}{1 + \sqrt{1 - x^2}}\right)^2 .$$

Setting $r = \frac{1}{2}$ in the right-hand side of (2.5), we obtain

$$b(f) \geqslant 0.21 .$$

Hence $\beta \geqslant 0.21$. The theorem is established.

Actually, much better information is available concerning the value of β. Ahlfors and Grunsky (*Math. Zeitschrift*, 1937) have shown that $\beta < 0.472$, and Ahlfors (*Trans. AMS*, **43**: 359—364, 1938) has shown that $\beta > 0.433$. We shall give an account of Ahlfors's work in the next chapter. The determination of the exact value of β remains an outstanding problem.

For papers concerning the Bloch theorem we recommend the paper of Ahlfors just cited and R. M. Robinson: "Bloch Functions," *Duke Math. J.*, 2:453—459, 1936.

EXERCISES

1. Show with the aid of

$$z \to \frac{1}{2} \operatorname{Log} \frac{1+z}{1-z}, \qquad |z| < 1,$$

that the Landau constant satisfies $\lambda \leqslant \pi/4$. (Here Log denotes the function L of Ex. 2, § 2, Chap. 1.)

2. Let Φ_2 denote the class of functions f analytic on $\Delta(0;1)$ and satisfying: $f(0) = 0$, $\max |f(e^{i\theta}/2)| \geqslant 1$. Show that

$$\inf_{f \in \Phi_2} b(f) > 0 .$$

3. Show that there exists $f \in \Phi$ such that $b(f) = \beta$.

Hint: Consider a sequence (f_n) satisfying $f_n \in \Phi_1$, $b(f_n) \to \beta$, and replace f_n by h_n, where h_n stands in the same relation to f_n as h to f in the proof of Theorem 2.1. Show that some subsequence of (h_n) converges uniformly in $\Delta(0;1)$ and that its limit h satisfies $b(h) = \beta$.

4. Show that if f is analytic and not constant on $\Delta(0;1)$, then

$$(1 - |z|^2)\,|f'(z)| \leqslant \frac{b(f)}{\beta}, \qquad |z| < 1 .$$

5. Show that if f is analytic and non constant in $\{\operatorname{Re} z > 0\}$, then

$$|f'(z)| \leqslant \frac{b(f)}{2\beta} \frac{1}{\operatorname{Re} z}, \qquad \operatorname{Re} z > 0 . \tag{2.6}$$

Hint: Consider for Re $a > 0$ the function g_a with domain $\Delta(0;1)$ satisfying

$$g_a\left(\frac{z-a}{z+\bar{a}}\right) = f(z)$$

and note that $b(g_a) = b(f)$.

6. Show that if f is analytic on K and non constant, $b(f) = +\infty$.

3. A Lemma. In this section we state and establish a lemma that we shall use in the proof of the Picard theorem as well as for other purposes.

LEMMA 3.1. *Let f be analytic on a simply-connected region Ω, and let $f(z) \neq 0,1$, $z \in \Omega$. Then there exists a function g analytic on Ω satisfying $f = \exp \circ (2\pi i \cosh \circ g)$. If $a \in \Omega$, g may be normalized to satisfy*

$$| g(a) | \leqslant \log \left[2 + \frac{| \log | f(a) | |}{\pi}\right] + \pi .$$

The point of this lemma is that with an admitted f there is associated a g that omits the lattice of points

$$\{\pm \cosh^{-1} (n + 1) + 2\pi im\}_{n \in N, m \in I}. \tag{3.1}$$

For such a g we have, if g is not constant,

$$b(g) \leqslant \sqrt{\left(\frac{\cosh^{-1} 2}{2}\right)^2 + \pi^2} \tag{3.2}$$

and hence, the possibility of controlling g'. Here $\cosh^{-1} a$ is the nonnegative solution of $\cosh x = a$, $a \geqslant 1$.

PROOF: Let F be analytic on Ω and satisfy

$$f = \exp \circ (2\pi iF) , \qquad -\frac{1}{2} \leqslant \operatorname{Re} F(a) < \frac{1}{2} . \tag{3.3}$$

It is clear that F omits every real integer. Further $| \operatorname{Im} F(a) | = | \log | f(a) | |/2\pi$. Now let S denote an analytic square root of $F^2 - 1$, and let G denote one of the functions $F + S$, $F - S$ satisfying $| G(a) | \geqslant 1$. Since $(F + S)(F - S) = 1$, we see that G is nonvanishing, and we let g denote the analytic logarithm of G satisfying $-\pi \leqslant \operatorname{Im} g(a) < \pi$. Retracing our steps, we see that $F = \cosh \circ g$, and consequently, $f = \exp \circ (2\pi i \cosh \circ g)$. [Of course this could have been achieved by analytic continuation. We do not presuppose a full-scale treatment of this subject.]

We see that

$$1 \leqslant | G(a) | \leqslant 1 + 2 | F(a) | \leqslant 1 + 2\left(\frac{1}{2} + \frac{| \log | f(a) | |}{2\pi}\right)$$
$$\leqslant 2 + \frac{| \log | f(a) | |}{\pi} .$$

The inequality for $| g(a) |$ now follows. We also have the inequality

$$| \log | f | | \leqslant 2\pi \cosh \circ | g | \leqslant 2\pi \exp \circ | g |. \tag{3.4}$$

4. Theorem of Schottky. Let $k \geqslant 0$. Let $\mathbf{P}(k)$ denote the class of functions f analytic on $\Delta(0;1)$ that omit 0 and 1 and satisfy $\log |f(0)| \leqslant k$. Let $\mathbf{Q}(k)$ denote the subclass of $\mathbf{P}(k)$ whose members f satisfy the stronger condition $|\log |f(0)|| \leqslant k$. We show

THEOREM 4.1. *There exist positive numbers A_1, A_2 such that*

$$(1)\ |\log |f(z)|| \leqslant A_1\Big(\frac{1+|z|}{1-|z|}\Big)^{A_2}, \ |z| < 1, \qquad f \in \mathbf{Q}(k);$$

$$(2)\ \log |f(z)| \leqslant A_1\Big(\frac{1+|z|}{1-|z|}\Big)^{2A_2}, \ |z| < 1, \qquad f \in \mathbf{P}(k)$$

(*Schottky*).

PROOF: We shall show that we may take A_1 as $2\pi e^{\pi}(2+k/\pi)$ and A_2 as

$$\frac{1}{2\beta}\sqrt{\Big(\frac{\cosh^{-1}2}{2}\Big)^2 + \pi^2}\,.$$

We may put aside the case where f is constant. Let us consider the inequality (1). Let g be associated with f in accordance with Lemma 3.1, it being understood that g is normalized at $a = 0$. By Ex. 4, § 2, this chapter, we have

$$|g'(z)| \leqslant 2A_2(1-|z|^2)^{-1}$$

and hence,

$$|g(z)| \leqslant |g(0)| + |g(z) - g(0)|$$
$$\leqslant |g(0)| + A_2 \log \frac{1+|z|}{1-|z|}\,.$$

From (3.4) and this last inequality we obtain Theorem 4.1 (1).

To establish (2), we note that it suffices to consider $f \in \mathbf{P}(k)$ for which $\log |f(0)| < -k$. Since f does not vanish in $\Delta(0;1)$, we see that for $0 < r < 1$,

$$\min_{|z|=r} \log |f(z)| \leqslant \log |f(0)| < 0\,.$$

If $\max_{|z|=r} \log |f(z)| \leqslant 0$, the inequality (2) holds trivially on $C(0;r)$. If, however, $\max_{|z|=r} \log |f(z)| > 0$, then there exists $a \in C(0;r)$ such that $\log |f(a)| = 0$. Applying (1) to

$$f \circ M_a,$$

we see that for $|z| = r$,

$$\log |f(z)| \leqslant A_1\Big(\frac{1+|L_a(z)|}{1-|L_a(z)|}\Big)^{A_2} \leqslant A_1\Big(\frac{1+|z|}{1-|z|}\Big)^{2A_2}.$$

Hence the inequality (2) holds.

EXERCISES

1. Conclude from the Schottky theorem the "little Picard theorem": If f is analytic on K and omits two distinct finite values, then f is constant.

2. Prove with the aid of the Schottky theorem the following theorem of Landau: Let a denote a given complex number $\neq 0,1$. Let E denote the set of functions f satisfying the following conditions: f is analytic on an open disk centered at $z = 0$; $f(0) = a$; $f'(0) = 1$; $f(z) \neq 0,1$ for all z in the domain of f. Let $r(f)$ denote the radius of the domain of f. Then $\sup_{f \in E} r(f) < +\infty$.

Give an explicit upper bound for the $r(f)$.

HINT: Apply the Schottky theorem to $F(z) = f[r(f)z]$.

3. Let Φ denote the class of functions f analytic on $\Delta(0;1)$ and satisfying $f(0) = 0$, $\max_{|z|=1/2} |f(z)| = 1$. Let $k(f)$ denote the supremum of the set of r for which $C(0;r) \subset f[\Delta(0;1)]$. Let $\kappa = \inf_{f \in \Phi} k(f)$. Show that $\kappa > 0$.

HINT: Suppose $k(f) < +\infty$. Let a and b denote points of modulus $k(f)$ and $2k(f)$ respectively omitted by f, and consider

$$g = \frac{f - a}{b - a}.$$

The function g belongs to the class $\mathbf{Q}$ (log 3).

REMARK: Essentially this theorem is given in Littlewood: *Lectures on the Theory of Functions*, Oxford University Press, 1944, p. 225. Littlewood remarks that the exact value of $\kappa_1 = \inf_{f \in \Phi_1} k(f)$ for the class Φ_1: f analytic on $\Delta(0;1)$, $f(0) = 0, f'(0) = 1$, is not known, but conjectures that $\kappa_1 = \frac{1}{4}$. This conjecture was settled affirmatively by W. K. Hayman in his paper "Some applications of the transfinite diameter to the theory of functions," *Journal d'Analyse Mathématique*, Vol. 1, pp. 155-179, 1951. The corresponding problem of determining κ is also settled there. The question is also discussed in his Cambridge University Press tract, *Multivalent Functions*. The conjecture of Littlewood can be demonstrated by use of the Lindelöf principle and appraisals of the Carleman-Milloux type for certain subharmonic functions. The value of κ can be similarly determined. A full discussion of this question is outside the program of the present book. However, we shall indicate the essential steps of the proof in § 8, Chap. 5.[1]

---

5. The Proof of the Big Picard Theorem.

Preliminary reductions. We may assume that the following restrictions hold. Reference is made to the statement of the big Picard theorem given at the beginning of this chapter.

$$a = \infty \text{ and } r < +\infty, \tag{1}$$

$$\nu_f(0) = \nu_f(1) = \nu_f(\infty) = 0. \tag{2}$$

It is trivial, of course, that we may require (1). That we may also require (2) is shown by the following argument. Replacing f by its restriction to a sufficiently small $\Delta(\infty; r_1) - \{\infty\}$, we see that we may assume that ν_f vanishes at three distinct points A, B, C. We may also suppose that $A = 0$, $B = 1$, $C = \infty$. For if, say, $C = \infty$, then

$$\varphi = \frac{f - A}{B - A}$$

does not vanish or take the value 1. If φ possesses a limit at ∞, so does f. If A, B, C are all finite and T is the rational function of degree 1 given by

$$T(z) = \frac{z - A}{z - B} \frac{C - B}{C - A},$$

then $T \circ f$ omits 0, 1, ∞, and if it possesses a limit at ∞, so does f.

We assume that we are dealing with a reduced f. We show that the *assumption that f does not possess a limit at ∞ implies that f does possess a limit at ∞.* Hence it follows that f does indeed possess a limit at ∞.

Let $m = \min_{|z|=2/r} |f(z)|$ and $M = \max_{|z|=2/r} |f(z)|$. Under the assumption that f does not possess a limit at ∞, we see that there exist points z_1, z_2 of modulus greater than $2/r$ such that

$$|f(z_1)| < \min\{1,m\} \leqslant \max\{1,M\} < |f(z_2)|.$$

Hence there exists $R > e/r$ such that for $\rho \geqslant R$,

$$\min_{|z|=\rho} |f(z)| < 1 < \max_{|z|=\rho} |f(z)|$$

since this is certainly the case by the maximum principle, for $\rho \geqslant \max\{|z_1|, |z_2|\}$. For each such ρ, there is a point, say $\rho e^{i\theta(\rho)}$, of $C(0;\rho)$ at which the modulus of f is 1. We now introduce the function F_ρ with domain $\{|\operatorname{Re} z| < 1\}$ defined by

$$F_\rho(z) = f(\rho e^{z+i\theta(\rho)}).$$

We have $|F_\rho(0)| = 1$. From the Schottky theorem with $k = 0$, we obtain $|\log |F_\rho(iy)|| \leqslant A_1 3^{A_2}$ for $0 \leqslant y \leqslant 1/2$; by repeated use of the Schottky theorem with successive centers $i/2$, i, $3i/2$, $\cdots$, $mi/2$, we conclude that

$$|\log |F_\rho(iy)|| \leqslant B_{m+1}, \qquad 0 \leqslant y \leqslant (m+1)/2$$

where B_{m+1} is independent of admitted ρ. Taking $m =$ the integral part of 4π, we conclude that f is bounded in $\Delta(\infty; R^{-1}) - \{\infty\}$ and hence, has a removable singularity at ∞. The proof is complete.

EXERCISES

1. Let $(f_n)_0^\infty$ denote a sequence of meromorphic functions, each mapping a region Ω_1 into a region Ω_2. Suppose that (f_n) tends uniformly to f in Ω_1 (in the sense of the chordal metric). Show that either $f(\Omega_1) \subset \Omega_2$ or f is a constant, the value of which is in fr Ω_2.

2. Suppose that $\Omega_2 = \hat{K} - \{a,b,c\}$, where a, b, c are three distinct points of $\hat{K}$, and that $(f_n)_0^\infty$ is a sequence of meromorphic functions each mapping Ω_1 into Ω_2. Show that there exists a subsequence $(f_{m(n)})$ converging uniformly (in the sense of the chordal metric) in Ω_1.

HINT: Treat the case $a = 0$, $b = 1$, $c = \infty$ with the aid of the Schottky theorem and Theorem 14.1, Chap. 2.

A paper that may be read profitably at this stage by the reader interested in further study of the Picard theorem and allied questions is R. M. Robinson, "A Generalization of Picard's and Related Theorems," *Duke Math. J.*, **5**: 118—132, 1939. This paper presupposes only a knowledge of the elements of the theory of functions of a complex variable.

6. A Theorem of Pólya. In this section we shall give an account of a theorem of Pólya (*J. London Math. Soc.*, **1**: 12–15, 1926) which finds its place in the present setting as an application of the theorem of Ex. 3, § 4, this chapter (although, to be sure, the theorem of the exercise in question actually finds its ultimate form in potential-theoretic terms rather than in the framework of the Picard theorem). It concerns *entire* functions of finite order (entire function = function analytic on K).

By the *order of growth* of an entire function f is meant

$$\limsup_{r \to +\infty} \frac{\overset{+}{\log}\,(\overset{+}{\log}\, M(r;f))}{\log r}. \tag{6.1}$$

Here $M(r;f)$ denotes $\max_{|z|=r} |f(z)|$, and $\overset{+}{\log}\, a$ denotes $\max\{\log a, 0\}$. We shall have occasion to study growth problems later in this book (Chap. 5). Let us note for the present that to say "f is of finite order" signifies the existence of some positive number α such that for r sufficiently large,

$$M(r;f) < \exp(r^\alpha).$$

The theorem of Pólya, which concerns the representation of entire functions of finite order as the composition of entire functions, follows.

THEOREM 6.1. *Let f be a nonconstant entire function of finite order, and let g and h denote entire functions satisfying*

$$f = g \circ h, \tag{6.2}$$

so that f is the composition of g and h. Then either (1) *the order of g is finite and h is a polynomial or* (2) *g is of zero order and h is not a polynomial.*

REDUCTION: It suffices to consider the situation where $h(0) = 0$. For if τ is the translation $\tau(z) = z - h(0)$, on the one hand, $\tau \circ h$ has the same order as h and is a polynomial if, and only if, h is, and, on the other hand, $g \circ \tau^{-1}$ has the same order as g.

Let us now turn to the proof. Let $\mu_1(r) = M(r;f)$, $\mu_2(r) = M(r;g)$, $\mu_3(r) = M(r;h)$. The proof hinges on the observation that for $r > 0$ we have

$$\mu_1(2r) \geqslant \mu_2\left(\frac{\kappa}{2}\,\mu_3(r)\right), \tag{6.3}$$

κ being defined in Ex. 3, § 4, this chapter. To see this we note that the image of $\Delta(0;1)$ with respect to $z \to h(2rz)/\mu_3(r)$ contains a $C(0;\rho)$ for some $\rho > \frac{1}{2}\kappa$. Hence $h[\Delta(0;2r)]$ contains a $C(0;\rho_1)$ for some $\rho_1 > \frac{1}{2}\kappa\mu_3(r)$. Hence

$$f[\Delta(0;2r)] \supset g[C(0;\rho_1)].$$

Hence $f[\Delta(0;2r)]$ contains a point of modulus $\mu_2(\rho_1)$,and so

$$\mu_1(2r) > \mu_2(\rho_1) > \mu_2\left(\frac{\kappa}{2}\,\mu_3(r)\right).$$

The proof is now readily completed, when we note that for r large we have

$$\frac{\log(\log \mu_1(2r))}{\log 2r} \geqslant \frac{\log(\log \mu_2(\frac{1}{2}\kappa\,\mu_3(r)))}{\log(\frac{1}{2}\kappa\,\mu_3(r))} \cdot \frac{\log(\frac{1}{2}\kappa\,\mu_3(r))}{\log(2r)} \tag{6.4}$$

If h is a polynomial of degree n, then

$$\lim_{r \to +\infty} \frac{\log \mu_3(r)}{\log r} = n .$$

If h is not a polynomial (in this case h is termed *transcendental*), then, thanks to the Cauchy inequalities,

$$\lim_{r \to +\infty} \frac{\log \mu_3(r)}{\log r} = +\infty .$$

The assertion of the theorem is seen to follow from (6.4).

[4]

Harmonic and Subharmonic Functions

1. Introduction. We now come to the consideration of aspects of the theory of functions of a complex variable where the relation between analytic functions of a complex variable and harmonic functions of two real variables dominates. This relation stems from the fact that locally harmonic functions and the real parts of analytic functions are the same; this implies that the logarithm of the modulus of an analytic function is harmonic save at the zeros of the analytic function. In the present chapter we shall give prominence to the notion of a subharmonic function. We may say, roughly speaking, that "subharmonic" and "harmonic" stand in the same relation as "convex" and "linear" for functions of a single variable. This is just a hint of why we shall be justified in expecting the notion of subharmonicity to make its importance felt in the theory of harmonic functions and, consequently, also in the theory of analytic functions of a complex variable. Actually, it will be seen that many theorems pertaining to the logarithm of the modulus of an analytic function are really special cases of theorems concerning subharmonic functions.

The present chapter is inevitably somewhat long. It will be divided into the following sections:

(A) Properties of harmonic functions,
(B) Poisson-Stieltjes integral and Fatou theorem,
(C) Subharmonic functions and applications,
(D) Dirichlet problem.

A) Properties of Harmonic Functions

2. Harmonic Functions. We do not presuppose prior experience with harmonic functions and shall develop the subject from first principles. Two useful references on the subject which are readily available are G. C. Evans, "Logarithmic Potential," *Colloquium Series of the American Mathematical Society*, **6**, 1927; and O. D. Kellogg, *Foundations of Potential Theory*, original edition published by Springer Verlag, 1929, available in a Dover Press paperback reprint.

We say that a function u is *harmonic at* $a \in K$ provided that its domain is a neighborhood of a and that its restriction to some $\Delta(a;r)$ contained in its domain belongs to the class $C''(\Delta(a;r))$ and satisfies the Laplace equation. It is to be recalled that, if Ω is an open subset $\neq \emptyset$ of $R \times R$, then $C''(\Omega)$ denotes the set of real-valued functions on Ω admitting continuous partial derivatives of the first two orders. We make a frank but harmless identification of points and sets in $R \times R$ and their images with respect to $(x,y) \to x + yi$ in K. It should also be remarked that it will be *convenient* to confine our attention to real-valued functions; there would be no difficulty in the complex-valued case. To be complete, when we say that u satisfies the *Laplace equation* on an open set $\Omega \subset K$ contained in the domain of u, we mean that $u_{xx}(z)$ and $u_{yy}(z)$ exist at each point of Ω and that

$$u_{xx}(z) + u_{yy}(z) = 0, \qquad z \in \Omega. \tag{2.1}$$

[In spite of the notational instability of our times, certainly the "old-fashioned" $u_{xx}(z)$ and $u_{yy}(z)$ need no gloss—though possibly apologies.] We shall denote $u_{xx} + u_{yy}$, termed the *Laplacian* of u, by Δu.

We say that u is *harmonic* at ∞ provided that its domain is a neighborhood of ∞ and that

$$z \to u(z^{-1})$$

is harmonic at 0. We shall see later that this is a "natural" definition and that, in particular, it forces u to be harmonic at each finite point sufficiently near ∞ (compare Exs. 1, 7, this §).

Given an open set $\Omega(\neq \emptyset) \subset \hat{K}$, we say that a function u is *harmonic* in Ω provided that u is harmonic at each point of Ω. We say that u is *harmonic on* Ω provided that the domain of u is Ω and u is harmonic in Ω.

Let us first study the relation between analyticity and harmonicity. Suppose that $f = u + iv$ is analytic at $a \in K$. Then it is easy to see that u and v each possess continuous partial derivatives of the first two orders in some neighborhood of a (in fact, continuous partial derivatives of all orders). It suffices to observe that

$$f'(z) = u_x(z) + iv_x(z) = -iu_y(z) + v_y(z) \tag{2.2}$$

for z sufficiently near a and that corresponding relations pertaining to derivatives of the second order are obtained on differentiating (2.2). We note explicitly that

$$f''(z) = u_{xx}(z) + iv_{xx}(y) = -iv_{yy}(z) - u_{yy}(z).$$

From these observations we conclude that u and v are harmonic at a.

Conversely, given a function u harmonic at $a \in K$, there exists a function v on some $\Delta(a;r)$ satisfying

$$v_x(z) = -u_y(z), \qquad v_y(z) = u_x(z),$$

since u_x and u_y have continuous derivatives in $\Delta(a;r)$ and satisfy the integrability condition

$$-u_{yy}(z) = u_{xx}(z)$$

in $\Delta(a;r)$. Now u and v satisfy the Cauchy-Riemann equations, and v is differentiable. Hence, u is the real part of a function analytic at a.

EXERCISE

1. Develop corresponding results for functions analytic at ∞ and functions harmonic at ∞. Show that, if u is harmonic at ∞, then u is harmonic in some $\Delta(\infty;r)$.

Applications of Fourier-series Methods. Suppose that $u \in C''(\mathcal{A})$, where $\mathcal{A} = \{r_1 < |z - \zeta| < r_2\}$, $0 \leqslant r_1 < r_2 \leqslant +\infty$. We introduce polar coordinates with pole at ζ and define U by

$$U(r,\theta) = u(\zeta + re^{i\theta}), \qquad r_1 < r < r_2. \tag{2.3}$$

Clearly, U has continuous partial derivatives of the first two orders on its domain. The following result is standard:

$$\Delta u(\zeta + re^{i\theta}) = (U_{rr} + r^{-1}U_r + r^{-2}U_{\theta\theta})\,|_{(r,\theta)}. \tag{2.4}$$

This identity has important implications for harmonic functions.

It will be convenient to have available the so-called *trigonometric* Fourier series of a function f with domain R, which is continuous (and real or complex-valued) on its domain and is periodic with period 2π. Let the sequences $(\alpha_k(f))_0^\infty$ and $(\beta_k(f))_0^\infty$ be defined by

$$\alpha_k(f) + i\beta_k(f) = \frac{1}{\pi}\int_0^{2\pi} f(x)e^{kix}\,dx, \qquad \alpha_k(f) - i\beta_k(f) = \frac{1}{\pi}\int_0^{2\pi} f(x)e^{-kix}\,dx.$$

By the *trigonometric* Fourier series of f is meant

$$\frac{\alpha_0(f)}{2} + \sum_{k=1}^{\infty} \left[\alpha_k(f)\cos kx + \beta_k(f)\sin kx\right]. \tag{2.5}$$

It is to be observed that the nth partial sum of this series is equal to

$$\sum_{k=-n}^{n} C_k(f)e^{kix}.$$

We shall refer also to the $\alpha_k(f)$ and $\beta_k(f)$ as the *Fourier coefficients* of f. When the term "Fourier coefficients" is employed, the sense of the term will be clear from context.

We return to u and propose to study the dependence of the Fourier coefficients of

$$\theta \to U(r,\theta)$$

on r for u harmonic in $\mathcal{A}$. We denote them by $A_k(r)$, $B_k(r)$, $k \in N$. It follows from (2.4) that A_k and B_k are both solutions of the differential equation

$$Y'' + r^{-1}Y' - k^2r^{-2}Y = 0 \tag{2.6}$$

on the interval $(r_1 < r < r_2)$. To see this, it suffices to multiply the right-hand side of (2.4) by $e^{ki\theta}/\pi$ and to integrate the product on $\{0 \leqslant \theta \leqslant 2\pi\}$. We apply two integrations by parts to

$$\int_0^{2\pi} U_{\theta\theta}(r,\theta)e^{ki\theta}\,d\theta$$

and obtain

$$\int_0^{2\pi} U_{\theta\theta}(r,\theta)e^{ki\theta}\,d\theta = -k^2\int_0^{2\pi} U(r,\theta)e^{ki\theta}\,d\theta\,.$$

It is now readily concluded that $A_k + iB_k$ satisfies (2.6). Hence so do A_k and B_k. This means that we have obtained valuable information about the A_k and B_k, for the solutions of (2.6) are well known. We see that

$$\begin{aligned} A_0(r) &= a_0 + b_0 \log r; \\ A_k(r) &= a_k r^k + b_k r^{-k},\ k \geqslant 1; \\ B_k(r) &= c_k r^k + d_k r^{-k},\ k \geqslant 1. \end{aligned} \tag{2.7}$$

Here the a_k, b_k, c_k, d_k are (uniquely determined) real numbers.

It is to be noted that $A_0(r)/2$ is simply the *circumferential mean*

$$m(r) = \frac{1}{2\pi}\int_0^{2\pi} u(\zeta + re^{i\theta})\,d\theta \tag{2.8}$$

of u on $C(\zeta;r)$. With the aid of the first of the relations (2.7), we conclude the *Gauss mean-value theorem:*

THEOREM 2.1. *Given u harmonic on a region Ω. Let $0 < R < +\infty$, and suppose that $\overline{\Delta(z_0;R)} \subset \Omega$. Then the circumferential mean of u on $C(z_0;R)$ is equal to $u(z_0)$.*

It suffices to observe that, when we take $\mathfrak{A} = \{0 < |z - z_0| < R\}$ (resp., $\{R^{-1} < |z| < +\infty\}$), the coefficient b_0 in the first of the equalities (2.7) must vanish for $\lim_{r\to 0} A_0(r)$ [resp., $\lim_{r\to+\infty} A_0(r)$] $= 2u(z_0)$. Hence $A_0(r)$ is independent of r. The theorem is readily concluded.

EXERCISES

2. Conclude the Gauss mean-value theorem by using the fact that a function harmonic on a disk is the real part of a function f analytic on the disk and by representing the value of f at the center of the disk by the usual integral formula.

3. Show that the maximum principle holds for harmonic functions: *Given u harmonic on a region Ω, $z_0 \in \Omega$. If $u(z_0) \geqslant u(z)$, $z \in \Omega$,* then u *is constant.*

HINT: Apply the Gauss mean-value theorem to show that $\{u(z) = u(z_0)\}$ is open. Obviously, $\{u(z) < u(z_0)\}$ is open.

REMARK: It is clear that a corresponding minimum principle holds.

4. Given u harmonic on $\Delta(z_0;R)$. If $z_0 \neq \infty$ and $\mathfrak{A} = \{0 < |z - z_0| < R\}$, then $b_k = d_k = 0$, $k \geqslant 1$, in formulas (2.7). If $z_0 = \infty$ and

$$\mathfrak{A} = \{R^{-1} < |z| < +\infty\}$$

then $a_k = c_k = 0$, $k \geqslant 1$.

5. Show the following theorem:

Given u harmonic on a region Ω. If int $\{u(z) = c\} \neq \emptyset$, then u is constant.

HINT: Applying formulas (2.7), we see that if $z_0 \in$ int $\{u(z) = c\}$ and $\Delta(z_0;r) \subset \Omega$, then $u(z) = c$ on $\Delta(z_0;r)$.

6. With the aid of the theorem of the preceding exercise show: Given u harmonic on a region Ω. If u has a relative maximum (resp., minimum) at $z_0 \in \Omega$, then u is constant.

7. ISOLATED SINGULARITIES OF HARMONIC FUNCTIONS. Given

$$\mathfrak{A} = \{0 < |z - \zeta| < R\}$$

and u harmonic on $\mathfrak{A}$. Let $\sigma(r) = \max. |u(\zeta + re^{i\theta})|$ and $\mu(r) = \min u(\zeta + re^{i\theta})$, $0 < r < R$. Show: (a) If $\liminf_{r\to 0} \sigma(r)/|\log r| = 0$, then b_k and d_k of (2.7) all vanish and u possesses a finite limit at ζ. (b) If α is a positive real number and $\liminf_{r\to 0} \sigma(r) r^\alpha < +\infty$, then $b_k = d_k = 0$ for $k \geqslant [\alpha] + 1$. (c) If $u > 0$, then $|A_k(r)|, |B_k(r)| \leqslant A_0(r)$, and so $b_k = d_k = 0$ for $k \geqslant 1$ and $b_0 \leqslant 0$. (d) If $\limsup_{r\to 0} \mu(r)/|\log r| > -\infty$, then $b_k = d_k = 0$ for $k \geqslant 1$.

HINT: To establish (d), let α satisfy $-\infty < \alpha < \limsup_{r\to 0} \mu(r)/|\log r|$, and verify that $u(z) - \alpha \log(1/|z|)$ is positive and harmonic in some $\Delta(\zeta;r) - \{\zeta\}$.

State and prove the corresponding theorems for a function harmonic on $\{R < |z| < +\infty\}$.

8. Given u harmonic on $\Delta(0;R)$. Show that for $0 < r < R$ the following inequalities hold:

$$a_0 + |a_n| r^n \leqslant 4\overset{+}{\sigma}(r),$$

$$a_0 + |b_n| r^n \leqslant 4\overset{+}{\sigma}(r),\ n = 1,2, \cdots.$$

Here $\sigma(r)$ denotes $\max u(re^{i\theta})$, and $\overset{+}{\sigma}(r) = \max \{0,\sigma(r)\}$.

Show that if u is harmonic on K and is not constant, then $\lim_{r\to+\infty} \sigma(r)r^{-1}$ exists and is positive. Under what circumstances is this limit finite?

---

3. The Poisson Integral. We are preparing the way for a study of the Dirichlet problem (§ 12, this chapter) under conditions extensive enough for the applications we shall meet. Let us consider for the present a function u

with domain $\overline{\Delta(0;1)}$, continuous and real-valued on its domain and harmonic in $\Delta(0;1)$. We note that u is "determined by its boundary values" in the sense that if v fulfills the same requirements as u and if $u(z) = v(z)$, $|z| = 1$, then $u = v$. For $u - v$ attains both its maximum and its minimum on $C(0;1)$ by virtue of the maximum principle for harmonic functions. Let us now examine the question of representing $u(z)$, $|z| < 1$, in terms of the restriction of u to $C(0;1)$. We consider the formulas (2.7) for the present situation and note that

$$a_k = \frac{1}{\pi} \int_0^{2\pi} u(e^{i\theta}) \cos k\theta \, d\theta \,,$$

$$b_k = \frac{1}{\pi} \int_0^{2\pi} u(e^{i\theta}) \sin k\theta \, d\theta \,,$$

thanks to the continuity of u in $\overline{\Delta(0;1)}$. Hence, for $0 \leqslant r < 1$, we have

$$u(re^{i\theta}) = \frac{a_0}{2} + \sum_{k=1}^{\infty} (a_k \cos k\theta + b_k \sin k\theta) \, r^k$$

$$= \frac{1}{\pi} \int_0^{2\pi} u(e^{i\varphi}) \left[\frac{1}{2} + \sum_{k=1}^{\infty} r^k \cos k(\theta - \varphi)\right] d\varphi \,,$$

the second equality being justified with the aid of the uniform convergence (with respect to φ) of the series in the integrand. It follows that

$$u(re^{i\theta}) = \frac{1}{\pi} \int_0^{2\pi} u(e^{i\varphi}) \operatorname{Re} \left[\frac{1}{2} + \sum_{k=1}^{\infty} r^k e^{ki(\theta-\varphi)}\right] d\varphi$$

$$= \frac{1}{2\pi} \int_0^{2\pi} u(e^{i\varphi}) \operatorname{Re} \left[\frac{1 + re^{i(\theta-\varphi)}}{1 - re^{i(\theta-\varphi)}}\right] d\varphi \,.$$

We conclude the *Poisson integral formula* for u:

$$u(z) = \frac{1}{2\pi} \int_0^{2\pi} u(e^{i\varphi}) \operatorname{Re} \left[\frac{e^{i\varphi} + z}{e^{i\varphi} - z}\right] d\varphi \,, \qquad |z| < 1 \,. \tag{3.1}$$

Thus we have obtained a formula representing the value of u at a point of $\Delta(0;1)$ in terms of the boundary values of u. We denote

$$\operatorname{Re} \left[\frac{e^{i\varphi} + z}{e^{i\varphi} - z}\right]$$

by $K(e^{i\varphi}, z)$ and term it the *Poisson kernel for the unit disk.* Note that $K(e^{i\varphi}, z) > 0$, $|z| < 1$. The positiveness of a kernel is a useful property (cf. Fejér kernel).

EXERCISES

1. Show that

$$K(e^{i\varphi},z) = \frac{1 - |z|^2}{|e^{i\varphi} - z|^2} \tag{3.2}$$

and that

$$K(1, -|z|) \leqslant K(e^{i\varphi},z) \leqslant K(1, |z|). \tag{3.3}$$

2. Derive the Poisson integral formula by the following consideration: With $M_a(z) = (z + a) / (1 + \bar{a}z)$, $|a| < 1$, let $u_a = u \circ M_a$. It follows that $u(a)$ is the circumferential mean of u_a on $C(0;1)$.

The Dirichlet Problem for $\Delta(0;1)$. Given U a continuous real-valued function with domain $C(0;1)$. Does there exist a function u meeting the requirements laid down at the beginning of this section whose restriction to $C(0;1)$ is U? [This is the Dirichlet problem for $\Delta(0;1)$, continuous boundary function.]

From the developments of this section up to this point, the only possibility is the function u defined by

$$u(z) = \begin{cases} U(z), & |z| = 1; \\ \dfrac{1}{2\pi}\displaystyle\int_0^{2\pi} U(e^{i\varphi})\, K(e^{i\varphi},z)\, d\varphi\,, & |z| < 1\,. \end{cases} \tag{3.4}$$

Let us now verify that u so defined meets the imposed specifications. We note that

$$z \to \frac{1}{2\pi}\int_0^{2\pi} U(e^{i\varphi}) \left[\frac{e^{i\varphi} + z}{e^{i\varphi} - z}\right] d\varphi\,, \qquad |z| < 1\,,$$

is analytic on $\Delta(0;1)$. *The harmonicity* of u in $\Delta(0;1)$ follows. It suffices now to verify that u is *continuous* at each point of $C(0;1)$. To that end, we note the following properties of the Poisson kernel:

$$(2\pi)^{-1}\int_0^{2\pi} K(e^{i\varphi},z)\, d\varphi = 1, \qquad |z| < 1\,. \tag{a}$$

$$\lim_{z\to e^{i\alpha}} \left[\int_{\alpha-\pi}^{\alpha-\varepsilon} + \int_{\alpha+\varepsilon}^{\alpha+\pi} K(e^{i\varphi},z)\, d\varphi\right] = 0\,, \qquad 0 < \varepsilon < \pi\,. \tag{b}$$

The first formula may be seen from (3.1) with $u = 1$. The second follows from (3.2) on noting that the denominator is bounded from zero for z in a sufficiently small neighborhood of $e^{i\alpha}$. With ε restricted as in (b), we conclude from (a) and (b) that

$$\lim_{z\to e^{i\alpha}} \frac{1}{2\pi}\int_{\alpha-\varepsilon}^{\alpha+\varepsilon} K(e^{i\varphi},z)\, d\varphi = 1\,, \qquad |z| < 1\,. \tag{c}$$

Starting with

$$u(z) = \frac{1}{2\pi}\int_{|\varphi-\alpha|\leqslant\varepsilon} U(e^{i\varphi})\, K(e^{i\varphi},z)\, d\varphi + \frac{1}{2\pi}\int_{\varepsilon\leqslant|\varphi-\alpha|\leqslant\pi} U(e^{i\varphi})\, K(e^{i\varphi},z)\, d\varphi, \quad |z| < 1,$$

we see, thanks to (b) and (c), that

$$\limsup_{z\to e^{i\alpha}} u(z) \leqslant \max_{|\varphi-\alpha|\leqslant\varepsilon} U(e^{i\varphi})$$

and

$$\liminf_{z\to e^{i\alpha}} u(z) \geqslant \min_{|\varphi-\alpha|\leqslant\varepsilon} U(e^{i\varphi}) .$$

It follows that $\lim_{z\to e^{i\alpha}} u(z) = U(e^{i\alpha})$. That is, u is *continuous* at each point of $C(0;1)$.

It is now immediate that the Dirichlet problem for an arbitrary disk $\Delta(a;r)$, $0 < r < +\infty$, and continuous real-valued boundary function b admits a unique solution. In fact, when $a \neq \infty$, this solution is

$$u\left(\frac{z-a}{r}\right), \tag{3.5}$$

where u is given by (3.4) with $U(z) = b(a + rz)$; and when $a = \infty$, it is

$$u\left(\frac{1}{rz}\right), \tag{3.6}$$

where u is again given by (3.4) but with $U(z) = b(1/rz)$.

EXERCISES

3. A continuous function f on R which is periodic with period 2π admits a unique representation of the form $f(\theta) = F(e^{i\theta})$, where F is a continuous function with domain $C(0;1)$. Show with the aid of (3.4), taking $U = F$, that f admits a uniform approximation by a trigonometric polynomial.

HINT: Approximate $f(\theta)$ by $u(re^{i\theta})$ and use the expansion for $u(re^{i\theta})$. Show that this approach to the Weierstrass approximation theorem may be made to depend only on (3.4) and not on considerations involving Fourier series.

4. Given u harmonic on $\Delta(a;r) - \{a\}$. Suppose that u possesses a finite limit at a. Show that u is the restriction of a function harmonic on $\Delta(a;r)$.

5. Let Ω denote a region $\subset K$ that is symmetric with respect to the real axis. Suppose that u is harmonic on Ω and vanishes at each point of Ω on the real axis. Show that $u(\bar{z}) = -u(z)$, $z \in \Omega$.

HINT: Consider the harmonic function $z \to u(z) + u(\bar{z})$, $z \in \Omega$, and show that it vanishes in a neighborhood of each point of Ω on the real axis.

Show that, if u_1 is a function continuous on $\Omega \cap \{\operatorname{Im} z \geqslant 0\}$ and harmonic in $\Omega \cap \{\operatorname{Im} z > 0\}$ that vanishes at each point of $\Omega \cap \{\operatorname{Im} z = 0\}$, then there exists a unique harmonic function u on Ω whose restriction to $\Omega \cap \{\operatorname{Im} z \geqslant 0\}$ is u_1 (Schwarz reflexion principle).

Some Applications. The fact that we can solve the Dirichlet problem for the disk, and indeed explicitly, means that we have at our disposal a powerful tool for the study of harmonic functions. By way of illustration, let us consider two well-known theorems that show how differentiability conditions may be weakened or dropped in characterizations of harmonicity.

Theorem 3.1 (Looman). *Let Ω denote a region $\subset K$. Let u be a continuous real-valued function on Ω satisfying the following conditions:* (1) u_{xx} *and* u_{yy} *exist on* Ω; (2) $\Delta u = 0$. *Then u is harmonic on Ω.*

Proof: Given $\overline{\Delta(a;r)} \subset \Omega$; let h denote the solution of the Dirichlet problem for $\Delta(a;r)$ satisfying $h(z) = u(z)$, $z \in C(a;r)$. We assert that $u(z) = h(z)$, $z \in \Delta(a;r)$. Suppose that $u(z) - h(z)$ is positive for some $z \in \Delta(a;r)$. Then, for some $\eta > 0$,

$$z \to w(z) = \eta |z|^2 + [u(z) - h(z)], \qquad z \in \overline{\Delta(a;r)},$$

would attain its maximum at a point $\zeta \in \Delta(a;r)$. This would imply that $\Delta w(\zeta) \leqslant 0$; but $\Delta w(z) = 4\eta$ in $\Delta(a;r)$. Hence, $u(z) - h(z) \leqslant 0$, $z \in \Delta(a;r)$. The same argument shows that $h(z) - u(z) \leqslant 0$, $z \in \Delta(a;r)$. Hence, u coincides with h in $\Delta(a;r)$, and, consequently, u is harmonic at a. Since a is an arbitrary point of Ω, u is harmonic on Ω.

Theorem 3.2 (Koebe). *Let Ω denote a region $\subset \hat{K}$. Let u be a continuous real-valued function on Ω satisfying the mean-value property: If $\overline{\Delta(a;r)} \subset \Omega$, ($r$ finite), then $u(a)$ is the circumferential mean of u on $C(a;r)$. Then u is harmonic on Ω.*

Proof: We repeat the first two sentences of the proof of Theorem 3.1. The function $z \to u(z) - h(z)$, $z \in \Delta(a;r)$, has the mean-value property and hence satisfies the maximum and minimum principles (see Ex. 3, § 2, this chapter). Hence,

$$\max_{z \in \overline{\Delta(a;r)}} [u(z) - h(z)] = \max_{z \in C(a;r)} [u(z) - h(z)] = 0,$$

and

$$\min_{z \in \overline{\Delta(a;r)}} [u(z) - h(z)] = \min_{z \in C(a;r)} [u(z) - h(z)] = 0.$$

Hence, u is harmonic at a. It follows that u is harmonic on Ω.

Uniform Limits of Sequences of Harmonic Functions. Given functions u, u_n, $n \in N$, u and each u_n being continuous and real-valued on $\overline{\Delta(a;r)}$ and harmonic in $\Delta(a;r)$. Then, if (u_n) tends to u uniformly on $C(a;r)$, (u_n) tends to u uniformly on $\overline{\Delta(a;r)}$, as is seen by the equality

$$\max_{\overline{\Delta(a;r)}} |u - u_n| = \max_{C(a;r)} |u - u_n|,$$

which is an immediate consequence of the maximum and minimum principles.

Suppose now that we are given a sequence of functions $(h_n)_0^\infty$, where each h_n is harmonic on a given region Ω, and suppose that (h_n) tends to a function h uniformly in Ω. *Then h is harmonic on Ω.* In fact, given $\overline{\Delta(a;r)} \subset \Omega$, r finite, let u denote the solution of the Dirichlet problem for $\Delta(a;r)$ satisfying $u(z) = h(z)$, $z \in C(a;r)$. Then, since h_n tends uniformly to u on $C(a;r)$, we conclude that $u = h$ on $\Delta(a;r)$. Hence, h is harmonic at a. Consequently, h is harmonic on Ω.

EXERCISES

6. Show with the aid of Theorem 3.2, this chapter, that the uniform limit of a sequence of harmonic functions is harmonic.

7. Let $(f_n)_0^\infty$ denote a sequence of functions analytic on a region Ω, and let $a \in \Omega$. Given that $(f_n(a))_0^\infty$ possesses a finite limit and that $(\operatorname{Re} f_n)_0^\infty$ converges uniformly in Ω, show that $(f_n)_0^\infty$ converges uniformly in Ω.

HINT: Consider the set E of $z \in \Omega$ for which there exists a disk $\Delta(z;r)$ on which $(f_n)_0^\infty$ converges uniformly, and develop a proof based on the fact that Ω is connected.

This result implies that if $(u_n)_0^\infty$ is a sequence of functions harmonic on Ω and converging uniformly in Ω and if for each n, u_n is the real part of a function analytic on Ω, then $\lim_{n\to\infty} u_n$ is also the real part of a function analytic on Ω.

8. DIRICHLET PROBLEM FOR ANNULUS. Let $\mathcal{O} = \{r_1 < |z| < r_2\}$, $0 < r_1 < r_2 < +\infty$. Let U_k denote a continuous real-valued function on $C(0;r_k)$, $k = 1,2$. Show that there exists a unique real-valued continuous function u on $\overline{\mathcal{O}}$ that is harmonic in $\mathcal{O}$ and satisfies $u(z) = U_k(z)$, $z \in C(0;r_k)$, $k = 1,2$.

HINT: Consider first the case where the $U_k(r_k e^{i\varphi})$ are each trigonometric polynomials of order n. The coefficients a_k, b_k, c_k, d_k can be so determined that

$$V(r,\varphi) = \frac{a_0 + b_0 \log r}{2} + \sum_{k=1}^{n} [(a_k r^k + b_k r^{-k}) \cos k\varphi + (c_k r^k + d_k r^{-k}) \sin k\varphi]$$

satisfies

$$V(r_k, \varphi) = U_k(r_k e^{i\varphi}), \qquad \text{all real } \varphi,\ k = 1,2.$$

Verify that

$$v(z) = \frac{a_0 + b_0 \log |z|}{2} + \operatorname{Re}\left\{\sum_1^n [(a_k - ic_k)z^k + (b_k + id_k)z^{-k}]\right\}$$

yields the solution of the Dirichlet problem. Proceed to the general case with the aid of the Weierstrass approximation theorem (compare Ex. 3, this §).

Determine the coefficients a_k, b_k, c_k, d_k in the expansion of the solution u of the Dirichlet problem in the general case in terms of U_1 and U_2.

Harnack's Theorems. From the inequalities of Ex. 1, this §, and the Poisson integral we obtain: If u is continuous and nonnegative on $\overline{\Delta(0;1)}$ and harmonic on $\Delta(0;1)$, then

$$u(z) \leqslant \frac{1}{2\pi}\int_0^{2\pi} u(e^{i\varphi})K(1, |z|)\, d\varphi = u(0)\, K(1, |z|)$$

and

$$u(z) \geqslant \frac{1}{2\pi}\int_0^{2\pi} u(e^{i\varphi})\, K(1, -|z|)\, d\varphi = u(0)\, K(1, -|z|)\,, \quad |z| < 1\,.$$

It is to be observed that the right-hand members involve information on u only at $z = 0$. We are led to suspect that the same inequalities hold for the wider class of u harmonic and nonnegative in $\Delta(0;1)$. That this is the case may be seen as follows. Given such a u, for $0 < r < 1$ we define u_r by

$$u_r(z) = u(rz), \qquad |z| < 1.$$

From

$$u(0)\frac{1 - |z|}{1 + |z|} \leqslant u_r(z) \leqslant u(0)\frac{1 + |z|}{1 - |z|}$$

we obtain the Harnack inequality:

$$u(0)\frac{1 - |z|}{1 + |z|} \leqslant u(z) \leqslant u(0)\frac{1 + |z|}{1 - |z|}\,, \qquad |z| < 1\,. \tag{3.7}$$

Now it turns out, as we shall see, that a qualitative form of (3.7) remains valid for nonnegative harmonic functions on an arbitrary region. Let Ω denote a given region $\subset \hat{K}$, let $a \in \Omega$, and let Φ denote the class of functions u harmonic on Ω, positive, and satisfying $u(a) = 1$. Let

$$\lambda(z) = \inf_{u \in \Phi} u(z)\,, \qquad \mu(z) = \sup_{u \in \Phi} u(z)\,, \qquad z \in \Omega\,.$$

We have

THEOREM 3.3. *λ is continuous and positive on Ω; μ is a continuous finite-valued function.*

PROOF: If $\Delta(\zeta;r) \subset \Omega$, r finite, then from (3.7) applied to $u(\zeta + rz)$ if $\zeta \neq \infty$ and to $u(1/rz)$ if $\zeta = \infty$, we conclude

$$u(\zeta)\frac{r - |z - \zeta|}{r + |z - \zeta|} \leqslant u(z) \leqslant u(\zeta)\frac{r + |z - \zeta|}{r - |z - \zeta|}, \qquad z \in \Delta(\zeta;r) \tag{3.8}$$

when $\zeta \neq \infty$, and

$$u(\infty)\frac{r - |z|^{-1}}{r + |z|^{-1}} \leqslant u(z) \leqslant u(\infty)\frac{r + |z|^{-1}}{r - |z|^{-1}}, \qquad z \in \Delta(\infty;r). \tag{3.9}$$

From the inequalities (3.8) and (3.9) we conclude that $\{\mu(z) < +\infty\}$ and $\{\mu(z) = +\infty\}$ are open. Since a belongs to the first set, we see that $\mu < +\infty$, Ω being connected. A similar argument shows that $\lambda > 0$. It is readily verified that the inequalities (3.8) and (3.9) hold when u is replaced by μ and that they also hold when u is replaced by λ. The resulting inequalities imply the continuity of λ and μ on Ω.

It is easy to see that the following inequality of the Harnack type holds: *If u is nonnegative harmonic on Ω, then*

$$u(a)\lambda \leqslant u \leqslant u(a)\mu. \tag{3.10}$$

Here, if $u \neq 0$, it suffices to consider $u/u(a)$.

The facts stated in Theorem 3.3 and the inequality (3.10) lead to the *Harnack convergence theorem* for monotone sequences of harmonic functions, namely:

THEOREM 3.4. Let $(u_n)_0^\infty$ *denote a nondecreasing sequence of harmonic functions on a region* $\Omega \subset \hat{K}$. *Then either* $u_n \to +\infty$ *uniformly in* Ω *or else* (u_n) *converges uniformly in* Ω.

PROOF: It suffices to note that if $n > m$, then $u_n - u_m \geqslant 0$. Thus by (3.10) we have

$$[u_n(a) - u_m(a)]\lambda(z) \leqslant u_n(z) - u_m(z) \leqslant [u_n(a) - u_m(a)]\mu(z). \tag{3.11}$$

If $u_n(a) \to +\infty$, the left-hand inequality of (3.11) ensures that $u_n \to +\infty$ uniformly in Ω. If $\lim u_n(a) < +\infty$, then the right-hand inequality of (3.11) ensures the uniform convergence of (u_n) in Ω.

EXERCISES

9. We now return to the Koebe proof of the Riemann mapping theorem, § 15, Chap. 2, and set the problem of treating the uniform convergence of the sequence $(f_n)_0^\infty$ by the methods developed in the present chapter. Let $g_n(z) = f_n(z)/z$, $z(\neq 0) \in \Omega$, $g_n(0) = f_n'(0) > 0$. Let $\Delta(0;r) \subset \Omega$. Let l_n denote the analytic logarithm of the restriction of g_n to $\Delta(0;r)$ satisfying $\operatorname{Im} l_n(0) = 0$.

Apply Theorem 3.4 to (Re l_n) and thereupon the theorem of Ex. 7 of the present section. It now suffices to show that the set of z in Ω having the property that there exists $\Delta(z;r) \subset \Omega$ on which (g_n) converges uniformly is closed relative to Ω.

If we assume that Ω has the property (l), we are assured that g_n itself has an analytic logarithm. The uniform convergence of (f_n) then follows somewhat more simply.

10. What can be said about a sequence of harmonic functions uniformly convergent in the sense of the chordal metric?

B) Poisson-Stieltjes Integral. Fatou Theorem

4. Positive Harmonic Functions on $\Delta(0;1)$. We shall be concerned with a study of the positive harmonic functions on $\Delta(0;1)$ and, in particular, with the representation theorem of Herglotz which asserts that such a function admits a representation as a Poisson-Stieltjes integral. The Harnack inequality (3.7) of this chapter has already shown us that the assumption of positivity forces considerable restriction on the behavior of a harmonic function. Positivity will play a fundamental role in the present section. We shall approach the Herglotz theorem via positive additive functionals and shall first consider such functionals in a special setting.

Let **C** denote the set of functions that are real-valued and continuous on R and are periodic with period 2π. (The reader familiar with the notion of a Banach space of course knows the standard manner of endowing **C** with a Banach space structure. A familiarity with Banach space ideas is not, however, presupposed here.) A map λ of **C** into R is termed a *positive additive functional* on **C** provided that the following conditions are fulfilled: (1) $\lambda(f) \geqslant 0$ if $f \geqslant 0$; (2) $\lambda(f_1 + f_2) = \lambda(f_1) + \lambda(f_2)$. Examples of such λ are easily given, for instance,

$$f \to f(0), \tag{a}$$

$$f \to \int_0^{2\pi} f(x)\, dx\,. \tag{b}$$

We shall denote the set of the positive additive functionals on **C** by Λ. It will be convenient to develop a few simple properties of such λ.

We see at once from (2) that $\lambda(0) = 0$ and that for each positive integer n, $\lambda(nf) = n\lambda(f)$. It then follows that for each nonnegative rational number q, $\lambda(qf) = q\lambda(f)$. From (1) and (2) we see that λ is monotone nondecreasing in f; that is, if $f_1 \leqslant f_2$, then $\lambda(f_1) \leqslant \lambda(f_2)$. Hence, for α a positive real number and $f \geqslant 0$, we see that

$$q_1\lambda(f) = \lambda(q_1 f) \leqslant \lambda(\alpha f) \leqslant \lambda(q_2 f) = q_2\lambda(f),$$

where q_1 and q_2 are rational numbers satisfying $0 \leqslant q_1 \leqslant \alpha \leqslant q_2$. It follows that for α positive real and $f \geqslant 0$, $\lambda(\alpha f) = \alpha\lambda(f)$. Suppose now that $\alpha > 0$, but f is an unrestricted member of **C**. From

$$\lambda(\alpha\,|f\,|) = \lambda[\alpha(\,|f\,| - f)] + \lambda(\alpha f)$$

and

$$\alpha\lambda(\,|f\,|) = \alpha\lambda(\,|f\,| - f) + \alpha\lambda(f)$$

we conclude that

$$\lambda(\alpha f) = \alpha\lambda(f).$$

If $\alpha < 0$,

$$\lambda(\alpha f) = -\,\lambda(-\,\alpha f) = -\,[(-\alpha)\lambda(f)] = \alpha\lambda(f).$$

We conclude

$$\lambda(\alpha f) = \alpha\lambda(f), \qquad \alpha \in R, f \in \mathbf{C}. \tag{4.1}$$

From the monotoneity of λ and from (4.1) we obtain

$$(\min f)\lambda(1) \leqslant \lambda(f) \leqslant (\max f)\lambda(1). \tag{4.2}$$

This inequality implies that if $(f_n)_0^\infty$ is a sequence of functions in **C** that tends uniformly to f, then $\lim_{n\to\infty} \lambda(f_n) = \lambda(f)$.

We are now in a position to arrive at a theorem equivalent to the Herglotz theorem. We shall seek to relate Λ with the set of nonnegative harmonic functions on $\Delta(0;1)$. To that end we consider (what amounts to a simple generalization of the Poisson integral) for $\lambda \in \Lambda$, the function u_λ with domain $\Delta(0;1)$ defined by

$$u_\lambda(z) = \lambda\big(K(e^{i\theta},z)\big) \tag{4.3}$$

$\big[$or, perhaps better, $\lambda(\theta \to K(e^{i\theta},z))\big]$ The basic result is

THEOREM 4.1. *The map $\lambda \to u_\lambda$ is a univalent map of Λ onto the set of nonnegative harmonic functions on $\Delta(0;1)$.*

PROOF: It is obvious that $u_\lambda \geqslant 0$. Further, given $z \in \Delta(0;1)$,

$$1 + 2\sum_{k=1}^{\infty} \Big\{\text{Re}\,[(e^{-i\theta}z)^k]\Big\}$$

converges uniformly to $K(e^{i\theta},z)$. Hence,

$$u_\lambda(z) = \lambda(1) + 2\,\text{Re}\left\{\sum_{k=1}^{\infty} [\lambda(\cos k\theta) - i\lambda(\sin k\theta)]z^k\right\}.$$

It follows that u_λ is *harmonic* on $\Delta(0;1)$.

Suppose that $u_\lambda = u_\mu$. Then we conclude that

$$\lambda(\cos k\theta) = \mu(\cos k\theta)\,, \quad \lambda(\sin k\theta) = \mu(\sin k\theta)\,, \qquad k \in N\,.$$

It follows that $\lambda(T) = \mu(T)$ for each trigonometric polynomial T and hence, by the Weierstrass approximation theorem for **C**, that $\lambda(f) = \mu(f)$, $f \in \mathbf{C}$. That is, $\lambda = \mu$. The map $\lambda \to u_\lambda$ is univalent.

It remains to be shown that $\lambda \to u_\lambda$ is an *onto* map. To that end we first make the immediate observation that if $(\lambda_n)_0^\infty$ is a sequence of members of Λ that tends pointwise on **C** to a map λ of **C** into R, then $\lambda \in \Lambda$. Given a nonnegative harmonic function u on $\Delta(0;1)$, we define

$$\lambda_r(f) = \frac{1}{2\pi}\int_0^{2\pi} u(re^{i\theta})f(\theta)\,d\theta\,, \qquad 0 \leqslant r < 1\,,$$

and note that $\lambda_r \in \Lambda$. Further, $\lim_{r\to1} \lambda_r(f)$ exists for $f(\theta) = \cos k\theta$, $\sin k\theta$, $k \in N$ Hence, $\lim_{r\to1} \lambda_r(T)$ exists for T a trigonometric polynomial. From

$$\lambda_r(f) = \lambda_r(T) + \lambda_r(f - T)$$

and

$$|\lambda_r(f - T)| \leqslant \lambda_r(1) \max |f - T| = u(0) \max |f - T|\,,$$

it follows by the Weierstrass approximation theorem that $\lim_{r\to1} \lambda_r(f)$ exists for $f \in \mathbf{C}$. Let λ denote the pointwise limit of λ_r. We assert that $u_\lambda = u$. In fact

$$\begin{aligned}\lambda\big(K(e^{i\theta},z)\big) &= \lim_{r\to1} \lambda_r\big(K(e^{i\theta},z)\big)\\ &= \lim_{r\to1} u(rz)\\ &= u(z).\end{aligned}$$

Hence, $\lambda \to u_\lambda$ is an *onto* map. The proof of Theorem 4.1 is complete.

To arrive at the Herglotz theorem, we shall want to use Riemann-Stieltjes integrals, which we assume are familiar to the reader. (Ref.: T. Apostol, *Mathematical Analysis*, Addison-Wesley, 1957, Chap. 9, in particular, p. 211.) We shall make use of the *Riesz representation theorem* for $\lambda \in \Lambda$:

Given $\lambda \in \Lambda$. *There exists a nondecreasing function* α *with domain* R *satisfying* $\alpha(x + 2\pi) = \alpha(x) + [\alpha(2\pi) - \alpha(0)]$, $x \in R$, *such that*

$$\lambda(f) = \int_a^{a+2\pi} f\,d\alpha\,, \qquad f \in \mathbf{C}\,. \tag{4.4}$$

The proof of this theorem is given in the appendix, § 1, pp. 139-141.

Taken together, Theorem 4.1 and the cited respresentation theorem yield

THEOREM 4.2 (Herglotz). *Given* u *harmonic on* $\Delta(0;1)$ *and nonnegative. There exists a monotone nondecreasing function* α *on* R *satisfying* $\alpha(\theta + 2\pi) = \alpha(\theta) + u(0)$ *such that*

$$u(z) = \int_a^{a+2\pi} K(e^{i\theta},z)\, d\alpha(\theta)\,, \qquad a \in R\,. \tag{4.5}$$

An integral of the form (4.5) is called a *Poisson-Stieltjes* integral, for obvious reasons. It is immediate that every Poisson-Stieltjes integral with α as restricted yields a nonnegative harmonic function on $\Delta(0;1)$.

5. The Fatou Theorem. Before we proceed to this theorem, which is concerned with the boundary behavior of functions on $\Delta(0;1)$ belonging to certain important classes, we shall want to introduce the concept of a set of zero measure. Given $E \subset R$, we say that E is a set of *zero* (Lebesgue) *measure* provided that for each positive number η, there exists a set S of open intervals i whose union contains E and which satisfies

$$\sum_{i \in S} |\, i\,| < \eta,$$

$|\, i\,|$ being the length of i. A corresponding definition holds for subsets E of $C\,(0;1)$, with intervals being replaced by arcs $\{e^{i\theta} \mid \alpha < \theta < \beta\}$ and lengths of intervals by arclength. It is easy to see that $E \subset C\,(0;1)$ is of zero measure if, and only if, $\{\theta \mid e^{i\theta} \in E\}$ is of zero measure.

We say that a property $P(x)$ holds for *almost all* x in a set E $[\subset R$ or $\subset C\,(0;1)]$ provided that the set of x in E for which $P(x)$ is false is of zero measure.

The Fatou Theorem for Nonnegative Harmonic Functions on $\Delta(0;1)$. This states

THEOREM 5.1. *Given* u *nonnegative harmonic on* $\Delta(0;1)$. *Then*

$$\lim_{r \to 1} u(r\zeta)$$

exists (finite) for almost all $\zeta \in C(0;1)$.

An essential role is played in the proof by the following theorem of Lebesgue:

Given α *monotone on the interval* $\{a \leqslant x \leqslant b\}$. *Then* $\alpha'(x)$ *exists (finite) for almost all* x *in the interval.*

F. Riesz's proof of the Lebesgue theorem is given in the appendix, § 2, pp. 141-145.

PROOF OF THEOREM 5.1: The proof pivots about the Herglotz theorem and Lebesgue's theorem. Starting with the representation (4.5) for u, we let E denote the image with respect to $\theta \to e^{i\theta}$ of the set of θ for which $\alpha'(\theta)$ either does not exist or exists but is not finite, and we verify that E contains the set of ζ that fail to have the property stated in Theorem 5.1. From this point on the proof proceeds in a straightforward manner. However, the use of the sign of $K_\theta(e^{i\theta}, re^{i\varphi})$ merits notice.

Let $\zeta = e^{i\varphi} \in C(0;1)$. We show that

$$\limsup_{r\to 1} u(r\zeta) \leqslant 2\pi \limsup_{h\to 0} \frac{\alpha(\varphi + h) - \alpha(\varphi)}{h} \tag{5.1}$$

and that

$$\liminf_{r\to 1} u(r\zeta) \geqslant 2\pi \liminf_{h\to 0} \frac{\alpha(\varphi + h) - \alpha(\varphi)}{h}. \tag{5.2}$$

Hence, if $\zeta \notin E$,

$$\lim_{r\to 1} u(r\zeta) = 2\pi\alpha'(\varphi).$$

The theorem of Fatou follows.

Let us consider (5.1). There is nothing to show when the right-hand side is equal to $+\infty$. We put this case aside and let A satisfy

$$\limsup_{h\to 0} \frac{\alpha(\varphi + h) - \alpha(\varphi)}{h} < A < +\infty.$$

We next fix η, $0 < \eta < \pi$, such that

$$\frac{\alpha(\varphi + h) - \alpha(\varphi)}{h} < A, \qquad 0 < |h| \leqslant \eta.$$

We have

$$u(r\zeta) = \int_{\eta \leqslant |\theta - \varphi| \leqslant \pi} + \int_{|\theta - \varphi| \leqslant \eta} K(e^{i\theta}, r\zeta)\, d\alpha(\theta). \tag{5.3}$$

Clearly, the first integral on the right tends to 0 as $r \to 1$. We also have

$$\int_{|\theta-\varphi|\leqslant\eta} K(e^{i\theta}, r\zeta)\, d\alpha(\theta) = K(e^{i\theta}, r\zeta)\,[\alpha(\theta) - \alpha(\varphi)]\Big|_{\varphi-\eta}^{\varphi+\eta} + \int_{\varphi-\eta}^{\varphi+\eta} [\alpha(\varphi) - \alpha(\theta)]\, K_\theta(e^{i\theta}, r\zeta)\, d\theta.$$

Hence,

$$\limsup_{r\to 1} u(r\zeta) = \limsup_{r\to 1} \int_{\varphi-\eta}^{\varphi+\eta} [\alpha(\varphi) - \alpha(\theta)]\, K_\theta(e^{i\theta}, r\zeta)\, d\theta$$
$$\leqslant \limsup_{r\to 1} \int_{\varphi-\eta}^{\varphi+\eta} A(\varphi - \theta)\, K_\theta(e^{i\theta}, r\zeta)\, d\theta.$$

Now

$$\int_{\varphi-\eta}^{\varphi+\eta} (\varphi - \theta)\, K_\theta(e^{i\theta}, r\zeta)\, d\theta = (\varphi - \theta)\, K(e^{i\theta}, r\zeta)\Big|_{\varphi-\eta}^{\varphi+\eta} + \int_{\varphi-\eta}^{\varphi+\eta} K(e^{i\theta}, r\zeta)\, d\theta.$$

Using the property (c) of the Poisson kernel given in § 3 of this chapter, we see that

$$\lim_{r\to 1}\int_{\varphi-\eta}^{\varphi+\eta}(\varphi-\theta)\,K_\theta(e^{i\theta},r\zeta)\,d\theta = 2\pi\,.$$

Hence,

$$\limsup_{r\to 1} u(r\zeta) \leqslant 2\pi A\,.$$

The inequality (5.1) follows. The inequality (5.2) is established similarly. We omit the details, which can now be readily supplied.

It is easy to see that Theorem 5.1 implies a corresponding theorem for bounded harmonic functions and bounded analytic functions on $\Delta(0;1)$.

EXERCISE

1. Show that if f is a univalent meromorphic function on $\Delta(0;1)$, then $\lim_{r\to 1} f(r\zeta)$ exists for almost all $\zeta \in C(0;1)$.

To be historically accurate, we should note that Fatou treated the case of a bounded analytic function in his celebrated paper: "Séries trigonométriques et séries de Taylor," *Acta Mathematica*, **30**: 335–400, 1906, which has been the impetus for a large number of important investigations on the boundary behavior of analytic, harmonic, and subharmonic functions.

C) Subharmonic Functions and Applications

6. References. (1) T. Radó, *Subharmonic Functions*. Berlin, 1939, (Chelsea reprint).

(2) J. E. Littlewood, *Theory of Functions*, Oxford 1944.

(3) C. Carathéodory, "On Dirichlet's Problem," *Am. J. Math.*, **59**: 709–731, 1937.

The modern literature on subharmonic functions and allied topics is vast. The account we give here pertains to only a small part of the subject (but a useful part for the theory of functions of a complex variable). The reader interested in pursuing the subject further would need the apparatus of modern integration theory. Among the modern improvements in the exposition of the subject is the proof of F. Riesz's fundamental theorem connecting the theory of subharmonic functions with potential theory which has been given by L. Schwartz with the aid of his theory of distributions.

7. Upper Semicontinuity. The fundamental definitions have already been given in § 7, Chap. 2. Here we shall be concerned with treating a fundamental approximation theorem in a special case and defining an integral for upper semicontinuous functions. The latter task devolves on us because we do not presuppose the Lebesgue theory of integration. However, the approach that we give derives from the modern theory.

We consider a function f with domain a finite interval $\{a \leqslant x \leqslant b\}$ that is upper semicontinuous on its domain and satisfies $f(a) = f(b)$. We show

THEOREM 7.1. *There exists a decreasing sequence* $(g_n)_0^\infty$ *of finite-valued continuous functions on* $\{a \leqslant x \leqslant b\}$, *satisfying* $g_n(a) = g_n(b)$, $n \in N$, *and tending pointwise to* f *on* $\{a \leqslant x \leqslant b\}$.

PROOF: Given $n \in N$, let $\mathscr{L}_n$ denote the family of continuous functions l on $\{a \leqslant x \leqslant b\}$ that satisfy the following conditions:

(a) $l(a) = l(b)$.

(b) l is linear on each subinterval $\{x_k \leqslant x \leqslant x_{k+1}\}$, $k = 0,1,\cdots,2^n - 1$, where $x_k = a + k(b - a)2^{-n}$.

(c) $l(x_k)$ is rational.

(d) $l > f$.

Let $\mathscr{L} = \bigcup_{n \in N} \mathscr{L}_n$. Clearly, $\mathscr{L}$ is countably infinite. Let $(l_j)_{j \in N}$ denote a univalent enumeration of $\mathscr{L}$ (that is, $j \to l_j$ is to be a one-to-one map of N onto $\mathscr{L}$). Let $g_n = \min \{l_1,\cdots,l_n\} + (n + 1)^{-1}$.

The sequence $(g_n)_0^\infty$ so specified meets the stipulated requirements. In fact, g_n is continuous, $g_n(a) = g_n(b)$, and $(g_n)_0^\infty$ is decreasing. Given x satisfying $a \leqslant x \leqslant b$, let r denote a finite real number exceeding $f(x)$. Thanks to the upper semicontinuity of f, there exists $l \in \mathscr{L}$ satisfying $f(x) < l(x) < r$. Hence,

$$f(x) \leqslant \lim g_n(x) \leqslant l(x) < r\,.$$

It follows that $f(x) = \lim g_n(x)$.

It is clear that Theorem 7.1 has its counterpart for functions that are upper semicontinuous on a circumference and also that a corresponding theorem holds for f not necessarily satisfying $f(a) = f(b)$ (with, of course, the g not subject to this boundary condition).

EXERCISES

1. Elaborate on the third from the last sentence of the proof.

2. Show that if f is upper semicontinuous on a compact metric space X, there exists a decreasing sequence $(g_n)_0^\infty$ of continuous finite-valued functions on X tending pointwise to f. The problem is to design a countable substitute for the family $\mathscr{L}$ of the proof of Theorem 7.1. Functions that are continuous and piecewise linear on $\{0 \leqslant x < +\infty\}$ yield on composition with the metric useful auxiliary functions.

3. *Dini's Theorem.* Let X be a compact Hausdorff space, let f be an upper semicontinuous function on X, let g denote a continuous finite-valued function on X satisfying $g > f$, and finally let $(f_n)_0^\infty$ denote a nonincreasing sequence of continuous finite-valued functions on X tending pointwise to f. Show that there exists $m \in N$ such that $f_m < g$.

A proof may be given by constructing an open covering suitably. A second approach is to introduce for each $x \in X$, $\nu(x) = \min\{n \mid f_n(x) < g(x)\}$ and to show that ν is upper semicontinuous.

Integral for Upper Semicontinuous Functions. Given f upper semicontinuous on a finite interval $\{a \leqslant x \leqslant b\}$. By the *integral of f* will be meant

$$\inf \int_a^b g\, dx\,, \tag{7.1}$$

where all continuous finite-valued functions g on $\{a \leqslant x \leqslant b\}$ satisfying $g \geqslant f$ are taken into account. When f is itself continuous and finite-valued on $\{a \leqslant x \leqslant b\}$, the present definition gives the customary Riemann integral of f. For this reason we denote (with propriety) the integral of f by $\int_a^b f\, dx$ or $\int_a^b f(x)\, dx$ for arbitrary upper semicontinuous f on $\{a \leqslant x \leqslant b\}$.

Several remarks are in order:

(1) Given f upper semicontinuous on $\{a \leqslant x \leqslant b\}$ and a nonincreasing sequence $(g_n)_0^\infty$ of continuous finite-valued functions on $\{a \leqslant x \leqslant b\}$ tending pointwise to f, then

$$\lim_{n\to\infty} \int_a^b g_n(x)\, dx = \int_a^b f(x)\, dx\,. \tag{7.2}$$

This follows on noting that if g is a continuous finite-valued function on $\{a \leqslant x \leqslant b\}$ satisfying $g \geqslant f$ and if η is a positive number, then for n sufficiently large (Dini theorem and monotoneity of Riemann integral)

$$\eta(b - a) + \int_a^b g(x)\, dx \geqslant \int_a^b g_n(x)\, dx \geqslant \int_a^b f(x)\, dx\,.$$

Hence,

$$\int_a^b g(x)\, dx \geqslant \lim_{n\to\infty} \int_a^b g_n(x)\, dx \geqslant \int_a^b f(x)\, dx\,.$$

We now see that (7.2) follows from the definition of $\int_a^b f(x)\, dx$.

(2) If f is an upper semicontinuous function with domain R and is periodic with period 2π, then

$$\int_a^{a+2\pi} f(x)\, dx$$

is independent of a. (The obvious gloss, that the integral refers to the restriction of f to $\{a \leqslant x \leqslant a + 2\pi\}$, is to be made.) The proof is straightforward. This remark is pertinent for the definition of the circumferential mean of an upper semicontinuous function.

(3) Given f upper semicontinuous on $\{a \leqslant x \leqslant b\}$ and A a finite real number such that $\max f \leqslant A$ and, for some x in the interval, $f(x) < A$; then

$$\int_a^b f(x)\,dx < A(b-a)\,.$$

It suffices to note there exists a continuous finite-valued g on $\{a \leqslant x \leqslant b\}$ satisfying $f \leqslant g \leqslant A$ and $g(x) < A$ for some x in $\{a \leqslant x \leqslant b\}$.

(4) Given f and g each upper semicontinuous on $\{a \leqslant x \leqslant b\}$ and a non-negative number c. Then

$$\int_a^b cf(x)\,dx = c\int_a^b f(x)\,dx$$

and

$$\int_a^b [f(x)+g(x)]\,dx = \int_a^b f(x)\,dx + \int_a^b g(x)\,dx\,.$$

We recall the conventions: $0\cdot(-\infty) = 0$, $a\cdot(-\infty) = -\infty$ for $a > 0$. We leave the proof of (4) as an exercise for the reader. A proof may be based on (1).

8. Definition of Subharmonicity. This notion can be defined in a number of different ways. We take as our starting point the definition originally given by F. Riesz. As we shall see, there are several alternative possibilities available for the definition of a subharmonic function.

A function u is said to be *subharmonic on a region* $\Omega \subset \hat{K}$ provided that u is upper semicontinuous on Ω and satisfies the following mean-value property: If $\overline{\Delta(a;r)} \subset \Omega$ (r finite), then

$$u(a) \leqslant \frac{1}{2\pi}\int_0^{2\pi} u(a+re^{i\theta})\,d\theta \tag{8.1}$$

when $a \neq \infty$, and

$$u(\infty) \leqslant \frac{1}{2\pi}\int_0^{2\pi} u(r^{-1}\,e^{i\theta})\,d\theta \tag{8.2}$$

when $a = \infty$. A function u is said to be *subharmonic at* a provided that there exists a region Ω contained in the domain of u and containing a such that the restriction of u to Ω is subharmonic on Ω. A function u is said to be *subharmonic in a region* Ω provided that u is subharmonic at each point of Ω. We shall see later that a function u whose domain is a region Ω and which is subharmonic in Ω is indeed subharmonic on Ω.

Given a function u with domain a region Ω which takes values in $\{-\infty \leqslant x < +\infty\}$, we say that u has the property HM (*harmonic-majorant property*) provided that for each h harmonic on a subregion of Ω, say $\Omega(h)$, $\Omega(h) \neq \hat{K}$, and satisfying

$$\limsup_{z(\in\Omega(h))\to\zeta} [u(z) - h(z)] \leqslant 0\,, \qquad \zeta \in \mathrm{fr}\,\Omega(h)\,, \tag{8.3}$$

we have

$$u(z) \leqslant h(z), \qquad z \in \Omega(h) . \tag{8.4}$$

We first show

THEOREM 8.1. *If u is subharmonic on a region Ω, then u has the property* HM. *In the opposite direction: If u is upper semicontinuous on Ω and u has the property* HM, *then u is subharmonic on Ω.*

PROOF: Given u subharmonic on Ω. Suppose that u fails to have the property HM, and let h denote a harmonic function of the admitted type which satisfies (8.3) but not (8.4). Let $v(z) = u(z) - h(z)$, $z \in \Omega(h)$. It follows from (8.3), from the negation of (8.4), and from the upper semicontinuity of v that there exists $a \in \Omega(h)$ at which v attains its maximum. Now v, as is easily verified, is subharmonic on $\Omega(h)$. We now complete the argument, using mean-value considerations as we did for harmonic functions. Let $A = \{v(z) = v(a)\}$, and let $B = \{v(z) < v(a)\}$. The set B is open, by virtue of the upper semicontinuity of v. The set A is seen to be open by observing that, if $z \in A \cap K$,

$$v(z) \leqslant \frac{1}{2\pi} \int_0^{2\pi} v(z + re^{i\theta}) \, d\theta \leqslant v(z)$$

for sufficiently small r (with the obvious variant holding for $z = \infty$); whence we see that a neighborhood of z belongs to A. Hence $A = \Omega(h)$. This contradicts (8.3). It follows that u has the property HM.

Let us now consider the second statement of the theorem. Given a closed disk $\overline{\Delta(a;r)} \subset \Omega$ (r finite), let g denote a continuous (finite-valued) function on $\overline{\Delta(a;r)}$, dominating u on $C(a;r)$ and harmonic in $\Delta(a;r)$. Since u has the property HM,

$$u(a) \leqslant g(a) .$$

Now $\inf_g g(a)$ is

$$\frac{1}{2\pi} \int_0^{2\pi} u(a + re^{i\theta}) \, d\theta$$

[resp., $(2\pi)^{-1}\int_0^{2\pi} u(r^{-1}e^{i\theta}) \, d\theta$]. The subharmonicity of u follows.

The mean-value considerations of the argument used in establishing the first half of Theorem 8.1 yield at once the *maximum principle for subharmonic functions*:

Given that u is subharmonic on a region Ω and that there exists $a \in \Omega$ such that $u(a) = \max u$. Then u is constant.

A consequence of Theorem 8.1 is the following result:

Given u upper semicontinuous on a region Ω. Suppose that for each $a \in \Omega$, there exists $\rho > 0$ such that for $0 < r < \rho$, $\overline{\Delta(a;r)} \subset \Omega$ and (8.1) [*resp.*, (8.2)] *holds. Then u is subharmonic on Ω.*

To establish this assertion, we note that the hypothesis implies that u has the property HM. This may be seen by the argument of the proof of the first half of Theorem 8.1, since it suffices to make only local use of the mean-value property.

The result just stated yields in turn a proof of the statement made at the beginning of this section, namely: *If u is a function whose domain is a region Ω which is subharmonic in Ω, then u is subharmonic on Ω.*

EXERCISES

1. If f is analytic on a region Ω, $\log |f|$ is subharmonic on Ω ($\log 0 = -\infty$).

2. Let u be upper semicontinuous on a region Ω. Suppose that for each $a \in \Omega$, there exists a nonconstant function φ meromorphic on a region containing $z = 0$ which maps its domain into Ω, satisfies $\varphi(0) = a$, and is such that

$$u(a) \leqslant \frac{1}{2\pi} \int_0^{2\pi} u[\varphi(re^{i\theta})]\, d\theta$$

for sufficiently small r. Show that u is subharmonic on Ω.

This is a convenient place to introduce an important maximum principle for subharmonic functions which was originally given for the modulus of an analytic function by Phragmén and Lindelöf. It has played an important role in many function-theoretic applications. The importance of the principle lies in the fact that it takes information of a mixed "quantitative-qualitative nature" and replaces it by more precise quantitative information.

THEOREM 8.2 (Phragmén-Lindelöf maximum principle). *Given u subharmonic on a region Ω. Suppose that E is a countable proper subset of the frontier of Ω. Suppose that $\sup u < +\infty$ and that there exists a real number M such that*

$$\limsup_{z \to \zeta} u(z) \leqslant M\,, \qquad \zeta \in \operatorname{fr} \Omega - E\,. \tag{8.5}$$

Then

$$\sup_{\Omega} u \leqslant M\,. \tag{8.6}$$

PROOF: Given a disk Δ (of finite radius), let $w \in \hat{K} - \overline{\Delta}$, and let l_w denote a rational function of degree 1 that maps $\hat{K} - \overline{\Delta}$ onto $\Delta(0;1)$ and satisfies $l_w(w) = 0$; we do not need to determine l_w explicitly.

Suppose now that $a \in \Omega$, that A is a finite real number greater than $u(a)$, and that r (finite) is such that $\overline{\Delta(a;2r)} \subset \Omega$ and

$$\max_{z \in \overline{\Delta(a;r)}} u(z) < A\,.$$

We take $\Delta = \Delta(a;r)$. We fix $b \in \Omega - \overline{\Delta}$ and let $\eta(w) > 0$ be such that

$$\sum_{w \in E} \eta(w) \log \left| \frac{1}{l_w(b)} \right| < +\infty\,. \tag{8.7}$$

We note that

$$z \to \sum_{w \in E} \eta(w) \log \left| \frac{1}{l_w(z)} \right| , \qquad z \in \Omega - \overline{\Delta} ,$$

is a nonnegative harmonic function on $\Omega - \overline{\Delta}$, thanks to (8.7) and the Harnack convergence theorem ("nonnegative" because the possibility that $E = \emptyset$ is allowed). We denote this function by v. We see that

$$v(z) \leqslant \{\max_{C(a;2r)} v\}\omega(z) , \qquad z \in \overline{\Delta(a;2r)} - \overline{\Delta(a;r)}, \tag{8.8}$$

where

$$\omega(z) = \frac{\log |(z - a)/r|}{\log 2}$$

if a is finite, and

$$\omega(z) = \frac{-\log |z\, r|}{\log 2}$$

if a is infinite. The function ω is just that solution for the Dirichlet problem for $\Delta(a;2r) - \overline{\Delta(a;r)}$ which takes the boundary value 1 on $C(a;2r)$ and the boundary value 0 on $C(a;r)$. The assertion (8.8) follows on noting that it holds for finite partial sums of the sum defining v. The inequality (8.8) yields the important conclusion that $\lim_{z \to \zeta} v(z) = 0$ for each $\zeta \in C(a;r)$. It follows from the definition of v that

$$\lim_{z \to w} v(z) = +\infty , \qquad w \in E .$$

We now introduce for each positive number ε,

$$u_\varepsilon(z) = u(z) - \varepsilon v(z) - \max \{A,M\}, \qquad z \in \Omega - \overline{\Delta(a;r)} . \tag{8.9}$$

The function u_ε is subharmonic on $\Omega - \overline{\Delta(a;r)}$ and satisfies

$$\limsup_{z \to \zeta} u_\varepsilon(z) \leqslant 0$$

for each frontier point ζ of $\Omega - \overline{\Delta(a;r)}$. It follows from Theorem 8.1 that

$$u(z) \leqslant \varepsilon v(z) + \max \{A,M\}, \qquad z \in \Omega - \overline{\Delta(a;r)} ,$$

and thereupon that

$$u(z) \leqslant \max \{A,M\} , \qquad z \in \Omega .$$

Consequently,

$$u(z) \leqslant \max \{u(a),M\} , \qquad z \in \Omega .$$

Now $u(a) \leqslant M$; otherwise not only would u be constant but also the boundary condition (8.5) would be violated. The theorem follows.

EXERCISE

3. Show that if frΩ is countable and u is a subharmonic function on Ω that is bounded above, then u is constant.

Superharmonic Functions. We arrive at the notion of a *superharmonic* function by replacing the requirement of upper semicontinuity by that of lower semicontinuity and reversing the sense of the inequalities (8.1) (resp., (8.2)). The notion of the integral of a lower semicontinuous function is defined in a manner analogous to that given by (7.1) of this chapter, with the obvious reversals of inequalities and of "sup" and "inf." It is immediate that a subharmonic function is the negative of a superharmonic function and that all the results established thus far for subharmonic functions have their counterparts for superharmonic functions.

9. Properties of Subharmonic Functions. We now establish some properties of subharmonic functions which are of frequent use. Let u_1 and u_2 denote subharmonic functions on a region Ω, and let c denote a nonnegative constant. Then

(a) $u_1 + u_2$, $\max\{u_1,u_2\}$, *and* cu_1 *are all subharmonic on* Ω.

It suffices to verify that each of the functions in question is upper semicontinuous on Ω and satisfies the mean-value property. It is to be observed that the convention $0\cdot(-\infty) = 0$ prevails.

(b) *Given a monotone nonincreasing sequence* $(u_n)_0^\infty$ *of functions subharmonic on a region* Ω. *Then* $u = \lim u_n$ *is subharmonic on* Ω.

The upper semicontinuity of u is readily concluded, since $(u_n)_0^\infty$ is monotone nonincreasing. On the other hand, we note that if $(f_n)_0^\infty$ is a monotone nonincreasing sequence of upper semicontinuous functions on a finite interval $\{a \leqslant x \leqslant b\}$ with pointwise limit f and if g is a finite-valued continuous function on $\{a \leqslant x \leqslant b\}$ satisfying $g > f$, then, as is seen by the argument of the Dini theorem,

$$g > f_n$$

for n sufficiently large. Hence,

$$\int_a^b f(x)\,dx \leqslant \lim_{n\to\infty} \int_a^b f_n(x)\,dx < \int_a^b g(x)\,dx\,.$$

It follows that

$$\int_a^b f(x)\,dx = \lim_{n\to\infty} \int_a^b f_n(x)\,dx\,.$$

On applying this result to $(u_n)_0^\infty$, we see that u satisfies the mean-value property.

(c) *Given* u *subharmonic on a region* Ω. *If* $\operatorname{int}\{u(z) = -\infty\} \neq \emptyset$, *then* u *is the constant* $-\infty$.

Actually, we may obtain much more refined results of this type with the aid of modern potential-theoretic methods (using the concept of capacity).

To prove the modest (c), let $E = \text{int}\,\{u(z) = -\infty\}$ and suppose that $a \in \bar{E} \cap \Omega$. There exists r (finite) such that $\overline{\Delta(a;r)} \subset \Omega$ and $C(a;r) \cap E \neq \emptyset$. There exists a nonincreasing sequence $(v_n)_0^\infty$ of functions continuous on $\overline{\Delta(a;r)}$ and harmonic in $\Delta(a;r)$ such that $\lim_{n\to\infty} v_n(z) = u(z)$ on $C(a;r)$. Now $v_n(z) \geqslant u(z)$, $z \in \overline{\Delta(a;r)}$, $n \in N$. Further, $\lim_{n\to\infty} v_n(a) = -\infty$, since u is equal to $-\infty$ on an arc of $C(a;r)$. By the Harnack convergence theorem, $\lim_{n\to\infty} v_n(z) = -\infty$, $z \in \Delta(a;r)$. Hence, $a \in E$. From $E \subset \bar{E} \cap \Omega \subset E$, we conclude, since Ω is connected, that $E = \Omega$. The assertion (c) follows.

(d) Composition with a meromorphic function. *Let u denote a subharmonic function on a region Ω_2, and let φ denote a meromorphic map of a region Ω_1 into Ω_2. Then $v = u \circ \varphi$ is subharmonic on Ω_1.*

We put aside the trivial case where φ is constant. The upper semicontinuity of v follows from the upper semicontinuity of u and the continuity of φ. We now use Ex. 2, § 8, this chapter. If $n(a;\varphi) = 1$, let ψ denote the inverse of the restriction of $\varphi - \varphi(a)$, (resp., $1/\varphi$, if $\varphi(a) = \infty$) to a sufficiently small $\Delta(a;r)$. Now $v \circ \psi(z) = u[\varphi(a) + z]$ (resp., $u(z^{-1})$) for z small, and $v \circ \psi$ satisfies the stipulated mean-value property.

If $n(a;\varphi) = m > 1$, we use Theorem 6.1 of Chap. 2 to infer the existence of a univalent meromorphic function ψ on a region Ω containing the origin satisfying $\psi(0) = a$, $\psi(\Omega) \subset \Omega_1$, and

$$\varphi \circ \psi(z) = \varphi(a) + z^m \left[\text{resp., } \varphi \circ \psi(z) = z^{-m}\right].$$

Thanks to these properties of ψ, $v \circ \psi(z) = u[\varphi(a) + z^m]$ [resp., $u(z^{-m})$] for z small. It is easily verified that in the first case the mean value of $v \circ \psi$ on $C(0;r)$ for r small is just the mean value of u on $C(\varphi(a);r^m)$ and in the second case is the mean value of u on $C(0;r^{-m})$. By Ex. 2, § 8, this chapter, property (*d*) follows.

EXERCISES

Most of the exercises that follow have as their theme the relation of convexity for functions of one real variable to subharmonicity. If we observe that the one-dimensional analogue of a harmonic function (= "solution" of Laplace's equation) is a linear function (= solution of $y'' = 0$), we see that the subharmonic functions (functions having the harmonic-majorant property + upper semicontinuity) parallel the convex functions. Exercises 1 to 9, which follow, serve to elaborate this remark.

1. To be complete, we recall that a finite real-valued function f whose domain D is a connected subset of R is termed *convex* provided that whenever $a,b(> a) \in D$,

$$f(x) \leqslant \frac{b-x}{b-a} f(a) + \frac{x-a}{b-a} f(b), \qquad a < x < b.$$

(Interpret this condition graphically!) Conclude for f convex on D:

(a) If $x_1 < x_2 \leqslant x_3 < x_4$, $x_k \in D$, then

$$\frac{f(x_2) - f(x_1)}{x_2 - x_1} \leqslant \frac{f(x_4) - f(x_3)}{x_4 - x_3}.$$

(b) f is continuous in int D.

(c) If $x_k \in D$, and $\mu_k \geqslant 0$, $k = 1,\cdots,n$ and $\sum_{k=1}^{n} \mu_k = 1$, then

$$f\Big(\sum_{k=1}^{n} \mu_k x_k\Big) \leqslant \sum_{k=1}^{n} \mu_k f(x_k)$$

(proof by induction).

2. Given a real-valued function f whose domain D is an open connected subset of R. Show: (a) If f is convex and $f''(a)$ exists, then $f''(a) \geqslant 0$. (b) If $f''(x)$ exists for each $x \in D$ and $f'' \geqslant 0$, then f is convex.

3. Given $u \in C''(\Omega)$, where Ω is a region $\subset K$ (compare § 2, this chapter). Show that u is subharmonic on Ω if, and only if, $\Delta u \geqslant 0$.

HINT: Given $u \in C''(\Omega)$, $a \in \Omega$, let $\mu(r) = (2\pi)^{-1}\int_0^{2\pi} u(a + re^{i\theta})\, d\theta$ for r small and positive, and note that (2.4) yields

$$\mu''(r) + r^{-1}\mu'(r) = \frac{1}{2\pi}\int_0^{2\pi} \Delta u(a + re^{i\theta})\, d\theta\,.$$

Relate subharmonicity with differential properties of μ, considering all $a \in \Omega$.

4. Given $u \not\equiv -\infty$ subharmonic on a region $\Omega \subset K$. Let

$$\mathfrak{A} = \{R_1 < |z - a| < R_2\} \subset \Omega,\ 0 \leqslant R_1 < R_2 \leqslant +\infty.$$

Let $\sigma(r) = \max_{z \in C(a;r)} u(z)$ and

$$\mu(r) = (2\pi)^{-1} \int_0^{2\pi} u(a + re^{i\theta})\, d\theta,\ R_1 < r < R_2.$$

Let $R_1 < r_1 < r_2 < R_2$. Show that

$$\mu(r) \leqslant \frac{\log r_2 - \log r}{\log r_2 - \log r_1}\mu(r_1) + \frac{\log r - \log r_1}{\log r_2 - \log r_1}\mu(r_2)\,, \tag{a}$$

$r_1 < r < r_2$, and that a corresponding relation holds for σ. Show that if equality holds in the μ inequality at any intermediate r, then it holds for all such r. Show also that equality occurs if and only if u is harmonic in $\{r_1 < |z - a| < r_2\}$. Show further that if equality holds in the σ inequality at an intermediate r, then it holds for all such r and also that equality occurs if, and only if, $u(z)$ is linear in $\log |z - a|$ for $\{r_1 \leqslant |z - a| \leqslant r_2\}$.

HINT: Consider the functions v continuous on $\{r_1 \leqslant |z - a| \leqslant r_2\}$ and harmonic in $\{r_1 < |z - a| < r_2\}$ which dominate u on $C(a;r_1)$ and $C(a;r_2)$.

Apply (2.7) and (2.8) of this chapter for the $\mu(r)$ pertaining to v. Take a sequence of v tending to u on $C(a;r_k)$, $k = 1,2$, in a nonincreasing fashion. Note that these considerations show that $\mu(r) > -\infty$, $r_1 \leqslant r \leqslant r_2$. For the σ inequality, employ the comparison function

$$v(z) = \frac{\log r_2 - \log | z - a |}{\log r_2 - \log r_1} \sigma(r_1) + \frac{\log | z - a | - \log r_1}{\log r_2 - \log r_1} \sigma(r_2) .$$

(The σ inequality is the Hadamard three-circles theorem in subharmonic form.)

5. Show that a finite real-valued function f on an interval (R_1,R_2) satisfies (a) of the previous exercise with f replacing μ for all r_1,r_2 satisfying $R_1 < r_1 < r_2 < R_2$ if, and only if, $f(r) \equiv F(\log r)$, where F is convex on $\{\log R_1 < x < \log R_2\}$.

6. Suppose that u is as in Ex. 4 of this set and that $\Delta(a;R) \subset \Omega$. Show that μ (now defined for $0 \leqslant r < R$) is nondecreasing and that if $\mu(r_1) = \mu(r_2)$, $0 \leqslant r_1 < r_2$ $(< R)$, then μ is constant on $\{0 \leqslant r \leqslant r_2\}$ and u is harmonic in $\Delta(a;r_2)$.

HINT: Using convex functions, one may proceed by first showing that if F is convex on $\{-\infty < x < x_0\}$, then either $\lim_{x\to-\infty} F(x) = +\infty$ or else F is nondecreasing.

7. Show that if u is subharmonic $(\not\equiv -\infty)$ on a strip $\{a < \operatorname{Re} z < b\}$ and u is constant on each vertical line $\{\operatorname{Re} z = c\}$, $a < c < b$, then u admits a representation of the form $F(\operatorname{Re} z)$, where F is convex on $\{a < x < b\}$. State and prove a corresponding result for functions subharmonic on an annulus $\{r_1 < | z | < r_2\}$ and constant on each $C(0;r)$, $r_1 < r < r_2$. Establish the converse theorems.

8. Given $u \not\equiv -\infty$ subharmonic on the finite plane. Let $u^+ = \max \{u,0\}$. Show that with

$$\mu_1(r) = \frac{1}{2\pi} \int_0^{2\pi} u^+(re^{i\theta})\, d\theta ,$$

$\lim_{r\to\infty} \mu_1(r)/\log r$ exists (finite or $+\infty$). If $\lim_{r\to\infty} \mu_1(r)/\log r = 0$, then u is a finite constant. Applied to $u = \log | f |$, where f is entire, the theorem of this exercise yields the theorem of Liouville.

9. Given u ($\not\equiv$ const.) subharmonic on a region Ω. Let f denote a continuous nondecreasing function on $\{\inf u \leqslant x < \sup u\}$ whose restriction to $\{\inf u < x < \sup u\}$ is convex. The possibility: $f(\inf u) = -\infty$ is allowed. Show that $f \circ u$ is subharmonic on Ω. The upper semicontinuity of $f \circ u$ is readily verified. To test the mean-value property, use may be made of the following lemma: Given g finite-valued and continuous on a finite interval $\{a \leqslant x \leqslant b\}$, taking values in the domain of f. Then

$$(b-a)^{-1} \int_a^b f \circ g(x)\, dx \geqslant f\left\{(b-a)^{-1} \int_a^b g(x)\, dx\right\} .$$

The lemma may be derived by using Ex. 1(c) of this set and approximating the integrals by finite sums.

10. Establish the following theorem: Let p satisfy $1 < p < +\infty$; let q satisfy $q^{-1} + p^{-1} = 1$; let a_k be finite, $k = 1,\cdots,n$. Then

$$\max\left\{ \left|\sum a_k x_k\right| \,\Big|\, \sum |x_k|^q = 1 \right\} = \left\{\sum |a_k|^p\right\}^{1/p}$$

(Hölder inequality). This theorem is readily established by the use of standard methods for maximum problems with constraints (for which see any good text on advanced calculus).

Apply this form of the Hölder inequality (note the "max"!) to show: If $u_1,\cdots,u_n$ are subharmonic and nonnegative in a region Ω and $1 < p < +\infty$, then

$$u = \left\{\sum_{k=1}^{n} u_k^p\right\}^{1/p}$$

is subharmonic on Ω.

HINT: In testing the mean-value property at $a \in \Omega$, represent $u(a)$ as $\Sigma\, x_k u_k(a)$, $x_k \geqslant 0$, $\Sigma\, x_k^q = 1$.

11. Let B be a compact set $\neq \emptyset$ in R^n having the property that $(x_1,\cdots,x_n) \in B$ implies $(|x_1|,\cdots,|x_n|) \in B$. Let $u_1,\cdots,u_n$ be as in Ex. 10. Let

$$u(z) = \max\left\{\sum x_k u_k(z) \,\big|\, (x_1,\cdots,x_n) \in B\right\}.$$

Then u is subharmonic on Ω. This result generalizes the theorem[2] of Ex. 10.

12. Establish with the aid of Ex. 10 the following theorem: Let u be subharmonic and nonnegative in an annulus $\{0 \leqslant r_1 < |z| < r_2 \leqslant +\infty\}$, and let $1 < p < +\infty$. Let $m(r;u)$ be the pth circumferential mean of u on $C(0,r)$; that is,

$$m(r;u) = \left\{\frac{1}{2\pi}\int_0^{2\pi} [u(re^{i\theta})]^p\, d\theta\right\}^{1/p} \qquad r_1 < r < r_2 .$$

Then $m(r;u)$ is convex in $\log r$.

HINT: Consider first the case where u is continuous, introduce

$$u_n(z) = \left\{\frac{1}{n}\sum_{k=0}^{n-1} \left[u(e^{2\pi ik/n}\, z)\right]^p\right\}^{1/p},$$

and study $\lim u_n$. To treat the general case, introduce v continuous on $\{R_1 \leqslant |z| \leqslant R_2\}$ and harmonic on $\{R_1 < |z| < R_2\}$, where $r_1 < R_1 < R_2 < r_2$, satisfying $v(z) \geqslant u(z)$ on the domain of v, and note that $m(r;u) \leqslant m(r;v)$. The proof is completed by considering a sequence of such v tending in a nonincreasing fashion to u on $C(0;R_k)$, $k = 1,2$.

A second proof of this theorem is to be found in Ex. 4, § 11, Chap. 5.

13. *A Lemma of I. N. Baker* (*Math. Zeitschrift*, **69**: 121). Let f be an entire function. Let $M(r;f) = \max_{|z|=r} |f(z)|$. If there exists an integer $n > 1$ and positive numbers A, B, r_0 such that $M(Ar^n;f) \leqslant B\,[M(r;f)]^n$ for $r \geqslant r_0$, then f is a polynomial.

HINT: If f is not identically zero, consider the convex function μ with domain R defined by $\mu(t) = \log M(e^t;f)$, and show that the hypothesis of the lemma implies that $\lim_{t\to+\infty} t^{-1}\mu(t)$ (this limit exists as a consequence of the convexity of μ) is finite.

---

10. $\beta \geqslant \sqrt{3}/4$ (Ahlfors). This theorem, which appears in Ahlfors's paper: "An Extension of Schwarz's Lemma," *Trans. AMS*, **43**: 359–364, 1938, affords an excellent opportunity to see put into action some of the ideas and methods exposed in Chap. 2 and in the present chapter. Ahlfors's paper has its roots in concepts of differential geometry such as Riemannian metric (specialized in the paper to conformal metric) and the Gaussian curvature of a Riemannian metric. In recent years the impact of differential-geometric methods on the theory of functions of a complex variable (quasi-conformal mapping, conformal metrics, etc.) has been considerable. The reader interested in this aspect of the theory of functions of a complex variable will find the paper of Ahlfors profitable. No improvement on the lower estimate of β given by Ahlfors has since been made, as far as I know.

In what follows, we shall not presuppose an acquaintance with differential-geometric concepts. The exposition will be cast in terms of classical function theory and some elementary observations concerning Laplacians. The connections with differential geometry will be pointed out parenthetically. We begin with some exercises of an elementary nature. They contain lemmas for the principal developments of this section as well as illustrative material.

EXERCISES

1. Let f be analytic on a region $\Omega \subset K$. Suppose that $|f(z)| < A < +\infty$. Let

$$\lambda(z) = \frac{A\,|f'(z)|}{A^2 - |f(z)|^2}.$$

Let $u(z) = \log \lambda(z)$. Suppose that $f'(a) \neq 0$. Show that

$$\Delta u(a) = 4[\lambda(a)]^2.$$

2. Suppose that f is analytic on a region $\Omega \subset K$ and that $|f| < A^2$, $0 < A < +\infty$. Let

$$\lambda(z) = \frac{A\,|f'(z)|}{2\,|f(z)|^{1/2}\,(A^2 - |f(z)|)}.$$

Let $u(z) = \log \lambda(z)$. Suppose that $f(a) \neq 0$, $f'(a) \neq 0$. Show that

$$\Delta u(a) = 4[\lambda(a)]^2.$$

HINT: Consider an analytic square root of f locally.

3. Let f be analytic on $\Delta(0;1)$ and satisfy $|f| < 1$. Let $a \in \Delta(0;1)$. Show that

$$\frac{|f'(a)|}{1 - |f(a)|^2} \leqslant \frac{1}{1 - |a|^2}$$

and that equality occurs if, and only if, f is a univalent conformal map of $\Delta(0;1)$ onto itself. This is the lemma of Schwarz-Pick.

HINT: Let $f(a) = b$, and consider the function $L_b \circ f \circ M_a$, where L_b and M_a are as defined in § 9, Chap. 2.

We consider a nonnegative continuous function λ on $\Delta(0;1)$. [This function leads to a conformal metric $\lambda(z)\,ds$ on $\Delta(0;1)$.] Suppose that $\lambda(a) \neq 0$. Then a function λ_a that possesses continuous partial derivatives of the first two orders in some neighborhood of a is said to *support* λ *at* a provided that

(1) $\lambda_a(a) = \lambda(a)$,

(2) $\lambda_a(z) \leqslant \lambda(z)$ in some neighborhood of a,

(3) With $u_a(z) = \log \lambda_a(z)$,

$$\Delta u_a(z) \geqslant 4[\lambda_a(z)]^2 \tag{10.1}$$

in some neighborhood of a.

NOTE: For $\lambda = \exp \circ u$ of class C'' and positive in a neighborhood of z, $K(z) = -\Delta u(z)/[\lambda(z)]^2$ is the *Gaussian curvature* at z of the metric $\lambda(z)\,ds$. The condition (10.1) states that the Gaussian curvature of $\lambda_a\,ds$ is no greater than -4 in some neighborhood of a. The first two exercises of the present section state that $K(a) = -4$ in each case for the metric $\lambda(z)\,ds$. The first exercise shows ($A = 1$) that each side of the Schwarz-Pick inequality gives rise to a metric in $\Delta(0;1)$ which is of constant Gaussian curvature -4 save for the singular z at which $f'(z) = 0$ in the case of the left-hand side and which is always of Gaussian curvature -4 for the right-hand side. The metric $(1 - |z|^2)^{-1}\,ds$ associated with the right-hand side is the *hyperbolic metric* of $\Delta(0;1)$. For a discussion of the hyperbolic metric, see C. Carathéodory, *Conformal Representation*, Cambridge University Press, 1932.

A mildly generalized version of Ahlfors's extension of the Schwarz lemma is given in the following theorem:

THEOREM 10.1. *Let there be given a nonnegative continuous function λ on $\Delta(0;1)$. Suppose that for each $z \in \Delta(0;1)$ for which $\lambda(z) \neq 0$, save possibly for a set of z clustering at no point of $\Delta(0;1)$, there exists λ_z that supports λ at z. Then*

$$\lambda(z) \leqslant (1 - |z|^2)^{-1}, \qquad |z| < 1. \tag{10.2}$$

This theorem differs from Ahlfors's version in that an exceptional set, where requirements concerning supporting functions are not made, is allowed here. (Actually one could allow even closed sets of zero capacity as exceptional sets. The proof would be essentially the same save for the use of more sophisticated tools from potential theory, such as Evans's theorem. In order to establish Ahlfors's lower estimate for the Bloch constant, one may operate with Ahlfors's extension of Schwarz's lemma. It is not necessary to take into account any exceptional sets. However, there is some interest in the fact that a Phragmén-Lindelöf argument may be used to ease the hypotheses of the extended form of Schwarz's lemma.) That the lemma of Schwarz-Pick may be subsumed under Theorem 10.1 follows from Ex. 1 of this section. The λ of that exercise is its own support at each z for which $\lambda(z) \neq 0$.

PROOF OF THEOREM 10.1: Let E denote the exceptional set. Let $0 < r < 1$. We show that

$$\lambda(z) \leqslant \frac{r}{r^2 - |z|^2} = \mu(z), \qquad |z| < r, \tag{10.3}$$

whence (10.2) follows. Let $\eta > 0$, and let

$$\lambda^*(z) = \lambda(z) \prod_{k=1}^{n} |L_{a_k}(z)|^\eta \tag{10.4}$$

where a_k, $k = 1,\cdots,n$, are the distinct points of E in $\Delta(0;r)$, n being possibly zero. We show that (10.3) holds with λ^* replacing λ. Letting $\eta \to 0$ and using the continuity of λ, we conclude that (10.3) holds. If (10.3) does not hold with λ^* replacing λ, there exists $b \in \Delta(0;r)$ such that

$$\frac{\lambda^*(b)}{\mu(b)} \geqslant \frac{\lambda^*(z)}{\mu(z)}, \qquad |z| < r, \tag{10.5}$$

and

$$\lambda^*(b) > \mu(b).$$

Let λ_b support λ at b. Then $\lambda_b^* = \lambda_b \prod_{k=1}^{n} |L_{a_k}|^\eta$ supports λ^* at b. It suffices to observe that the Laplacian of the logarithm of λ_b^* is no less than $4[\lambda_b(z)]^2 \geqslant 4[\lambda_b^*(z)]^2$ for z near b. From (10.5) we conclude that

$$\frac{\lambda_b^*(b)}{\mu(b)} \geqslant \frac{\lambda_b^*(z)}{\mu(z)}$$

in some neighborhood of b. Hence, with $u(z) = \log \lambda_b^*(z)$ and $v(z) = \log \mu(z)$, we see that $u - v$ has a relative maximum at b, so that the Laplacian of $u - v$ at b does not exceed zero. But the Laplacian of $u - v$ at b is at least as large as

$$4[\lambda_b^*(b)]^2 - 4[\mu(b)]^2 = 4\{[\lambda^*(b)]^2 - [\mu(b)]^2\} > 0\,.$$

The contradiction is manifest. Hence, (10.3) holds with λ^* replacing λ. The theorem now follows.

It is to be observed that the device of introducing (10.4) is reminiscent of the Phragmén-Lindelöf argument.

EXERCISE

4. Show that the logarithm of λ of Theorem 10.1 is subharmonic on $\Delta(0;1)$.

In order to apply Theorem 10.1 to a specific problem, we are led to design in terms of the data of the problem a λ meeting the support condition and yielding useful information through the mediation of Theorem 10.1. Let us turn to the λ constructed by Ahlfors in connection with the Bloch theorem.

We start with f analytic on $\Delta(0;1)$, satisfying $f'(0) = 1$. For each $z \in \Delta(0;1)$, we define $\rho(z)$ as follows: If $f'(z) = 0$, $\rho(z) = 0$; if $f'(z) \neq 0$, then $\rho(z)$ is the supremum of the set of $r > 0$ for which the restriction of f to the component of $f^{-1}[\Delta(f(z);r)]$ containing z maps this component univalently onto $\Delta(f(z);r)$. As is easily seen, $\rho(z)$ is the *maximum* of the set of r. We denote the component of $f^{-1}[\Delta(f(z);\rho(z))]$ containing z by Ω_z and note that there is a frontier point of Ω_z which is either on $C(0;1)$ or else is a zero of f'. [Establish!]

The function ρ is continuous, as we shall now see. If $f'(a) \neq 0$, then

$$\rho(a) - |f(z) - f(a)| \leqslant \rho(z) \leqslant \rho(a) + |f(z) - f(a)|, \qquad z \in \Omega_a\,.$$

If $f'(a) = 0$, then, using the local representation theorem for meromorphic functions (Theorem 6.1, Chap. 2), we see that for z sufficiently near a,

$$\rho(z) = |f(z) - f(a)|\,. \tag{10.6}$$

Hence ρ is continuous. Of course $\rho(z) \leqslant b(f)$, $|z| < 1$. We restrict our attention to f satisfying $b(f) < +\infty$.

Now let $A > \sqrt{3b(f)}$. We define λ by

$$\lambda(z) = \begin{cases} \dfrac{A\,|f'(z)|}{2\sqrt{\rho(z)}\,[A^2 - \rho(z)]}\,, & \text{when } f'(z) \neq 0; \\[2ex] \dfrac{1}{A}\sqrt{\dfrac{|f''(z)|}{2}}\,, & \text{when } n(z;f) \geqslant 2\,. \end{cases} \tag{10.7}$$

The condition (10.6) implies that λ is continuous.

Supporting λ_a. Suppose that $f'(a) \neq 0$. Let b denote a point of $C(f(a); \rho(a))$ that is *not* the image with respect to f of a frontier point of Ω_a in $\Delta(0;1)$, where f has multiplicity 1. We define $\rho_a(z)$ simply as $|f(z) - b|$, $z \in \Omega_a$, note that

$$\rho_a(z) \geqslant \rho(z)$$

in Ω_a, and thereupon define $\lambda_a(z)$ as

$$\frac{A\,|\,f'(z)\,|}{2\sqrt{\rho_a(z)}\,[A^2 - \rho_a(z)]}\,. \tag{10.8}$$

We note that $\rho_a(a) = \rho(a)$, $\rho_a(z) \leqslant 2b(f)$. Since $t^{1/2}(A^2 - t)$ is increasing on $\{0 \leqslant t \leqslant A^2/3\}$, we see that $\lambda_a(z) \leqslant \lambda(z)$ for z near a. Applying Ex. 2 of this section, we see that λ_a supports λ at a.

We conclude that λ is admitted by Theorem 10.1. From $\lambda(0) \leqslant 1$, we have

$$\begin{aligned} A &\leqslant 2\sqrt{\rho(0)}\,[A^2 - \rho(0)] \\ &\leqslant 2\sqrt{b(f)}\,[A^2 - b(f)]\,. \end{aligned}$$

Hence, letting $A \to \sqrt{3b(f)}$, we obtain

$$\sqrt{3b(f)} \leqslant 4[b(f)]^{3/2}\,.$$

Hence,

$$b(f) \geqslant \sqrt{3}/4\,,$$

and finally

$$\beta \geqslant \sqrt{3}/4\,.$$

EXERCISE

5. Show that the conclusion $\beta \geqslant \sqrt{3}/4$ can be established with Ahlfors's extension of Schwarz's lemma without concern for exceptional points. It suffices to study the points where the multiplicity of f is 2.

---

11. Perron Families. We now turn to the study of certain existence problems, notably the Dirichlet problem, with the aid of methods based on the consideration of families of subharmonic functions—these methods are due to Perron. It will be well to keep the analogy between convex functions of a single variable and subharmonic functions in mind.

Poisson Modification. Given a subharmonic function u on a region Ω, a function v with domain Ω is termed a *Poisson modification* of u provided that there exists $\overline{\Delta(a;r)} \subset \Omega$ (r finite) such that $v(z) = u(z)$, $z \in \Omega - \Delta(a;r)$, and

$$v(a + rz) = \frac{1}{2\pi}\int_0^{2\pi} u(a + re^{i\theta})\,K(e^{i\theta}, z)\,d\theta)\,, \qquad |\,z\,| < 1\,, \tag{11.1}$$

if $a \neq \infty$, and

$$v\left(\frac{1}{rz}\right) = \frac{1}{2\pi}\int_0^{2\pi} u\left(\frac{1}{re^{i\theta}}\right) K(e^{i\theta}, z)\, d\theta\,, \qquad |z| < 1\,, \tag{11.2}$$

if $a = \infty$. The integrals are taken in the sense of integrals of upper semicontinuous functions.

If V is continuous (finite) on $\overline{\Delta(a;r)}$ and harmonic in $\Delta(a;r)$ and satisfies $V(z) \geqslant u(z)$, $z \in C(a;r)$, then $V(z) \geqslant u(z)$, $z \in \Delta(a;r)$, by the harmonic-majorant property of subharmonic functions. We take a monotone decreasing sequence $(V_n)_0^\infty$ of such V which tends pointwise on $C(a;r)$ to u. The limit of the sequence is the restriction of v to $\overline{\Delta(a;r)}$. Hence we conclude:

$$v \geqslant u$$

and either $v \equiv -\infty$ *in* $\Delta(a;r)$ *or else* v *is harmonic in* $\Delta(a;r)$.

Now the function that agrees with u on $\Omega - \overline{\Delta(a;r)}$ and with V_n on $\overline{\Delta(a;r)}$ is easily seen to be upper semicontinuous on Ω. Hence, v is the limit of a monotone nonincreasing sequence of upper semicontinuous functions; consequently, v is itself upper semicontinuous. It is also seen that at each point of Ω, v satisfies the mean-value property for sufficiently small peripheries. It is clear that it suffices to consider only points of $C(a;r)$, for certainly v is subharmonic at each point of $\Omega - C(a;r)$. If $z \in C(a;r)$,

$$v(z) = u(z) \leqslant \frac{1}{2\pi}\int_0^{2\pi} u(z + \rho e^{i\theta})\, d\theta \leqslant \frac{1}{2\pi}\int_0^{2\pi} v(z + \rho e^{i\theta})\, d\theta$$

for ρ sufficiently small. Hence, v *is subharmonic* on Ω.

Perron Family. Given a region Ω. A family Φ of functions subharmonic on Ω is termed a *Perron family* provided that the following conditions are fulfilled:

(1) If $u_1, u_2 \in \Phi$, then $\max\{u_1, u_2\} \in \Phi$.

(2) If $u \in \Phi$, then each Poisson modification of u is also a member of Φ.

Given a Perron family Φ of functions subharmonic on Ω, let v denote the upper envelope of the family; that is,

$$v(z) = \sup\{u(z) \mid u \in \Phi\}\,, \qquad z \in \Omega\,.$$

The basic theorem concerning Perron families is

THEOREM 11.1. *One of the following alternatives occurs:* (a) $v \equiv -\infty$, (b) $v \equiv +\infty$, (c) v *is harmonic on* Ω.

PROOF: We put aside the case where Φ does not contain a member distinct from $-\infty$. We first show that either $v \equiv +\infty$ or else v is finite-valued. Suppose that $v(a) = +\infty$. Let $\overline{\Delta(a;r)} \subset \Omega$. We are assured that there exists a sequence $(u_n)_0^\infty$ whose members belong to Φ and are such that $u_n(a) \to +\infty$. We may assume that $u_n \leqslant u_{n+1}$, all n, by virtue of property (1) of Φ. It suffices to replace the nth term of the original sequence by $\max\{u_k\}_0^n$. We may also assume that u_n is harmonic in $\Delta(a;r)$ by virtue of property (2) of Φ. It now follows from the Harnack convergence theorem that $v(z) = +\infty$, $z \in \Delta(a;r)$. Hence, we see that the set $E = \{v(z) = +\infty\}$ is open. A similar argument shows that if $b \in \bar{E} \cap \Omega$, then $b \in E$. It suffices to take $\overline{\Delta(b;r)} \subset \Omega$, $c \in E \cap \Delta(b;r)$, and a sequence $(u_n)_0^\infty$ satisfying the stipulations: $u_n(c) \to +\infty$, $u_n \leqslant u_{n+1}$, u_n harmonic in $\Delta(b;r)$. Hence, either $E = \Omega$ or $E = \emptyset$. It follows that either $v \equiv +\infty$ or else $v < +\infty$. On the other hand, there exists $u \in \Phi$ that is not the constant $-\infty$. Since $\operatorname{int}\{u(z) = -\infty\} = \emptyset$, we see that, given $a \in \Omega$, there is a Poisson modification u_1 of u for which $u_1(a)$ is finite. Hence, when $v < +\infty$, v is finite-valued.

Let us now show that when v is finite-valued, it is also *harmonic on* Ω. The theorem will then follow. Again we consider $\overline{\Delta(a;r)} \subset \Omega$ and show that v is harmonic in $\Delta(a;r)$. To that end, we consider a sequence $(u_n)_0^\infty$ whose members belong to Φ satisfying: $u_n(a) \to v(a)$; $u_n \leqslant u_{n+1}$, all n; u_n harmonic in $\Delta(a;r)$. We assert that $\lim_{n\to\infty} u_n(z) = v(z)$, $z \in \Delta(a;r)$. To see this, let $b \in \Delta(a;r)$. There exists a sequence $(w_n)_0^\infty$, $w_n \in \Phi$ satisfying: $w_n(b) \to v(b)$; $w_n \leqslant w_{n+1}$, all n. Now let U_n denote the Poisson modification of $\max\{u_n, w_n\}$ associated with $\Delta(a;r)$. Then $(U_n)_0^\infty$ is nondecreasing. Now $\lim_{n\to\infty} U_n$ is harmonic in $\Delta(a;r)$, as is $\lim_{n\to\infty} u_n$. Since $\lim U_n \geqslant \lim u_n$ and both limits agree at a, they agree throughout $\Delta(a;r)$. Further, the value of $\lim U_n$ at b is $v(b)$. Hence, the value of $\lim u_n$ at b is $v(b)$. Since b is an arbitrary point of $\Delta(a;r)$, v is harmonic in $\Delta(a;r)$. It follows that v is harmonic on Ω.

Theorem 11.1 is rich in consequences, as we shall now see. All Perron families considered will pertain to Ω. Let Ψ denote a family of functions subharmonic on Ω. There is a smallest Perron family $\Phi[\Psi]$ containing Ψ; it is, as one verifies directly, simply the intersection of all the Perron families that contain Ψ. Suppose now that Ψ contains a member not the constant $-\infty$ and that there exists a function h harmonic on Ω satisfying

$$u \leqslant h, \qquad u \in \Psi.$$

Let Φ_1 denote the family of subharmonic functions u on Ω satisfying $u \leqslant h$. Clearly, Φ_1 is a Perron family and $\Phi[\Psi] \subset \Phi_1$. Hence, v, the upper envelope of $\Phi[\Psi]$, is no greater than h. Since v is finite-valued, v is harmonic. We see that v is the least harmonic function on Ω that dominates each member of Ψ. This follows on replacing the above h by an arbitrary harmonic function on Ω that dominates each member of Ψ. Hence, we are led to the following important conclusion:

THEOREM 11.2. *Given a family $\Psi \neq \emptyset$ of subharmonic functions $u \not\equiv -\infty$ on Ω. If there exists a harmonic function on Ω that dominates each $u \in \Psi$, there is a least such harmonic function h_Ψ.*

We term h_Ψ the *least harmonic majorant* (LHM) of Ψ. If Ψ reduces to a single member u, we speak of the *least harmonic majorant* of u and denote it by h_u. Corresponding results hold for families of superharmonic functions and their harmonic minorants. We are led to the notion of the *greatest harmonic minorant* (GHM) of a family of superharmonic functions (resp., of a superharmonic function). The details parallel those given for LHM and will be omitted.

EXERCISES

1. Given w superharmonic on Ω, the family Φ of functions u subharmonic on Ω that satisfy $u \leqslant w$ is a Perron family. If $s \not\equiv -\infty$ is subharmonic on Ω and $s \leqslant w \not\equiv +\infty$, then s possesses an LHM $h \leqslant w$, and the GHM of w is the upper envelope of Φ.

2. Let Ω denote a region whose frontier consists of $n \geqslant 2$ mutually disjoint circumferences $C_k = C(a_k;r_k)$, $0 < r_k < +\infty$, $k = 1,2,\cdots,n$, and let U_k be a continuous finite real-valued function on C_k. Show that there exists a unique function h continuous on $\bar{\Omega}$ and harmonic in Ω whose restriction to C_k is U_k. (Dirichlet problem for Ω with continuous boundary function.)

HINT: Let m denote the least value and M the greatest value attained by any of the U_k. Let A_k denote a closed annulus lying in $\bar{\Omega}$ one of whose boundary components is C_k and such that $A_k \cap A_l = \emptyset$ for $k \neq l$. Let u be defined on $\bar{\Omega}$ as follows: On $\Omega - \bigcup A_k$, u is to take the value m; the restriction of u to A_k is to be the solution of the Dirichlet problem for A_k with boundary function U_k on C_k and m on the other contour of fr A_k. Let w be correspondingly defined with M replacing m. Show that u is subharmonic in Ω and that w is superharmonic in Ω, and apply the preceding exercise.

3. Let f denote a nonconstant meromorphic function mapping a region Ω_1 into a region Ω_2. Let $u \not\equiv -\infty$ be subharmonic in Ω_2 and admit a harmonic majorant. Let $v = u \circ f$. Then $h_v \leqslant h_u \circ f$.

If $\Omega_1 = \Omega_2 = \Delta(0;1)$ and $f(0) = 0$, show that

$$\frac{1}{2\pi}\int_0^{2\pi} v(re^{i\theta})\,d\theta \leqslant \frac{1}{2\pi}\int_0^{2\pi} u(re^{i\theta})\,d\theta\,, \qquad 0 < r < 1\,.$$

(cf. Littlewood, *Theory of Functions*, p. 163 *et seq.*)

4. Suppose that u is subharmonic on $\Delta(0;R) - \{0\}$. Show that there is at most one subharmonic function v on $\Delta(0;R)$ whose restriction to $\Delta(0;R) - \{0\}$ is u. Show that a necessary and sufficient condition that such a v exist is that

$$\lim_{r \to 0} \frac{\int_0^{2\pi} \overset{+}{u}(re^{i\theta})\,d\theta}{\log (1/r)} = 0\,.$$

HINT: Consider for $0 < r < R$, the function u_r on $\Delta(0;R)$ that agrees with u for $r \leqslant |z| < R$ and is given by

$$\frac{1}{2\pi}\int_0^{2\pi} u(re^{i\theta})\, K(e^{i\theta}, r^{-1} z)\, d\theta$$

for $|z| < r$. Verify that u_r is subharmonic and that $u_{r_1} \leqslant u_{r_2}$ for $0 < r_1 < r_2 < R$.

5. Let u be harmonic on a region Ω. Suppose that there exists a function p harmonic on Ω and nonnegative such that $u \leqslant p$. Then u admits a representation as the difference of two nonnegative harmonic functions on Ω. In fact, there exist nonnegative harmonic functions p_1 and p_2 on Ω such that (1) $u = p_1 - p_2$, and (2) if q_1 and q_2 are nonnegative harmonic functions on Ω such that $u = q_1 - q_2$, then $p_1 \leqslant q_1$ and $p_2 \leqslant q_2$.

D) The Dirichlet Problem

12. The Dirichlet Problem. In this section we treat the Dirichlet problem for a fairly general class of regions, using the method of Perron families. Let Ω denote a region $\subset \hat{K}$ whose complement is not empty. Let U denote a continuous finite real-valued function with domain fr Ω. The classical Dirichlet problem for the datum (Ω, U) is: *Does there exist a function u continuous on $\bar{\Omega}$ and harmonic in Ω whose restriction to* fr Ω *is U?*

It is immediate there is at most one such u. We remark that if h is continuous and finite-valued on the closure of a region Ω and is harmonic in Ω, then $\max_{\bar{\Omega}} h = \max_{\text{fr}\,\Omega} h$ and $\min_{\bar{\Omega}} h = \min_{\text{fr}\,\Omega} h$. Application of this observation to the difference $u_1 - u_2$, where u_1 and u_2 each satisfy the conditions imposed on u, leads to the stated uniqueness assertion.

Let Φ denote the family of functions w subharmonic on Ω that satisfy the condition

$$\limsup_{z \to \zeta} w(z) \leqslant U(\zeta)\,, \qquad \zeta \in \text{fr}\,\Omega\,. \tag{12.1}$$

Clearly, Φ is a Perron family. Now the constant function on Ω taking the value min U belongs to Φ. Further, each $w \in \Phi$ satisfies $w(z) \leqslant \max U$, by Theorem 8.1 of this chapter. Hence v, the upper envelope of Φ, is harmonic and takes values lying between min U and max U. Further, if the Dirichlet problem possesses a solution u, then u_Ω, the restriction of u to Ω, belongs to Φ and satisfies $w \leqslant u_\Omega$ for each $w \in \Phi$, by Theorem 8.1. Hence, $v = u_\Omega$. We conclude that the *only candidate* for the solution of the Dirichlet problem with datum (Ω, U) is $v \cup U$.

Let us now seek to impose conditions that will assure us that the Dirichlet problem has a solution. We shall see subsequently that the conditions in question are fulfilled in the "usual" situations of practice.

Barrier. Given $\zeta \in \text{fr}\,\Omega$, the region Ω is said to possess a *barrier at* ζ provided that for each r, $0 < r$, there exists a function S_r superharmonic on Ω, positive, and satisfying (1) $\lim_{z\to\zeta} S_r = 0$, and (2) $S_r(z) = 1$, $z \in \Omega - \Delta(\zeta;r)$. We term a function meeting the requirements imposed on S_r an *r-normalized barrier function for* (Ω, ζ). We show

THEOREM 12.1. *If Ω possesses a barrier at ζ, then*

$$\lim_{z\to\zeta} v = U(\zeta)\,.$$

The proof is simple. Let $r > 0$, let S denote an r-normalized barrier function for Ω at ζ, let

$$\alpha(r) = \min\left\{U(z) \mid z \in \text{fr}\,\Omega \cap \overline{\Delta(\zeta;r)}\right\},$$

and

$$\beta(r) = \max\left\{U(z) \mid z \in \text{fr}\,\Omega \cap \overline{\Delta(\zeta;r)}\right\}.$$

Then

$$\alpha(r) + \left[\min_{\text{fr}\,\Omega} U - \alpha(r)\right] S \in \Phi\,,$$

and for each $w \in \Phi$,

$$w \leqslant \beta(r) + \left[\max_{\text{fr}\,\Omega} U - \beta(r)\right] S\,.$$

Hence, we have

$$\alpha(r) + [\min_{\text{fr}\,\Omega} U - \alpha(r)]\, S \leqslant v \leqslant \beta(r) + [\max_{\text{fr}\,\Omega} U - \beta(r)]\, S. \tag{12.1}$$

From (12.1) we conclude

$$\alpha(r) \leqslant \liminf_{z\to\zeta} v \leqslant \limsup_{z\to\zeta} v \leqslant \beta(r)\,, \tag{12.2}$$

and, thereupon, since $\lim_{r\to 0} \alpha(r) = \lim_{r\to 0} \beta(r) = U(\zeta)$, Theorem 12.1.

The following theorem is now obvious.

THEOREM 12.2. *If Ω possesses a barrier at each point of* fr Ω, *then the Dirichlet problem with datum (Ω, U) admits a solution.*

EXERCISE

1. The boundary problem of this exercise is of common occurrence in applications to the theory of analytic functions. Let E be a countable proper subset of fr Ω, where Ω is a region $\subset \hat{K}$. Let U now be continuous on fr $\Omega - E$ and bounded. Then, by Theorem 8.2, there is at most one function h harmonic on Ω and *bounded* that satisfies

$$\lim_{z\to\zeta} h(z) = U(\zeta)\,, \qquad \zeta \in \text{fr}\,\Omega - E\,. \tag{12.3}$$

Establish the associated existence theorem under the assumption that E is finite and Ω possesses a barrier function at each point of fr $\Omega - E$.

Note that the situation where $\Omega = \Delta(0;1)$, $U(\zeta) = 0$, $E = \{1\}$ shows that the boundedness condition is essential for uniqueness. If the boundedness condition is not imposed, $z \to K(1,z)$ and the constant 0 are both solutions.

A Sufficient Condition for the Existence of a Barrier. It is essential to have a sufficient condition guaranteeing the existence of a barrier which is easily verified and at the same time is adequate for applications. Such a criterion is given by

THEOREM 12.3. *If there exists a continuum C containing the point ζ of* fr Ω *and satisfying $C \subset \hat{K} - \Omega$, then the region Ω possesses a barrier at ζ.*

(We recall that a *continuum* is a closed connected set containing more than one point.)

In order to establish the theorem, it will be useful to have available the following lemma:

LEMMA 12.1. *If C is a continuum satisfying $0,\infty \in C$, and if Ω is a component of $\hat{K} - C$, then the identity map of Ω onto itself admits an analytic logarithm. That is, there exists an analytic function l on Ω satisfying*

$$\exp[l(z)] = z\,, \qquad z \in \Omega\,.$$

PROOF OF LEMMA: It suffices to show that if γ is a closed rectifiable path in Ω, then

$$\int_\gamma \frac{dz}{z} = 0\,, \tag{12.4}$$

for then Theorem 2.3 of Chap. 1 is applicable. To establish (12.4) we consider the analytic function f on the component of $\hat{K} - \gamma$ containing C which is defined by

$$f(a) = \int_\gamma (z - a)^{-1}\, dz.$$

Examining the Laurent expansion of f about ∞, we see that for a large,

$$f(a) = \sum_{k=1}^{\infty} C_k a^{-k}\,,$$

where

$$C_k = -\int_\gamma z^{k-1}\, dz = 0\,.$$

Hence, f is the constant 0, and consequently (2.4) holds. The lemma follows. A by-product of the proof: $z - a$ has an analytic logarithm on Ω for each $a \in C \cap K$.

Let us now show for Ω of the lemma that if $0,\infty \in \operatorname{fr} \Omega$, Ω possesses a barrier at ∞. The general situation of the theorem will be seen to reduce to this case.

We note that l is univalent. We also note that the intersection E of $l(\Omega)$ and the imaginary axis is the union of a countable set of mutually disjoint intervals $\{ix \mid \alpha_k < x < \beta_k\}$, where $\theta = \Sigma(\beta_k - \alpha_k) \leqslant 2\pi$. [Note that $\Sigma(\beta_k - \alpha_k)$ is the sum of the lengths of the arcs of $C(0;1)$ in the image of E with respect to the exponential map, which is univalent on E.] Now let $h_k(z)$, $\operatorname{Re} z > 0$, denote the determination of

$$\arg\left(\frac{z - i\alpha_k}{z - i\beta_k}\right)$$

lying between 0 and π, so that h_k is harmonic on $\{\operatorname{Re} z > 0\}$. It is clear on geometric grounds that $h(z) = \Sigma\, h_k(z)$ is the "angle" intercepted at the point z by the set E, so that $0 < h(z) < \pi$ for $\operatorname{Re} z > 0$ and that $\lim_{z\to\zeta} h = \pi$, $\zeta \in E$. We shall leave a more formal arithmetical study for the exercises at the end of this section (Exs. 2,3). Let us define w on $l(\Omega)$ by

$$w(z) = \begin{cases} h(z), & \operatorname{Re} z > 0\,, \\ \pi\,, & \operatorname{Re} z \leqslant 0\,. \end{cases}$$

We see that w is superharmonic on $l(\Omega)$ and positive. Further,

$$h(x + iy) \leqslant 2 \operatorname{Arctan} \frac{\theta}{2x}, \qquad \theta = \sum (\beta_k - \alpha_k)\,, \tag{12.5}$$

and so

$$\lim_{\operatorname{Re} z\to+\infty} w = 0\,.$$

We now introduce

$$S = \frac{1}{\pi}\, w \circ l\,,$$

and we observe that S is a superharmonic function on Ω which is positive and satisfies (1) $\lim_{z\to\infty} S = 0$, and (2) $S(z) = 1$ when $|z| \leqslant 1$. A similar argument leads to a corresponding function S_r, $0 < r < +\infty$ superharmonic on Ω and positive and satisfying (a) $\lim_{z\to\infty} S_r = 0$, and (b) $S_r(z) = 1$ when $|z| \leqslant r^{-1}$. It suffices to proceed from the intersection of $\{\operatorname{Re} z = \log r^{-1}\}$ and $l(\Omega)$. Thus Ω possesses a barrier at ∞.

To treat the case of the theorem, we refer to the statement of the theorem and let Ω_1 denote the component of $\hat{K} - C$ that contains Ω, let ζ' denote a point of $\operatorname{fr} \Omega_1$ distinct from ζ, and let λ denote a rational function of degree 1 satisfying

$$\lambda(\zeta) = \infty\,, \qquad \lambda(\zeta') = 0\,.$$

Now let the S_r pertain to the component $\lambda(\Omega_1)$ of $\hat{K} - \lambda(C)$. Note that the $S_r \circ \lambda$ restricted to Ω serve to show that Ω possesses a barrier at ζ.

EXERCISES

2. Given $z \in K$, let $\lambda_z(w)$ denote the logarithm of $z - w$, $\operatorname{Re} w < \operatorname{Re} z$, satisfying $|\operatorname{Im} \lambda_z(w)| < \pi/2$. Let $-\infty < \alpha < \beta < +\infty$. Show that for $\operatorname{Re} z > 0$, the argument of

$$\frac{z - i\alpha}{z - i\beta}$$

which lies between 0 and π, denoted by $h(z)$, satisfies

$$\begin{aligned} h(z) &= \operatorname{Im}\left[\lambda_z(i\alpha) - \lambda_z(i\beta)\right] \\ &= \operatorname{Re}\left(\int_\beta^\alpha \frac{1}{it - z}\,dt\right) \\ &= \int_\alpha^\beta \frac{x}{x^2 + (y - t)^2}\,dt \\ &= \operatorname{Arctan}\frac{y - \alpha}{x} - \operatorname{Arctan}\frac{y - \beta}{x}, \qquad z = x + yi\,. \end{aligned}$$

Note that h is harmonic on $\{\operatorname{Re} z > 0\}$. Show further that if $c > \beta$ or $c < \alpha$, $\lim_{z \to ic} h(z) = 0$. Show that if $\alpha < c < \beta$, then $\lim_{z \to ic} h(z) = \pi$. It follows now that h is the unique harmonic function on $\{\operatorname{Re} z > 0\}$ that is *bounded* and satisfies: $\lim_{z \to ic} h = \pi$, $\alpha < c < \beta$; $\lim_{z \to ic} h = 0$, $c < \alpha$ or $c > \beta$.

3. Note that

$$\int_{-\infty}^{+\infty} \frac{x}{x^2 + (y - t)^2}\,dt = \pi\,, \qquad x > 0\,. \tag{a}$$

Conclude that $h = \Sigma h_k$ of the text is harmonic on $\{\operatorname{Re} z > 0\}$ and satisfies $0 < h < \pi$. Show that if $ic \in E$, then $\lim_{z \to ic} h = \pi$. Give a rigorous proof of (12.5). It is convenient to treat the case of a finite number of intervals first and to seek a maximizing configuration for given θ and z.

4. Let f be a bounded real-valued function on $\{\operatorname{Re} z = 0\}$ continuous save at the points belonging to a set $E \subset \{\operatorname{Re} z = 0\}$ clustering at no point of the imaginary axis. Show that

$$z \to \frac{1}{\pi} \int_{-\infty}^{+\infty} \frac{x f(it)}{x^2 + (y - t)^2}\,dt\,, \qquad z = x + yi\,,\quad x > 0\,,$$

is the unique bounded harmonic function h on $\{\operatorname{Re} z > 0\}$ satisfying

$$\lim_{z \to \zeta} h = f(\zeta)\,, \qquad \operatorname{Re} \zeta = 0\,, \quad \zeta \notin E.$$

[5]

Applications

1. Introduction. We now have at our disposal powerful methods for treating questions concerning harmonic functions. It is now possible to introduce certain distinguished harmonic functions with whose aid we may obtain useful information concerning meromorphic functions subject to various conditions, the exact nature of which will be made explicit in the following sections.

2. Green's Function. Given a region $\Omega \subset \hat{K}$ and a point $a \in \Omega$, we are led to ask whether there exists a function g harmonic on $\Omega - \{a\}$, possessing the limit zero at each point of fr Ω, and such that

$$\log | z - a | + g(z) , \; a \neq \infty , \tag{2.1}$$

(resp., $-\log | z | + g(z)$ for $a = \infty$) possesses a removable singularity at a. If $\Omega = \hat{K}$, no such function can exist. In any other case there is at most one function g, as is seen by examining the difference of two such functions. Further, such a function g must clearly be positive, for $\inf_{z \in \Omega - \{a\}} g(z) = 0$ and g is not constant. If such a function g exists, the function g_a with domain Ω satisfying $g_a(a) = +\infty$ whose restriction to $\Omega - \{a\}$ is g is called *Green's function of Ω with pole a.*

The following exercises point out an important property of Green's functions and give sufficient conditions for their existence.

EXERCISES

1. Given that the region Ω possesses Green's function g_a with pole a. Suppose that w is a positive superharmonic function on Ω satisfying

$$\liminf_{z \to a} \{w(z) + \log | z - a |\} > -\infty$$

(resp., $\liminf_{z \to \infty} \{w(z) - \log | z |\} > -\infty$ when $a = \infty$).

Then

$$g_a \leqslant w .$$

This shows that g_a is the *smallest* w satisfying the stated condition. Note that, in particular, w may be harmonic save at a.

2. Suppose that Ω is a bounded region $\subset K$ satisfying the condition that for each point $\zeta \in$ fr Ω there exists a continuum C satisfying $\zeta \in C \subset \hat{K} - \Omega$.

Let $a \in \Omega$. Show that Ω possesses Green's function with pole a by treating a related Dirichlet problem.

3. Suppose that in Ex. 2 the condition that Ω be a bounded region of K is dropped, that instead $\hat{K} \neq \Omega$, and that the remainder of the hypothesis prevails. Show that Ω still possesses Green's function with pole a.

HINT: For $a = \infty$ we may proceed as follows. Fix $\overline{\Delta(\infty;r)} \subset \Omega$. Define $u(z) = \log |zr|$, $r^{-1} \leqslant |z| < +\infty$; $u(z) = 0$, $z \in \Omega - \overline{\Delta(\infty;r)}$. Let ω denote the solution of the Dirichlet problem for $\Omega - \overline{\Delta(\infty;r)}$ satisfying $\omega(z) = 1$, $z \in C(\infty;r)$, $\omega(z) = 0$, $z \in \text{fr}\, \Omega$. Let $w(z) = \log |zr| + A$, $r^{-1} \leqslant |z| < +\infty$, $w(z) = A\, \omega(z)$, $z \in \Omega - \overline{\Delta(\infty;r)}$. Show that for A sufficiently large, w is superharmonic. Conclude that LHM u is the restriction of g_∞ to $\Omega - \{\infty\}$. The case $a \neq \infty$ differs only in an obvious way.

The device of this exercise will be useful to us in the next section.

4. Let Ω denote a region $\subset \hat{K}$ that satisfies the hypotheses of the Riemann mapping theorem (§ 12, Chap. 2). Let f denote a one-to-one conformal map of Ω onto $\Delta(0;1)$. Let $f(a) = 0$. Then g_a, Green's function for Ω with pole a, is given by $g_a(z) = -\log |f(z)|$.

5. Let Ω denote a region $\subset \hat{K}$, let $a \in \Omega$. Suppose that Ω has Green's function with pole a and also is homotopically simply-connected. Then Ω is conformally equivalent to $\Delta(0;1)$. I.e., prove the Riemann mapping theorem.

---

3. Classification of Regions. The property of Green's function given in Ex. 1, § 2, this chapter, points to a way of formulating the notion of Green's function without making use of boundary considerations. Suppose that we are given a region Ω and $a \in \Omega$. Suppose further that the class P_a of positive harmonic functions h on $\Omega - \{a\}$ such that $z \to h(z) + \log |z - a|$, $a \neq \infty$, [resp., $z \to h(z) - \log |z|$, $a = \infty$] has a removable singularity at a is not empty. Under this assumption, as we shall see, the class P_a has a least member. If, in particular, Ω possesses Green's function g_a with pole a, then the restriction of g_a to $\Omega - \{a\}$ is the least member of P_a. Thus we may with propriety define *Green's function* of Ω *with pole a*, when $P_a \neq \emptyset$, as that function with domain Ω which takes the value $+\infty$ at a and whose restriction to $\Omega - \{a\}$ is the least member of P_a. We shall make this definition and shall not distinguish between Green's function (in the sense of § 2) and the generalized Green's function (as per definition of the present paragraph). For this general situation we denote Green's function with pole a by g_a.

We shall now treat Ahlfors's characterization of regions for which it makes sense to talk of Green's functions ("On the Characterization of Hyperbolic Riemann Surfaces," *Ann. Acad. Sci. Fennicae No.* 125, 1952). We shall also see that if Ω possesses Green's function with pole a, then Ω possesses Green's function with pole b for each $b \in \Omega$. We recall that we have already considered the possibility of classifying regions according to the behavior of the functions analytic on them (cf. holomorphic simple-connectivity). Here regions will be classified according to the positive superharmonic functions that they tolerate.

Given a region $\Omega \subset \hat{K}$, we shall say that Ω is *hyperbolic* provided the family of the positive superharmonic functions on Ω contains nonconstant members. A region that is not hyperbolic is termed *parabolic*. (We are following the nomenclature of Ahlfors here. There is a long tradition of the use of "hyperbolic" and "parabolic" in classifications of this sort. Weyl once stated in his lectures that the practice was originated by Felix Klein, who used these terms with great gusto.) If Ω is parabolic, then clearly $P_a = \emptyset$ for each $a \in \Omega$. There can be no question of Green's functions. An example of a parabolic region is a region whose complement with respect to $\hat{K}$ is finite.

EXERCISE

1. Establish the last assertion.

When Ω is hyperbolic, the situation is radically different. Here we have

THEOREM 3.1: *If Ω is hyperbolic, then for each $a \in \Omega$, $P_a \neq \emptyset$ and P_a has a least member. Hence, if Ω is hyperbolic, then Ω possesses Green's function with pole a for each $a \in \Omega$.*

(On the other hand, if Ω possesses Green's function with pole a for some $a \in \Omega$, of course Ω is hyperbolic.)

PROOF: Given a hyperbolic region Ω and $a \in \Omega$, we fix $\overline{\Delta(a;2r)} \subset \Omega$. There exists a nonconstant positive superharmonic function w on Ω. We assume that $\inf_{z \in \Omega} w(z) = 0$ (replacing, if necessary, a given w by $w - \inf w$) and that $w(z) = 1$, $z \in \overline{\Delta(a;2r)}$, [replacing, if necessary, w by $\min \{1, \mu^{-1}w\}$, where μ is the minimum value attained by w on $\overline{\Delta(a;2r)}$]. Let u be defined on $\Omega - \overline{\Delta(a;r)}$ as follows:

$$u(z) = \frac{\log(|z-a|/2r)}{\log \frac{1}{2}}, \qquad r < |z-a| \leqslant 2r,$$

if $a \neq \infty$ (resp., $\log |2rz|/\log 2$, $\frac{1}{2} \leqslant |rz| < 1$, if $a = \infty$); $u(z) = 0$, $z \in \Omega - \overline{\Delta(a;2r)}$. Clearly, u is subharmonic and is dominated on its domain by w. Let ω denote the least harmonic majorant of u. We have $u(z) \leqslant \omega(z) \leqslant w(z)$. Hence, ω possesses the limit 1 at each point of $C(a;r)$, and, further, $\inf \omega(z) = 0$. We now introduce the function s on $\Omega - \{a\}$ as follows: $s(z) = -\log(|z-a|/r)$ for $0 < |z-a| \leqslant r$ if $a \neq \infty$ (resp., $\log |rz|$ for $1 \leqslant |rz| < +\infty$ if $a = \infty$), $s(z) = 0$, $z \in \Omega - \overline{\Delta(a;r)}$. Clearly, s is subharmonic and nonnegative on its domain. We define the function S on $\Omega - \{a\}$ by:

$$S(z) = s(z) + A,\ z \in \overline{\Delta(a;r)} - \{a\};\ S(z) = A\,\omega(z),\ z \in \Omega - \overline{\Delta(a;r)}.$$

Here A is taken as a positive number chosen so large that S is superharmonic on its domain (compare Ex. 3, § 2, this chapter). It is clear that $s < S$ and that s possesses a least harmonic majorant h satisfying $s < h \leqslant S$. It is evident from this inequality that $h \in P_a$. If $h_1 \in P_a$, clearly $h_1 > s$; that is, h_1 is a harmonic majorant of s, and so $h_1 \geqslant h$. The function h is the least member of P_a. The remaining assertion of Theorem 3.1 is immediate.

EXERCISES

2. If Ω possesses a barrier at some $\zeta \in \operatorname{fr} \Omega$, then Ω is hyperbolic.

3. Determine g_a for $\Omega = \{0 < |z| < 1\}$.

4. If Ω is parabolic and f is a bounded analytic function on Ω, then f is constant (extension of Liouville's theorem).

5. Given hyperbolic regions Ω_1 and Ω_2 and a point a satisfying $a \in \Omega_1 \subset \Omega_2$. Let $g_a^{(k)}$ denote Green's function for Ω_k with pole a, $k = 1,2$. Show that

$$g_a^{(1)}(z) \leqslant g_a^{(2)}(z)\,, \qquad z \in \Omega_1\,,$$

and that equality may hold for all $z \in \Omega_1$ even though $\Omega_1 \neq \Omega_2$. If, however, $\lim_{z \to \zeta} g_a^{(1)}(z) = 0$ for each $\zeta \in \operatorname{fr} \Omega_1$ and $g_a^{(1)}(z) = g_a^{(2)}(z)$ for some $z (\neq a) \in \Omega_1$, then $\Omega_1 = \Omega_2$.

6. If g_a has the property that $\lim_{z \to \zeta} g_a(z) = 0$ for each point $\zeta \in \operatorname{fr} \Omega$, then g_b has the same property, b arbitrary $\in \Omega$.

---

4. The Lindelöf Principle. Suppose that Ω_1 and Ω_2 are regions, Ω_2 being hyperbolic, and suppose that there exists a nonconstant meromorphic function f mapping Ω_1 into Ω_2. Let g_a denote Green's function of Ω_2 with pole a. Then $g_a \circ f$ is clearly a nonconstant positive superharmonic function on Ω_1. Hence, Ω_1 *is hyperbolic*. This result yields contrapositively: *If f is meromorphic on a parabolic region Ω and is not constant, then $f(\Omega)$ is also parabolic.*

We now come to an important inequality pertaining to meromorphic functions that map hyperbolic regions into hyperbolic regions. Specifically, let Ω_k $(k = 1,2)$ be hyperbolic regions. In order to keep the notation simple, let us agree to denote Green's function of Ω_1 with pole a by g_a (as above) and Green's function of Ω_2 with pole b by G_b. Suppose that f is a meromorphic function mapping Ω_1 into Ω_2. Let us first fix our attention on a point $a \in \Omega_1$ and let $b = f(a)$. The *Lindelöf inequality* states

$$g_a \leqslant G_b \circ f\,. \tag{4.1}$$

This is very easy to see. It is trivial if f is constant. If f is not constant, we note that $G_b \circ f$ is positive superharmonic on Ω_1 and is such that

$$z \to G_b \circ f(z) + n(a;f) \log |z - a|\,, \qquad a \neq \infty\,,$$

(resp., $z \to G_b \circ f(z) - n(\infty; f) \log |z|$, $a = \infty$) has a removable singularity at a.

It follows that the subharmonic function s of § 3 taken in the present context is dominated by $G_b \circ f$. Since LHM s is just the restriction of g_a to $\Omega - \{a\}$, the Lindelöf inequality follows.

It is easy to see that if $\Omega_1 = \Omega_2 = \Delta(0;1)$ and $a = b = 0$, then (4.1) is equivalent to the first of the two inequalities of Schwarz's lemma.

The inequality of Lindelöf may be rephrased more vividly as follows. Given c, $0 < c < +\infty$, let $\Omega_1^{(c)} = \{g_a(z) > c\}$ and $\Omega_2^{(c)} = \{G_b(z) > c\}$. Then (4.1) is *equivalent* to the assertion that

$$f(\Omega_1^{(c)}) \subset \Omega_2^{(c)}, \qquad 0 < c < +\infty. \tag{4.2}$$

EXERCISE

1. Suppose that f is a meromorphic function mapping a hyperbolic region Ω into itself, and suppose that there exists $a \in \Omega$ which is a fixed point of f; that is, $f(a) = a$. Let f_n denote the nth iterate of f; that is, f_n is the nth term of the sequence $(f_n)_1^\infty$ defined recursively by $f_1 = f$, $f_{n+1} = f \circ f_n$, $n = 1,2,\cdots$. Show that either (f_n) converges uniformly in Ω to the constant a or else $g_a = g_a \circ f$. Show in the latter case that f is a conformal automorphism of Ω onto itself. Show further that if $a \neq \infty$, then $|f'(a)| \leqslant 1$, equality occurring if, and only if, f is a conformal automorphism of Ω.

HINT: For the first assertion show that if $g_a \neq g_a \circ f$, then $(g_a \circ f_n)_1^\infty$ is a nondecreasing sequence of positive superharmonic functions on Ω converging uniformly in Ω to $+\infty$. For the second assertion consider the case where $a \in K$, and note that there exists a subsequence $(f_{m(n)})_1^\infty$ that converges uniformly in Ω and satisfies $\lim f'_{m(n)}(a) = 1$. Relate the behavior of f to that of $\lim f_{m(n)}$. For the third assertion, when f is a conformal automorphism of Ω, consider also the inverse of f.

Sharp Form of the Lindelöf Principle. The inequality (4.1) may of course be replaced by the more precise inequality

$$n(a;f)g_a \leqslant G_b \circ f. \tag{4.3}$$

Thanks to this fact, we now see that if b is a given point of Ω_2 and $a_1,\cdots,a_m$ are distinct points of Ω_1 satisfying $f(a_k) = b$, $k = l,\cdots,m$, then

$$\sum_{k=1}^{m} n(a_k;f)g_{a_k} \leqslant G_b \circ f. \tag{4.4}$$

It suffices to treat the nontrivial situation: $m > 0$, f not constant, and to proceed inductively. When $m = 1$, (4.4) is true. If we have $m + 1$ distinct a_k satisfying $f(a_k) = b$, we see that

$$w = G_b \circ f - \sum_{k=1}^{m} n(a_k;f)g_{a_k}$$

(appropriately defined at $a_1,\cdots,a_m$) is a positive superharmonic function on Ω_1 such that

$$w - n(a_{m+1}; f)g_{a_{m+1}}$$

possesses a finite limit at a_{m+1}. Hence, $w \geqslant n(a_{m+1};f)g_{a_{m+1}}$ and consequently

$$G_b \circ f \geqslant \sum_{k=1}^{m+1} n(a_k;f)g_{a_k} .$$

It now follows that if f is a nonconstant meromorphic function mapping Ω_1 into Ω_2, then

$$\sum_{f(a)=b} n(a;f)g_a \leqslant G_b \circ f \tag{4.5}$$

and the sum on the left-hand side is harmonic at each point of $\Omega_1 - f^{-1}(\{b\})$, as may be seen with the aid of (4.4) and Harnack's convergence theorem. At the same time, we see that for a given point a_0 satisfying $f(a_0) = b$,

$$\sum_{f(a)=b,\, a\neq a_0} n(a;f)g_a$$

is harmonic at a_0. Hence, we conclude the sharp form of the Lindelöf principle:

If f is a meromorphic function mapping the hyperbolic region Ω_1 into the hyperbolic region Ω_2, then

$$G_b \circ f = \Big[\sum_{f(a)=b} n(a;f)g_a\Big] + h , \tag{4.6}$$

where h is harmonic on Ω_1 and is nonnegative. The residual term h is unique if f is not the constant b.

EXERCISES

2. Let f denote a nonconstant analytic function on $\Delta(0;1)$ of modulus less than 1. Show that

$$\sum_{f(a)=b} n(a;f)\,(1 - |a|) < +\infty .$$

3. Given sequences $(a_k)_1^\infty$, $(m_k)_1^\infty$, where $|a_k| < 1$ for all k, m_k is a positive integer for all k, and the a_k are distinct. Show that if

$$\sum m_k(1 - |a_k|) < +\infty ,$$

then there exists a nonconstant analytic function on $\Delta(0;1)$, say f, $|f| < 1$, whose zeros are precisely the a_k and whose multiplicity at a_k is m_k, $k = 1,2,\cdots$.

HINT: Consider an analytic function f satisfying

$$\log |f| = - \sum_{k=1}^{\infty} m_k\, g_{a_k} ,$$

where g_a is Green's function for $\Delta(0;1)$ with pole a (Poincaré, Blaschke).

---

5. Iversen's Theorem. It is easy to see that if Ω is a parabolic region, then $\bar{\Omega} = \hat{K}$ and $\hat{K} - \Omega$ is totally disconnected; that is, contains no continuum (closed connected set containing more than one point). Hence, if f is a nonconstant meromorphic function on Ω, $\hat{K} - f(\Omega)$ is also totally disconnected. We shall now consider a theorem concerning f which casts light on the behavior of f in a given component of $f^{-1}(\omega)$, where ω is a region. The theorem for the case where $\Omega = K$ is due to Iversen. It has since received numerous generalizations. The proof that follows is due in part to Valiron.

THEOREM 5.1. *Given f meromorphic on a parabolic region Ω and not constant. Let ω denote a region, and let $a \in \omega$. Let Ω_1 denote a component of $f^{-1}(\omega)$. Then either f attains a at some point of Ω_1, or else there exists a path $\gamma : z = Z(t)$, $0 \leqslant t \leqslant 1$ that lies in Ω_1 save for the endpoint $Z(1) \notin \Omega$ and is such that*

$$\lim_{t\to 1} f(Z(t)) = a\,. \tag{5.1}$$

REMARK: In general, if f is meromorphic on a region Ω, $a \in \hat{K}$ is termed an *asymptotic* value of f provided that there exists a continuous map Z of $\{0 \leqslant t < 1\}$ into Ω that satisfies the following two conditions: (1) for each compact $C \subset \Omega$, $Z(t) \in \Omega - C$ for t sufficiently near 1; (2) $\lim_{t\to 1} f \circ Z = a$. The Iversen theorem assures us that if the restriction of f to Ω_1 does not attain a, then it has a as an asymptotic value. The Iversen theorem thus yields important qualitative information concerning the behavior of f on *each* component of $f^{-1}(\omega)$.

We now turn to the proof and show first that, at least, *$f(\Omega_1)$ is dense in ω.* If this were not the case, there would exist $b \in \omega - \overline{f(\Omega_1)}$ satisfying the condition that for some finite $r > 0$, $\overline{\Delta(b;r)} \subset \omega$ and $\Delta(b;r) \cap f(\Omega_1) \neq \emptyset$. We fix such an r, and we let g denote Green's function of $\Delta(b;r)$ with pole b. Let δ denote a component of $f^{-1}[\Delta(b;r)]$ that lies in Ω_1. That there is such a component follows from the condition $\Delta(b;r) \cap f(\Omega_1) \neq \emptyset$. We define u with domain Ω by

$$u(z) = \begin{cases} g_b(f(z))\,, & z \in \delta\,, \\ 0\,, & z \in \Omega - \delta\,. \end{cases}$$

It is easy to see that u is a continuous bounded nonconstant subharmonic function on Ω. But this means that $(\sup u) - u$ is a positive nonconstant superharmonic function on Ω. The contradiction is obvious, since Ω is parabolic.

The remainder of the proof will be based on the property of f just established (called by Stoilow the *Iversen property*). The fact that f is meromorphic plays no role in the rest of the argument except to ensure that f is continuous. The argument that follows may be traced back to that given by Valiron.

If f attains a on Ω_1, there is no need for further consideration. Suppose that f omits a on Ω_1. Let $(r_n)_1^\infty$ denote a monotone-decreasing sequence of positive numbers satisfying: $\lim_{n\to\infty} r_n = 0$, $\overline{\Delta(a;r_1)} \subset \omega$. Let $(\delta_n)_1^\infty$ satisfy the following conditions: for each n, δ_n is a component of $f^{-1}[\Delta(a;r_n)]$; $\delta_1 \subset \Omega_1$; $\delta_{n+1} \subset \delta_n$, all n. The existence of such a sequence is established recursively, thanks to the Iversen property. Thus, since $f(\Omega_1)$ is dense in ω, there exists a component of $f^{-1}[\Delta(a;r_1)]$ that contains a point of Ω_1 and, consequently, is a subset of Ω_1. We denote this component of $f^{-1}[\Delta(a;r_1)]$ by δ_1. We now continue step by step, taking $\delta_2 \subset \delta_1$, etc. The existence of a path with the stated properties is easily established. In fact, there exists a continuous map φ of $\{0 \leqslant t < 1\}$ into Ω_1 satisfying $\varphi(\{1 - 2^{-(n-1)} \leqslant t \leqslant 1 - 2^{-n}\}) \subset \delta_n$, $n = 1,2,\cdots$. To see this, let $z_n \in \delta_n$, $n = 1,2,\cdots$, and let Z_n denote a continuous map of

$$\{1 - 2^{-(n-1)} \leqslant t \leqslant 1 - 2^{-n}\}$$

into δ_n satisfying

$$Z_n(1 - 2^{-(n-1)}) = z_n ,$$

$$Z_n(1 - 2^{-n}) = z_{n+1} , \qquad n = 1,2,\cdots .$$

Clearly, $\varphi = \bigcup Z_n$ has the stated property. We now verify that $\lim_{t\to 1} \varphi$ exists and is not in Ω. We may then take Z of the theorem as the continuous extension of φ to $\{0 \leqslant t \leqslant 1\}$.

Suppose that O is an arbitrary open set containing $\hat{K} - \Omega$. We assert that $\varphi(t) \in O$ for t sufficiently near 1. Otherwise there would exist a sequence $(t_n)_1^\infty$ satisfying: $t_1 \geqslant 0$, $(t_n)_1^\infty$ is increasing, $\lim t_n = 1$, $(\varphi(t_n))_1^\infty$ possesses a limit $\alpha \in \Omega$. But then $f(\alpha) = a$ and $\alpha \in \Omega \cap \overline{\Omega}_1$, and this is not possible.

To complete the proof, it will be convenient to assume that $\infty \in \Omega$, as we may without loss of generality. For each positive integer n, let σ_n denote the union of the squares

$$\{2^{-n}j \leqslant \operatorname{Re} z \leqslant 2^{-n}(j + 1); 2^{-n}k \leqslant \operatorname{Im} z \leqslant 2^{-n}(k + 1)\} ,$$

where j and k are integers, which have points in common with $K - \Omega$. Clearly, $K - \Omega \subset \operatorname{int} \sigma_n$. Now, for given n, $\varphi(t) \in \operatorname{int} \sigma_n$ for t sufficiently near 1. Let τ_n denote the component of $\operatorname{int} \sigma_n$ that contains $\varphi(t)$ for t sufficiently near 1. The sequence $(\bar{\tau}_n)_1^\infty$ is monotone nonincreasing. The intersection $\bigcap_1^\infty \bar{\tau}_n$ is connected and is contained in $K - \Omega$. Hence, $\bigcap_1^\infty \bar{\tau}_n$ reduces to a point, say α. Given $r > 0$, $\bar{\tau}_n \subset \Delta(\alpha;r)$ for n sufficiently large. Hence, $\varphi(t) \in \Delta(\alpha;r)$ for t sufficiently near 1. That is, $\lim_{t\to 1} \varphi = \alpha$. The proof is complete.

EXERCISE

Determine the asymptotic values of the entire functions: e^z, $\cos z$.

---

6. Harmonic Measure. The notion of harmonic measure was introduced by R. Nevanlinna as a systematic method for the study of meromorphic functions that map regions of a suitably restricted type into regions of the same type and are subject to certain boundary conditions. In the account that follows we do not aim for generality; rather we shall consider the case—adequately general for the applications—where the regions considered are Jordan regions.

It is important for some purposes to be able to replace a harmonic measure by a majorant or minorant that is easily calculated in terms of the geometric data and is sufficiently good to yield useful information. Aspects of this problem concerning the application of harmonic measure will be treated below (cf. Theorem 7.1, this chapter).

We recall that a *Jordan curve* in $\hat{K}$ is a homeomorph in $\hat{K}$ of $C(0;1)$. In other words, it is the image of $C(0;1)$ with respect to a univalent continuous map of $C(0;1)$ into $\hat{K}$. A region Ω is said to be a *Jordan region* provided that fr Ω is the union of a finite number > 0 of mutually disjoint Jordan curves. A set contained in the frontier of a Jordan region Ω will be termed *elementary* provided that it is either a component of fr Ω or else the image of an open interval $\{a < t < b\}$ with respect to a univalent continuous map of $\{a < t < b\}$. A subset α of fr Ω will be termed *admissible* provided that it is the union of a finite number $\geqslant 0$ of elementary sets. By the *harmonic measure* ω_α of an admissible α with respect to Ω is meant the unique bounded harmonic function on Ω satisfying

$$\lim_{z \to \zeta} \omega_\alpha(z) = \begin{cases} 1, & \zeta \in \alpha; \\ 0, & \zeta \in \text{fr}\,\Omega - \bar{\alpha}\,. \end{cases} \tag{6.1}$$

If reference is made to a region Ω_k instead of Ω, we shall write $\omega_\alpha^{(k)}$ for the harmonic measure of α with respect to Ω_k. The existence of ω_α is assured by Ex. 1, § 12, Chap. 4.

EXERCISES

1. Let $\beta = \text{fr}\,\Omega - \bar{\alpha}$, and show that β is also admissible. Show that

$$\omega_\alpha + \omega_\beta = 1\,.$$

Show also that if $\alpha_1 \subset \alpha_2$, then $\omega_{\alpha_1} \leqslant \omega_{\alpha_2}$.

2. Suppose that $\Omega = \{r_1 < |z| < r_2\}$, $0 < r_1 < r_2 < +\infty$. Determine ω_α when $\alpha = C(0;r_1)$ and when $\alpha = C(0;r_2)$. Determine explicitly the Fourier expansion of ω_α when α is an elementary subset of $C(0;r_2)$.

We shall now see how harmonic measure may be applied to function-theoretic situations. The following theorem is typical of the comparison theorems usually encountered. We do not strive for the ultimate in generality.

THEOREM 6.1 (R. Nevanlinna). *Let f be a meromorphic function mapping a Jordan region Ω_1 into a Jordan region Ω_2.* Let α *denote an admitted subset of* fr Ω_1, *and let β denote an admitted subset of* fr Ω_2. *Suppose that for each $t \in \alpha$, $B(f;t) \subset \bar{\beta}$. Then*

$$\omega_\alpha^{(1)} \leqslant \omega_\beta^{(2)} \circ f\,. \tag{6.2}$$

PROOF: Let γ denote an admitted subset of fr Ω_2 containing $\bar{\beta}$. Considering

$$\omega_\alpha^{(1)} - \omega_\gamma^{(2)} \circ f$$

and applying the Phragmén-Lindelöf maximum principle, we conclude that

$$\omega_\alpha^{(1)} \leqslant \omega_\gamma^{(2)} \circ f .$$

We next observe that $\omega_\beta^{(2)}$ is the lower envelope of the $\omega_\gamma^{(2)}$, and (6.2) follows. [The notation "$B(t;f)$" is that of § 8, Chap. 2.]

EXERCISES

3. Suppose that, in the situation of Theorem 6.1, f is the identity map, $f(z) = z$, $z \in \Omega_1$, and $\alpha = \beta$. From Theorem 6.1 conclude:

$$\omega_\alpha^{(1)}(z) \leqslant \omega_\alpha^{(2)}(z) , \qquad z \in \Omega_1 .$$

(This is Carleman's principle of *monotoneity* for harmonic measure, "Prinzip von Gebietserweiterung." It is a very useful tool for considerations involving appraisals of harmonic measure.)

When does equality occur?

4. Apply Theorem 6.1 to the following situation: $\Omega_1 = \Omega_2 = \Delta(0;1)$, $f(0) = 0$. Show that the length of α does not exceed the length of β (Löwner). Show that if $\alpha \neq \emptyset$, then f possesses a limit at each point of α.

---

7. The Sectorial-limit Theorem. This theorem pertains to functions that are analytic on a half-plane and bounded. It may be formulated as follows:

THEOREM 7.1. *Given f analytic on $\{\text{Im } z > 0\}$ and bounded. Suppose that there exists a "path": $z = Z(t)$, $0 \leqslant t < 1$ (sic!), in $\{\text{Im } z > 0\}$* (that is, *Z is a continuous map of $\{0 \leqslant t < 1\}$ into $\{\text{Im } z > 0\}$*) *such that $\lim_{t \to 1} Z(t) = 0$ and $\lim_{t \to 1} f \circ Z(t)$ exists. Let the latter limit be a. Then for each positive ε and b satisfying $0 < b < \pi/2$, there exists $r > 0$ such that*

$$|f(z) - a| < \varepsilon \tag{7.1}$$

for z satisfying $|\text{Arg } z - \pi/2| < b , \qquad |z| < r .$

The function f is said to possess the *sectorial limit a at* 0 provided that the assertion of the last sentence holds. This explains the designation "sectorial-limit theorem." Two preliminary remarks are in order:

(1) Theorem 7.1 may be regarded as a corollary of a theorem pertaining to positive superharmonic functions in a half-plane. For, if w is a positive superharmonic function on $\{\text{Im } z > 0\}$ satisfying $\lim_{t \to 1} w \circ Z(t) = +\infty$, then, as we shall see, w possesses the sectorial limit $+\infty$ at 0. Taking

$$w = \log \left| \frac{2M}{f - a} \right| ,$$

where $\sup |f| < M < +\infty$, we conclude Theorem 7.1.

(2) We may assume that Z is univalent (and even piecewise linear). (The reader should verify this assertion). We make this reduction.

The proof of Theorem 7.1 will be based on the following lemma. (We recall: *Jordan arc* = homeomorph of $\{0 \leqslant t \leqslant 1\}$; *endpoint* = image of 0 or 1.)

LEMMA 7.1. *Let γ denote a Jordan arc one of whose endpoints is* 0 *and the other is of the form $e^{i\theta}$, $0 < \theta < \pi$, and all of whose other points lie in*

$$\Omega = \{\text{Im } z > 0\} \cap \Delta(0;1).$$

Let w be positive superharmonic on Ω and satisfy

$$w(z) \geqslant 1\,, \qquad z \in \Omega \cap \gamma\,.$$

Then, given $\varepsilon > 0$, there exists r, $0 < r < 1$ such that

$$w(z) \geqslant \pi^{-1} \min \{\text{Arg } z, \pi - \text{Arg } z\} - \varepsilon, \qquad |z| < r\,. \tag{7.2}$$

PROOF OF THE LEMMA: We shall want to examine the set $\Omega - \gamma$. Actually it consists of exactly two components, the frontier of each of which may be specified completely with the aid of the Jordan-curve theorem and arguments involving the order of a point with respect to a closed curve. However, for our purposes it is not necessary to have this precise information. In what follows, we shall make only limited use of separation considerations.

Let

$$\alpha = \{-1 < \text{Re } z < 0, \text{Im } z = 0\},$$

and let

$$\beta = \{0 < \text{Re } z < 1, \text{Im } z = 0\}.$$

Let Ω_α denote the component of $\Omega - \gamma$ for which $\alpha \subset \text{fr } \Omega_\alpha$. There is precisely one such component. Similarly, let Ω_β denote the component of $\Omega - \gamma$ for which $\beta \subset \text{fr } \Omega_\beta$.

The first fact that we observe is that α *is in the exterior of* Ω_β and β *is in the exterior of* Ω_α. This may be seen as follows. The region Ω_β is contained in (and, in fact, as may easily be concluded, is) a component of the complement of δ, where δ is the closed Jordan curve consisting of γ,β, and the arc of $C(0;1)$ in the closed upper half-plane joining 1 and the point of γ on $C(0;1)$. Further, $|O(z;\delta)| = 1$ for $z \in \Omega_\beta$, as may be seen by studying the change in $O(z;\delta)$ when z transits β (see Appendix, § 3). Now α is contained in the unbounded component of $K - \delta$. Hence, $O(z;\delta) = 0$, $z \in \alpha$. Our assertion follows for α and Ω_β, for β and Ω_α. It follows also, of course, that $\Omega_\alpha \cap \Omega_\beta = \emptyset$.

Now let ω_α denote the harmonic measure of α with respect to Ω, and let ω_β denote the harmonic measure of β with respect to Ω. We can show with the aid of the Phragmén-Lindelöf maximum principle that

$$w(z) \geqslant \omega_\beta(z)\,, \qquad z \in \Omega_\alpha\,,$$

$$w(z) \geqslant \omega_\alpha(z)\,, \qquad z \in \Omega_\beta\,.$$

Thus, to establish the second of these inequalities, we note that fr $\Omega_\beta \subset \delta$ (for present purposes we do not need to know that fr $\Omega_\beta = \delta$) and consider the limiting behavior of $w(z) - \omega_\alpha(z)$ at the points of fr Ω_β different from the endpoints of γ.

Suppose that Ω' were a component of $\Omega - \gamma$ different from Ω_α and from Ω_β (cf. our remarks at the beginning of the proof). Then fr $\Omega' \subset \gamma$, and another application of the Phragmén-Lindelöf maximum principle shows that $w(z) \geqslant 1$, $z \in \Omega'$. Hence,

$$w \geqslant \min \{\omega_\alpha, \omega_\beta\}.$$

We note that

$$\lim_{z\to 0} [\pi^{-1} \operatorname{Arg} z - \omega_\alpha(z)] = 0 \tag{7.3}$$

and that

$$\lim_{z\to 0} [1 - \pi^{-1} \operatorname{Arg} z - \omega_\beta(z)] = 0 \tag{7.4}$$

The lemma follows.

EXERCISE

1. Establish (7.3) and (7.4).

The theorem is now readily established. We consider the superharmonic formulation given above: w superharmonic positive on $\{\operatorname{Im} z > 0\}$, $\lim w \circ Z = +\infty$. Given $a > 0$, there exists a finite positive r such that $w(rz) \geqslant a$, z on $\Omega \cap \gamma$, where γ is a Jordan arc of the type specified in the lemma. Hence, given $\varepsilon > 0$, there exists R, $0 < R < r$, such that

$$w(z) \geqslant a[\pi^{-1} \min \{\operatorname{Arg} z, \pi - \operatorname{Arg} z\} - \varepsilon], \qquad |z| < R,$$

and we conclude that w possesses the sectorial limit $+\infty$ at 0.

EXERCISE

2. Show that if h is a positive harmonic function on $\Delta(0;1)$, then h possesses a finite sectorial limit at almost every point of $C(0;1)$. [*Sectorial limit* is similarly defined here. Given $\zeta \in C(0;1)$, one considers the limiting behavior at ζ of the restriction of h to $\Delta(0;1) \cap \{|\operatorname{Arg}(1 - \zeta^{-1}z)| < \delta\}$, $0 < \delta < \pi/2$.]

HINT: Consider $\exp \circ f$, where f is an analytic function satisfying $\operatorname{Re} f = h$.

REMARK: Actually the requirement that there exist a "path" on which f tends to a may be considerably weakened. In fact, it has been shown by Tord Hall (*Arkiv Mat. Astron. Fysik*, Bd25A, N:o 28) that it suffices to assume that

$$\lim_{r\to 0} \{\inf_{0<\theta<\pi} |f(re^{i\theta}) - a|\} = 0.$$

Hall's work applies also to the superharmonic variant formulated above. His argument is based on considerations of potential theory.

A known open problem connected with Hall's paper is the following: Given w superharmonic on $\{\operatorname{Im} z > 0\}$ and positive. Suppose that

$$\sup_{0 \leqslant \theta \leqslant \pi} w(re^{i\theta}) \geqslant 1$$

for all positive r. Is it true that

$$w(z) \geqslant \pi^{-1} \min \{\operatorname{Arg} z, \pi - \operatorname{Arg} z\} ? \tag{7.5}$$

Hall's work shows that the inequality

$$w(z) \geqslant \tfrac{2}{3}\pi^{-1} \min \{\operatorname{Arg} z, \pi - \operatorname{Arg} z\}$$

is true. The basis for the conjecture (7.5) is to be found in the "extreme" (albeit the propriety of this designation is precisely the problem) case: $w(z) = \pi^{-1} \operatorname{Arg} z$.

8. The Inequality of Milloux-Schmidt. The problem whose study leads to the inequality of Milloux-Schmidt is the following:

Suppose that $0 < m < 1$ and that f is analytic on $\Delta(0;1)$, has modulus less than 1, and, further, satisfies

$$\min |f(re^{i\theta})| \leqslant m, \qquad 0 < r < 1. \tag{8.1}$$

To what restrictions is the following subject?

$$M(r;f) = \max |f(re^{i\theta})|, \qquad 0 < r < 1,$$

We may distinguish two questions. (1) We may ask whether the condition (8.1) does indeed force $\sup_f M(r;f) < 1$ for $0 < r < 1$ and, if so, whether it is possible to give a simple upper estimate for $\sup_f M(r;f)$ that yields useful information for applications. (2) We may seek to determine the exact value of $\sup_f M(r;f)$ and the functions subject to the given restrictions whose maximum moduli on $C(0;r)$ are equal to the extreme value. We shall treat only the first question. An account of the solution of the second question is to be found in M. Heins: "On the Problem of Milloux for Functions Analytic throughout the Interior of the Unit Circle," *Am. J. Math.*, **67**: 212–234, 1945.

Given f fulfilling the imposed conditions, we see, on considering the sharp form of the Lindelöf principle, Eq. (4.6) of this chapter, with $\Omega_1 = \Omega_2 = \Delta(0;1)$, $b = 0$, that

$$-\log |f| = \sum_{f(a)=0} n(a;f) g_a + h,$$

where h is a nonnegative harmonic function on $\Delta(0;1)$. Let us introduce the auxiliary positive superharmonic function w given by

$$w(z) = \sum_{f(a)=0} n(a;f) g_{-|a|}(z) + h(0) \operatorname{Re}\left(\frac{-1+z}{-1-z}\right). \tag{8.2}$$

From the inequality

$$g_{-|a|}(|z|) \leqslant g_a(z) \leqslant g_{-|a|}(-|z|)$$

[see Chap. 2, (10.2)] and the Harnack inequality [see Chap. 4 (3.7)], we see that

$$w(-|z|) \geqslant -\log|f(z)| \geqslant w(|z|). \qquad (8.3)$$

Thus a lower estimate for $w(r)$ will yield an upper estimate for $M(r;f)$. From (8.3) we also see that $w(-r) \geqslant -\log m$ for $0 \leqslant r < 1$. Thus we obtain

$$w(r) \geqslant (-\log m)\,\omega(r), \qquad 0 < r < 1, \qquad (8.4)$$

where ω is the unique bounded harmonic function whose domain is $\Delta(0;1)$ slit along $\{-1 < x \leqslant 0\}$ which possesses the limit 1 at each point of $\{-1 < x \leqslant 0\}$ and the limit 0 at each point of $C(0;1)$ different from -1. Now $\omega(r)$ is explicitly given by

$$\omega(r) = 1 - \frac{4}{\pi}\operatorname{Arctan}\sqrt{r}. \qquad (8.5)$$

Hence, we conclude the inequality of Milloux-Schmidt:

$$\log M(r;f) \leqslant (\log m)\left(1 - \frac{4}{\pi}\operatorname{Arctan}\sqrt{r}\right). \qquad (8.6)$$

EXERCISES

1. Establish (8.5).

HINT: Determine the harmonic measure u of $\{it \mid -1 < t < 1\}$ with respect to $\Delta(0;1) \cap \{\operatorname{Re} z > 0\}$, and note that $\omega(z) = u(\sqrt{z})$, where $\sqrt{z}$ is the square root of z with positive real part, z in domain of ω. Show that

$$u(z) = \frac{2}{\pi}\operatorname{Arg}\left(\frac{z+i}{z-i}\right) - 1.$$

2. Establish with the aid of (8.6) the following theorem of Wiman: *Given f analytic on K and not constant. Suppose that there exists a finite positive number m such that* $\min|f(re^{i\theta})| \leqslant m$, $0 < r < \infty$.
Then

$$\alpha = \liminf_{r\to\infty} \frac{\log M(r;f)}{\sqrt{r}} > 0.$$

HINT: Consider $F_R(z) = f(Rz)/M(R;f)$ in $\Delta(0;1)$, $0 < R < \infty$.

3. Show also that in the situation of Wiman's theorem,

$$\limsup_{r\to\infty} \frac{\log M(r;f)}{\sqrt{r}} \leqslant \frac{4}{\pi}\alpha.$$

[We shall obtain the sharper conclusion that $\lim_{r\to\infty} r^{-1/2}\log M(r;f)$ exists (finite or not) in § 11 of the present chapter.]

A Conjecture of Littlewood. This is a convenient place to discuss the conjecture of Littlewood to which allusion was made in the remark added to Ex. 1, § 4, Chap. 3. We recall that we are concerned with the class Φ_1 of functions f analytic on $\Delta(0;1)$ and satisfying $f(0) = 0$ and $f'(0) = 1$, and that for given $f \in \Phi_1$, $k(f)$ is the supremum of the set of r for which $C(0;r) \subset f[\Delta(0;1)]$. If we consider the function $f_0 \in \Phi_1$ which maps $\Delta(0;1)$ univalently onto K less a slit $\{-\infty < t \leqslant -a\}$ of the negative real axis, we see that the inverse of f_0 is given by

$$z \to \frac{\sqrt{z+a} - \sqrt{a}}{\sqrt{z+a} + \sqrt{a}}, \tag{8.7}$$

where $\sqrt{z+a}$ is the determination of the square root of $z+a$ with positive real part. From

$$1 = f_0'(0) = 4a\,,$$

we conclude that $a = \frac{1}{4}$. Thus inf $k(f) \leqslant \frac{1}{4}$.

We now indicate *heuristically* how the argument employed in deriving the Milloux-Schmidt inequality may be used as a basis for a proof of the inequality: $k(f) \geqslant \frac{1}{4}$. Suppose that $f \in \Phi_1$ is such that $k(f) < +\infty$. Suppose that $0 < \rho < 1$. Let $F_\rho(z) = f(\rho z)$, $|z| < 1$. Then F_ρ omits an open set O such that $O \cap C(0;r) \neq \emptyset$, $k(f) \leqslant r$. Hence, there exists a region Ω satisfying the following conditions: (1) $F_\rho[\Delta(0;1)] \subset \Omega$; (2) fr Ω is the union of segments $\{e^{i\varphi_k} t \mid 0 < \sigma_k \leqslant t \leqslant \tau_k < +\infty\}$, $k = 1,2,\cdots$, where $\sigma_k < \tau_k$ and lim $\sigma_k = +\infty$; (3) $\bigcup\{\sigma_k \leqslant t \leqslant \tau_k\} \supset \{t \geqslant k(f)\}$. Let G denote Green's function for Ω with pole 0, and let g denote Green's function with pole 0 for K slit along $\{-\infty < x \leqslant -k(f)\}$. By the Lindelöf inequality, we have

$$G \circ F_\rho(z) \geqslant -\log |z|\,. \tag{8.8}$$

What the reader is now asked to accept is the following inequality:

$$G(z) \leqslant g(|z|)\,, \qquad z \in \Omega\,. \tag{8.9}$$

This inequality plays a role corresponding to that of the inequality following (8.2) of the present section. The proof of (8.9) may be based on elementary potential-theoretic considerations. In particular, one may consider first regions of the form $\Omega \cap \Delta(0;r)$ and establish representation formulas for Green's function with pole 0 for such $\Omega \cap \Delta(0;r)$ in terms of Green's functions for $\Delta(0;r)$. One obtains integral formulas that permit estimations paralleling those obtained with the aid of (8.2) in the case of the Milloux-Schmidt inequality. However, integrals rather than sums now appear.

We now see by (8.8) and (8.9) that

$$g(|F_\rho(z)|) \geqslant -\log|z|\,, \qquad |z| < 1\,,$$

and, hence, that

$$g(|f(z)|) \geqslant -\log|z|, \qquad |z|<1. \tag{8.10}$$

Using Ex. 4, § 2, this chapter, we see that

$$g(z) = \log\left|\frac{\sqrt{z+k(f)}+\sqrt{k(f)}}{\sqrt{z+k(f)}-\sqrt{k(f)}}\right|. \tag{8.11}$$

This coupled with (8.10) implies that $\log|4k(f)| \geqslant 0$, or $k(f) \geqslant \frac{1}{4}$. Hence, Littlewood's conjecture follows that

$$\inf_{f\in\Phi_1} k(f) = \tfrac{1}{4}.$$

9. The Phragmén-Lindelöf Theorem. This theorem was originally given for analytic functions. It may be stated as follows:

Given a function f analytic on $\{\operatorname{Im} z > 0\}$ *and satisfying*

$$\limsup_{z\to\eta}|f(z)| \leqslant 1, \qquad \eta\in R.$$

Then either $|f| \leqslant 1$, *or else*

$$\liminf_{r\to\infty}\frac{\log S(r;f)}{r} > 0, \qquad S(r;f) = \sup_{0<\theta<\pi}|f(re^{i\theta})|. \tag{9.1}$$

We have already met phenomena of this type on several occasions. For example, Liouville's theorem may be formulated in this manner: If f is a function analytic on K, then either f is constant or $\lim\limits_{r\to\infty} M(r;f)r^{-1} > 0$. A theorem of a similar type is: If f is analytic on K but is not a polynomial, then $\lim\limits_{r\to\infty}\log M(r;f)/\log r = +\infty$. Still another example is afforded by the theorem of Wiman given in the exercises of the preceding section.

The original version of the Phragmén-Lindelöf theorem has received a number of refinements. Contributions in this direction have been made by F. and R. Nevanlinna, L. Ahlfors, and M. Heins. Since the logarithm of the modulus of an analytic function is subharmonic, the statement of the Phragmén-Lindelöf theorem may be paraphrased for subharmonic functions. The theorem thus extended remains true. The developments of the present section are quite suitable for exercise treatment.

EXERCISES

1. Let

$$\mathfrak{A} = \{r_1 < |z| < r_2\}, \quad 0 \leqslant r_1 < r_2 \leqslant +\infty,$$

and let

$$\Omega = \mathfrak{A} \cap \{\operatorname{Im} z > 0\}.$$

Given that h is harmonic on Ω and satisfies $\lim_{z\to\eta} h(z) = 0$, η real, $r_1 < |\eta| < r_2$. Show that $\bar{h}$, the harmonic extension of h to $\mathcal{O}\!\ell$, admits a Fourier representation of the form

$$\bar{h}(re^{i\theta}) = \sum_{k=1}^{\infty} (a_k r^k + b_k r^{-k}) \sin k\theta .$$

Conclude that

$$\int_0^{\pi} h(re^{i\theta}) \sin\theta \, d\theta$$

is of the form $\alpha r + \beta r^{-1}$.

2. If h is harmonic on $\Delta(0;R) \cap \{\operatorname{Im} z > 0\}$ and satisfies $\lim_{z\to\eta} h(z) = 0$, $-R < \eta < R$, then $\bar{h}$, its harmonic extension to $\Delta(0;R)$, admits a Fourier representation of the form

$$\bar{h}(re^{i\theta}) = \sum_{k=1}^{\infty} a_k r^k \sin k\theta .$$

Using the inequality $|\sin k\theta| \leqslant k |\sin\theta|$, show that if h is *nonnegative*, the coefficients a_k satisfy the inequalities:

$$|a_k| r^{k-1} \leqslant k a_1 , \qquad 0 \leqslant r < R , \qquad k = 1,2,\cdots . \tag{9.2}$$

Also show that

$$a_1\Big[\operatorname{Im} z - \frac{2R - |z|}{(R - |z|)^2} |z|^2\Big] \leqslant h(z) \leqslant a_1\Big[\operatorname{Im} z + \frac{2R - |z|}{(R - |z|)^2} |z|^2\Big] . \tag{9.3}$$

3. Show that if h is a positive harmonic function on $\{\operatorname{Im} z > 0\}$ satisfying $\lim_{z\to\eta} h(z) = 0$ for each real η, then $h(z) = \alpha \operatorname{Im} z$, where $\alpha > 0$.

4. Suppose that u is subharmonic in Ω of Ex. 1 and satisfies $\limsup_{z\to\eta} u(z) \leqslant 0$, η real, $r_1 < |\eta| < r_2$ as well as $u(\eta) = 0$. Suppose further that the restriction of u to Ω is not identically $-\infty$. Let

$$\mu(r;u) = \int_0^{\pi} u(re^{i\theta}) \sin\theta \, d\theta$$

Then $\mu(r;u) > -\infty$, $r_1 < r < r_2$. Further, $r \to \mu(r;u)$ is *convex* with respect to the family of functions $\alpha r + \beta r^{-1}$ on $\{r_1 < r < r_2\}$. That is, if $r_1 < \rho_1 < \rho_2 < r_2$ and $\alpha\rho_k + \beta\rho_k^{-1} = \mu(\rho_k;u)$, $k = 1,2$, then $\mu(r;u) \leqslant \alpha r + \beta r^{-1}$, $\rho_1 < r < \rho_2$.

HINT: Let $(h_n)_1^{\infty}$ denote a monotone nonincreasing sequence of continuous functions on $\{\rho_1 \leqslant |z| \leqslant \rho_2\} \cap \{\operatorname{Im} z \geqslant 0\}$ satisfying:

(1) h_n is harmonic in $\{\rho_1 < |z| < \rho_2\} \cap \{\operatorname{Im} z > 0\}$;

(2) $h_n(x) = 0$, $\rho_1 < |x| < \rho_2$, x real;

(3) $\lim_{n\to\infty} h_n(\rho_k e^{i\theta}) = u(\rho_k e^{i\theta})$, $0 < \theta < \pi$, $k = 1,2$. Let $h = \lim_{n\to\infty} h_n$. Then h is harmonic in $\{\rho_1 < |z| < \rho_2\} \cap \{\mathrm{Im}\, z > 0\}$ and dominates u there. Apply Ex. 1 to h_n, and note that h is continuous at each real x satisfying $\rho_1 < |x| < \rho_2$ [this may be seen with the aid of (9.3)] and that

$$\lim_{n\to\infty} \mu(\rho_k;h_n) = \mu(\rho_k;u)\,, \qquad k = 1,2\,.$$

REMARK: The convexity property is due to Ahlfors in the case where u is of the form $\overset{+}{\log} |f|$, f being analytic (L. Ahlfors, "On Phragmén-Lindelöf's Principle," *Trans. AMS*, **41**: 1–8, 1937).

5. Suppose that $u \not\equiv -\infty$ is subharmonic on $\{\mathrm{Im}\, z > 0\}$ and satisfies the boundary condition $\limsup_{z\to\eta} u(z) \leqslant 0$, η real. Show that

$$r \to r^{-1}\,\mu(r;u)$$

is monotone nondecreasing on $\{0 < r < +\infty\}$, basing the proof on the convexity property of $\mu(r;u)$ of Ex. 4 and the imposed boundary condition.

REMARK: This result is also due to Ahlfors (*loc. cit.*) for the case referred to in the previous exercise. With $u = \overset{+}{\log} |f|$, f analytic, it had been shown earlier by F. and R. Nevanlinna that if f is not of modulus $\leqslant 1$, then

$$\liminf_{r\to\infty} r^{-1}\,\mu(r;u) > 0\,.$$

6. Establish the monotoneity of $r^{-1}\mu(r;u)$ of Ex. 5 by the following argument. Let H_r denote the class of functions h continuous on $\overline{\Delta(0;r)} \cap \{\mathrm{Im}\, z \geqslant 0\}$ which vanish at each point of $\{-r < \mathrm{Re}\, z < r;\ \mathrm{Im}\, z = 0\}$, satisfy $h(re^{i\theta}) \geqslant u(re^{i\theta})$, $0 < \theta < \pi$, and in addition are harmonic in $\Delta(0;r) \cap \{\mathrm{Im}\, z > 0\}$. Show that

$$r^{-1}\,\mu(r;u) = \frac{\pi}{2} \inf \{h_y(0) \mid h \in H_r\}\,,$$

and conclude the monotoneity theorem.

The fact that $\lim_{r\to\infty} r^{-1}\,\mu(r;u) < +\infty$ does not in itself yield any positive information on the rate of growth of u. Thus, with $u(z) = \mathrm{Im}\, z^{2n+1}$, $n = 1,2,\cdots$, we have $\mu(r;u) = 0$ and $\sigma(r;u) = \sup_{0<\theta<\pi} u(re^{i\theta}) = r^{2n+1}$. However, the following exercises show that the growth of $u^+ = \max\{u,0\}$ is definitely connected with the behavior of $r^{-1}\mu(r;u^+)$. In Exs. 7 and 8 it is assumed that u satisfies the conditions of Ex. 5.

EXERCISES

7. If u^+ possesses a harmonic majorant, then the least harmonic majorant $\bar{h}$ of u^+ is given by $h(z) = \alpha\, \mathrm{Im}\, z$, where $\alpha = (2/\pi) \lim_{r\to\infty} r^{-1}\mu(r;u^+)$. If

$$\lim_{r\to\infty} r^{-1}\mu(r;u^+) < +\infty,$$

then u^+ admits a harmonic majorant.

HINT: Let h_r denote the least harmonic majorant of the restriction of u^+ to $\Delta(0;r) \cap \{\operatorname{Im} z > 0\}$, and consider $\lim_{r\to\infty} h_r$. Here (9.3) is useful.

8. Suppose that u^+ possesses a harmonic majorant. Let

$$\beta = (2/\pi) \lim_{r\to\infty} r^{-1}\mu(r;u).$$

Show that β is the least γ such that $u(z) \leqslant \gamma \operatorname{Im} z$, $\operatorname{Im} z > 0$.

HINT: Consider now the lower envelope of the original family H_r.

We note that $\beta^+ = \alpha$.

We next turn to the consideration of the following gauge for the size of u on $C(0;r) \cap \{\operatorname{Im} z > 0\}$:

$$\sigma(r;u) = \sup_{0<\theta<\pi} u(re^{i\theta}),$$

the gauge originally considered by Phragmén and Lindelöf. The growth of $\sigma(r;u)$ is related to that of $\mu(r;u^+)$. In fact, the following exercises yield:

$$\lim_{r\to\infty} r^{-1}\sigma(r;u) = \frac{2}{\pi} \lim_{r\to\infty} r^{-1}\mu(r;u^+).$$

EXERCISES

9. Show that if $u^+ \not\equiv 0$, then $\sigma(r;u) \geqslant \frac{1}{2}\mu(r;u^+)$ for r sufficiently large. Conclude that, given any u meeting the conditions of Ex. 5, either $\lim_{r\to\infty} r^{-1}\sigma(r;u) = +\infty$ or u^+ has a harmonic majorant.

10. Investigate $\delta_b(a) = \int_0^\pi (a - b \sin\theta)^- \sin\theta \, d\theta$, where a and b are finite real and $x^- = \min\{x, 0\}$. Clearly, $a \to \delta_b(a)$ is continuous. Show that $a \to \delta_b(a)$ is monotone increasing for $a \leqslant b^+$ and vanishes for $a \geqslant b^+$.

11. Show that if u^+ has a harmonic majorant, then $\lim_{r\to\infty} r^{-1}\sigma(r;u) = \alpha$ (reference being made to α of Ex. 7).

HINT: With $v(z) = u(z) - \beta \operatorname{Im} z$ (β of Ex. 8), $\lim_{r\to\infty} r^{-1}\mu(r;v) = 0$. Show that

$$r^{-1}\mu(r;v) \leqslant \delta_\beta\left(\frac{\sigma(r)}{r}\right) \leqslant 0,$$

and apply Ex. 10.

The result of this exercise is due to M. Heins (*Trans. AMS*, **60**: 238–244, 1946).

The Phragmén-Lindelöf theorem stated at the beginning of this section, as well as its subharmonic counterpart, is subsumed under the results of the present exercises. Further, it is easily verified that if $0 \leqslant A \leqslant +\infty$, there exists f satisfying the hypotheses of the Phragmén-Lindelöf theorem such that with $u = \log|f|$, $\lim_{r\to\infty} r^{-1}\sigma(r;u) = A$. If $0 \leqslant A < +\infty$, it suffices to take $f(z) = e^{-iAz}$, and if $A = +\infty$, to take $f(z) = e^{-iz^2}$.

10. Wiman's Theorem. We now turn to a study of the limit problem connected with Wiman's theorem (Ex. 2, § 8, this chapter). The present section, and for that matter Wiman's theorem itself, are really concerned with subharmonic functions. Since the Riesz representation theorem for subharmonic functions, which appears to be essential for studying the general subharmonic situation, is not treated in this book, we shall confine our attention to analytic functions. The reader interested in the subharmonic case will find that the discussion of the present section is immediately applicable. We start with some preliminaries that are classical tools of the theory of entire functions.

Poisson-Jensen Formula. Let f be analytic in $\Delta(0;R)$ and not identically zero. Then

$$\log |f(z)| = \sum\nolimits_r n(a;f) \log \left| \frac{r(z-a)}{r^2 - \bar{a}z} \right| + h_r(z), \qquad |z| < r < R, \quad (10.1)$$

where Σ_r is used to mean that the sum is extended over the zeros of f in $\Delta(0;r)$ and where h_r is the Poisson integral

$$\frac{1}{2\pi}\int_0^{2\pi} \log |f(re^{i\theta})| \, K\left(e^{i\theta}, \frac{z}{r}\right) d\theta .$$

The formula (10.1) is the Poisson-Jensen formula. The proof is simple. If $f(z) \neq 0$ for $|z| = r$, the assertion is immediate. If f vanishes at some point of $C(0;r)$, we note first that $h_\rho(z)$ is monotone in ρ, $|z| < \rho < R$, since $\log |f|$ is subharmonic, and second that $h_\rho(0)$ is continuous in ρ by virtue of the convexity property of the mean value of a subharmonic function. Hence, $\lim_{\rho \to r} h_\rho = h_r$, and we see that (10.1) holds without restriction.

EXERCISE

1. State and prove the analogue of (10.1) for meromorphic functions.

We introduce $\nu(r)$, the valence at 0 of the restriction of f to $\Delta(0;r)$; that is,

$$\nu(r) = \sum_{f(a)=0, |a|<r} n(a;f) .$$

If $f(0) \neq 0$, then, setting $z = 0$ in (10.1), we obtain

$$\log |f(0)| = \int_0^r \log \frac{t}{r} \, d\nu(t) + h_r(0)$$

$$= -\int_0^r \frac{\nu(t)}{t} \, dt + h_r(0), \qquad (10.2)$$

the latter equality following by an integration by parts.

If $f(0) = 0$ and if c is the coefficient of order $n(0;f)$ in the power-series expansion of f, then, by an obvious variant of the above consideration, we obtain

$$\log |c| = -\int_0^r \frac{\nu(t) - n(0;f)}{t}\, dt - n(0;f) \log r + h_r(0)\,. \tag{10.3}$$

The formulas (10.2) and (10.3) are the *Jensen formulas.*

EXERCISE

2. Show that if f is an entire function and $f(0) \neq 0$, then

$$\nu(r) \leqslant \frac{1}{\log 2} \{\log M(2r;f) - \log |f(0)|\}\,. \tag{10.4}$$

An Infinite-product Representation. We now consider an entire function $f \not\equiv 0$ satisfying the growth condition

$$\lim_{r\to\infty} r^{-1} \log M(r;f) = 0\,. \tag{10.5}$$

We seek to establish an infinite-product representation for f. It is to be observed that the product representations afforded by the Weierstrass infinite-product theorem have the serious inconvenience of possibly containing exponential convergence factors, the control of which may be difficult. We suppose, as we may without loss of generality, that $f(0) = 1$. The case where $f(0) \neq 1$ is readily reduced to the case we are considering. Using (10.1), we obtain

$$\begin{aligned}\log |f(z)| &= [h_r(z) - h_r(0)] + \sum\nolimits_r n(a;f) \left\{\log \left| \frac{r(z-a)}{r^2 - \bar{a}z} \right| - \log \left| \frac{a}{r} \right| \right\} \\ &= [h_r(z) - h_r(0)] + \sum\nolimits_r n(a;f) \log |1 - a^{-1}z| \\ &\quad - \sum\nolimits_r n(a;f) \log \left| 1 - \frac{\bar{a}z}{r^2} \right|, \qquad |z| < r\,. \end{aligned} \tag{10.6}$$

Hence,

$$\log |f(z)| - \sum\nolimits_r n(a;f) \log |1 - a^{-1}z| = [h_r(z) - h_r(0)] - \sum\nolimits_r n(a;f) \log \left| 1 - \frac{\bar{a}z}{r^2} \right|, \qquad |z| < r\,, \tag{10.7}$$

where the summations extend, as above, over the zeros of f in $\Delta(0;r)$ and the left-hand side is properly construed at the zeros. We note that

$$\begin{aligned}\frac{1}{2\pi}\int_0^{2\pi} |\log |f(re^{i\theta})||\, d\theta &\leqslant \frac{1}{2\pi}\int_0^{2\pi} \{|\log |f(re^{i\theta})|| + \log |f(re^{i\theta})|\}\, d\theta \\ &\leqslant 2 \log M(r;f)\,.\end{aligned}$$

This observation, (10.5), and the Poisson integral formula for h_r, taken together, yield the result that $h_r - h_r(0)$ tends uniformly to zero as $r \to \infty$ for z on a given bounded set of the complex plane. Further,

$$\left| \sum_r n(a;f) \log \left| 1 - \frac{\bar{a}z}{r^2} \right| \right| \leqslant \sum_r n(a;f) \frac{|\bar{a}z/r^2|}{1 - |\bar{a}z/r^2|}$$

$$\leqslant \frac{\nu(r)\,|z|}{r - |z|}, \qquad |z| < r. \tag{10.8}$$

Hence, using (10.4) and (10.5), we see that the left-hand side of (10.8) tends uniformly to zero as $r \to \infty$ for z on a given bounded set. It follows that

$$\log |f(z)| = \lim_{r\to\infty} \sum_r n(a;f) \log |1 - a^{-1}z|, \tag{10.9}$$

the convergence being uniform in the complement of the set of zeros of f with respect to the finite plane.

EXERCISES

3. Show that

$$f(z) = \lim_{r\to\infty} \prod_r \left(1 - \frac{z}{a}\right)^{n(a;f)},$$

the convergence being uniform on each bounded subset of the plane. Here $\prod_r$ has a significance corresponding to that of $\sum_r$.

Show that if f satisfies (10.5) or merely $\liminf_{r\to\infty} r^{-1} \log M(r;f) = 0$ and is not a polynomial, then f attains each finite value infinitely many times.

4. Let f denote an entire function satisfying $f(0) = 1$. Consider the condition

$$\int_1^\infty t^{-2} \log M(t;f)\, dt < +\infty. \tag{10.10}$$

Show (a) that (10.10) implies (10.5), and (b) that (10.10) is fulfilled if the order of f is less than 1. Show that (10.10) implies that

$$\int_0^\infty t^{-2}\, \nu(t)\, dt < +\infty \tag{10.11}$$

and that (10.11) is equivalent to

$$\sum_{f(a)=0} n(a;f)\, |a|^{-1} < +\infty. \tag{10.12}$$

5. Show that if (10.10) is fulfilled, then

$$\sum_{(a)=0} n(a;f)\, \big|\log |1 - a^{-1}z|\big| < +\infty,$$

for z not a zero of f, and, further,

$$\log |f(z)| = \sum_{f(a)=0} n(a;f) \log |1 - a^{-1}z| \tag{10.13}$$

and

$$f(z) = \prod_{f(a)=0} (1 - a^{-1}z)^{n(a;f)} . \tag{10.14}$$

Show further that the convergence is uniform for (10.13) and (10.14) in the complement of the set of zeros of f when f is not a polynomial and Σ and Π are taken in terms of a given univalent enumeration of the zeros of f.

6. Given f satisfying (10.10), we associate with f the function F given by

$$F(z) = \prod_{f(a)=0} (1 + |a|^{-1}z)^{n(a;f)} . \tag{10.15}$$

(Each zero of f is moved to the point of the negative real axis having the same modulus.) Clearly, F is an entire function satisfying

$$|F(-|z|)| \leqslant |F(z)| \leqslant F(|z|) \tag{10.16}$$

and

$$|F(-|z|)| \leqslant |f(z)| \leqslant F(|z|) . \tag{10.17}$$

Show that

$$\begin{aligned} \log F(|z|) &= \int_0^\infty \log(1 + t^{-1}|z|)\, d\nu(t) \\ &= |z| \int_0^\infty \frac{\nu(t)}{t(t + |z|)}\, dt . \end{aligned} \tag{10.18}$$

We are now prepared to consider the refined Wiman theorem. We consider an entire function f that fulfills the hypotheses of Wiman's theorem and is such that

$$\liminf_{r\to\infty} r^{-1/2} \log M(r;f) < +\infty . \tag{10.19}$$

We show

Theorem 10.1. $\lim_{r\to\infty} r^{-1/2} \log M(r;f)$ *exists.*

PROOF: The demonstration starts with the observation that

$$\limsup_{r\to\infty} r^{-1/2} \log M(r;f) < +\infty \tag{10.20}$$

(Ex. 3, § 8, this chapter). We assume that $f(0) = 1$. The unrestricted case is readily reduced to this one. We consider along with f the ancillary functions F (defined above) and G with domain $\{\text{Re } z > 0\}$ defined by

$$G(z) = F(z^2) . \tag{10.21}$$

(1) From (10.20), (10.4), and (10.18) we conclude that

$$\limsup_{r\to\infty} r^{-1/2} \log M(r;F) < +\infty . \tag{10.22}$$

It suffices to note that the upper estimate obtained from (10.4) for $\nu(r)$ yields $\nu(r) \leqslant Ar^{1/2}$ for some finite A and to apply this result to (10.18). An elementary calculation shows the validity of (10.22).

(2) Applying the Phragmén-Lindelöf theorem in its sharp form (Exs. 9, 11, § 9, this chapter) to $\log |m^{-1} G|$, we infer that $\lim_{r\to\infty} r^{-1} \log M(r;G)$ exists and is a finite and positive number, say α. It follows that $\lim_{r\to\infty} r^{-1/2} \log M(r;F) = \alpha$.

(3) In order to relate the growth of f, in which we are interested, to that of F, concerning which we have definite information, it is convenient to have a control on the nature of the subset of the negative real axis on which F is "small" in a sense we shall make precise. To be exact, *let finite positive numbers a and b be given with $b > 1$. Let E denote the subset of the negative real axis*

$$\{-t \mid \log |m^{-1} F(-t)| < -at^{1/2}, t > 1\} . \tag{10.23}$$

Then any family of mutually disjoint intervals

$$I = \{-c(I) > x > -d(I)\} \subset E$$

satisfying $d(I)/c(I) \geqslant b^2$ is finite.

To see this, we consider $u(z) = \log |m^{-1} G(z)| - \alpha \operatorname{Re} z$ in $\{\operatorname{Re} z > 0\}$ and let ω denote the harmonic measure of $\{it \mid 1 < t < b\}$ with respect to $\{\operatorname{Re} z > 0\}$. Then

$$u(z) \leqslant -a[c(I)]^{1/2}\, \omega\Big(\frac{z}{[c(I)]^{1/2}}\Big) , \qquad \operatorname{Re} z > 0 .$$

By (9.3), if $(\lambda_n)_1^\infty$ is a monotone-increasing sequence of positive numbers, satisfying $\lim \lambda_n = +\infty$,

$$\lim_{n\to\infty} \lambda_n\, \omega(\lambda_n^{-1} z) = p \operatorname{Re} z , \qquad p = \frac{\partial \omega}{\partial x}(0) > 0 .$$

Hence, if there are infinitely many mutually disjoint I satisfying the stated condition, then

$$u(z) \leqslant -ap \operatorname{Re} z ,$$

and hence

$$\log |m^{-1} G(z)| \leqslant (\alpha - ap) \operatorname{Re} z, \qquad \operatorname{Re} z > 0 .$$

This implies

$$\overset{+}{\log} |m^{-1} G(z)| \leqslant (\alpha - ap)^+ \operatorname{Re} z , \qquad \operatorname{Re} z > 0 .$$

This is impossible because of the extremal nature of α.

(4) The rest of the argument proceeds in a straightforward manner. We consider $f(z)f(-z)$, and using the infinite-product representations for f and F we obtain

$$|f(z)f(-z)| = \left|\prod_{f(a)=0} (1 - a^{-2}z^2)^{n(a;f)}\right|$$

$$\geqslant \prod \left|1 - |a|^{-2}|z|^2\right|^{n(a;f)}$$

$$= F(|z|)\,|F(-|z|)|$$

and hence,

$$M(r;f)m \geqslant M(r;F)\,|F(-r)|\,. \tag{10.24}$$

This means of controlling f in terms of F is a standard device in the theory of entire functions. Given $a < \alpha$, b as in (3), we see by (3) and (10.24) that if we take $r_1 > 1$ and sufficiently large,

$$\alpha - a < r^{-1/2} \log M(r;F) < \alpha + a\,, \qquad r \geqslant r_1\,,$$

and each maximal interval $\{-c > t > -d\}$ of E satisfying $c^{-1}d \geqslant b^2$ is such that $d < r_1$. We suppose, as we may, that $-r_1 \notin E$. Further,

$$\log M(r;f) \geqslant \log M(r;F) - ar^{1/2}$$

when $-r \notin E$ and $r > 1$. If $r \geqslant r_1$ and $-r$ belongs to a maximal interval $\{-c > t > -d\} \subset E$, we have $c^{-1}d < b^2$, $c \geqslant r_1$, and

$$\log M(r;f) \geqslant \log M(c;f) \geqslant \log M(c;F) - ac^{1/2} > \log M(c;F) - ar^{1/2}\,.$$

Hence, for $r \geqslant r_1$, we have

$$\alpha + a > r^{-1/2} \log M(r;F) \geqslant r^{-1/2} \log M(r;f) > \frac{\alpha - a}{b} - a\,.$$

Given the arbitrary character of a and b, we see that

$$\lim_{r\to\infty} r^{-1/2} \log M(r;f) = \alpha\,. \tag{10.25}$$

Theorem 10.1 follows.

EXERCISE

7. Define $C(z) = \sum_{k=0}^{\infty} \frac{(-1)^k z^k}{(2k)!}$ so that $\cos z = C(z^2)$. Show that

$$C(z) = \prod_{n=0}^{\infty} \left\{1 - \frac{z}{[(n + \frac{1}{2})\pi]^2}\right\},$$

and that

$$\lim_{r \to \infty} r^{-1/2} \log M(r;C) = 1 \,.$$

We see that the case of a finite positive limit is realized in the situation of the Wiman theorem. The exponential function yields an obvious example for the case of an infinite limit.

---

11. A Method of Carleman. In this section we shall analyze the growth of an entire function about which we possess information concerning the "size" of the set where *the modulus of the function does not exceed a given positive bound.* In the Wiman theorem the only stipulation is that

$$\min |f(re^{i\theta})| \leqslant m$$

for all finite positive r. Suppose, however, that the arclength of the set

$$\{z \mid |z| = r, \quad |f(z)| > m\}$$

is no greater than $\alpha\pi r$ for all finite positive r, α satisfying $0 < \alpha < 2$. Then it is natural to expect that the growth of f will be conditioned by this additional requirement on f. In the present section we shall see that this is indeed the case. In our study the set

$$\{z \mid |f(z)| > m\}$$

plays an essential role. Now this set may be of considerable complexity, and the resources from the theory of subharmonic functions that we have developed thus far do not appear to be adequate to study the problem at hand (subjective opinion of the author). However, there is a method, due to Carleman, that permits easy access to the problem we are considering. Carleman described his method in a short note in the Comptes Rendus of the Académie des Sciences de Paris in 1933 entitled "*Sur une inégalité différentielle dans la théorie des fonctions analytiques*" and used it to furnish a proof of the celebrated conjecture of Denjoy concerning the number of finite asymptotic values of an entire function of finite order, which had been settled shortly before by Ahlfors. The method of Carleman has an "elementary" character. It is available for subharmonic functions. However, we shall not consider that aspect of the question here.

Carleman's Lemma. Let $a < b$, and let Y_1 and Y_2 denote two continuous finite real-valued functions with domain $\{a < x < b\}$ which satisfy $Y_1(x) < Y_2(x)$, $a < x < b$. Let S denote the strip

$$\bigcup_{a<x<b} \{x + iy \mid Y_1(x) \leqslant y \leqslant Y_2(x)\}\,.$$

Let h be harmonic at each point of S, be positive in the interior of S, and satisfy

$$h(z) = 0,\ h_y(z) \neq 0, \qquad z = x + iY_k(x),\ a < x < b,\ k = 1,2\,. \tag{11.1}$$

We now associate with h and x, $a < x < b$, the quadratic norm

$$q(x) = \left\{ \int_{Y_1(x)}^{Y_2(x)} [h(x + iy)]^2 \, dy \right\}^{1/2}. \tag{11.2}$$

The function q is the focus of attention. Let $\delta(x) = Y_2(x) - Y_1(x)$. Then Carleman's lemma asserts

$$q''(x) \geqslant \left[\frac{\pi}{\delta(x)}\right]^2 q(x)\,, \qquad a < x < b \tag{11.3}$$

(Carleman's differential inequality).

Proof: We note that, thanks to the condition (11.1), Y_1 and Y_2 are real analytic. It suffices for the present, however, to note merely that Y_1 and Y_2 both possess continuous derivatives of the first order on $\{a < x < b\}$ (implicit-function theorem). It follows from the definition (11.2) that q^2 possesses a derivative at each point of $\{a < x < b\}$. Since, further, $q(x) > 0$, $a < x < b$, it follows that $q'(x)$ exists and that

$$q(x)q'(x) = \int_{Y_1(x)}^{Y_2(x)} hh_x \, dy\,, \qquad a < x < b\,. \tag{11.4}$$

It follows that $q''(x)$ exists and that

$$[q'(x)]^2 + q(x)q''(x) = \int_{Y_1(x)}^{Y_2(x)} (h_x^2 + hh_{xx}) \, dy\,, \qquad a < x < b\,. \tag{11.5}$$

Applying the Schwarz inequality (see any good advanced calculus text) to (11.4), we obtain

$$[q(x)q'(x)]^2 \leqslant [q(x)]^2 \int_{Y_1(x)}^{Y_2(x)} h_x^2 \, dy\,,$$

so that

$$[q'(x)]^2 \leqslant \int_{Y_1(x)}^{Y_2(x)} h_x^2 \, dy\,, \qquad a < x < b\,.$$

Hence, we infer from (11.5)

$$\begin{aligned} q(x)q''(x) &\geqslant \int_{Y_1(x)}^{Y_2(x)} hh_{xx} \, dy \\ &= -\int_{Y_1(x)}^{Y_2(x)} hh_{yy} \, dy\,, \qquad a < x < b\,. \end{aligned}$$

Integrating by parts, we obtain

$$q(x)q''(x) \geqslant \int_{Y_1(x)}^{Y_2(x)} h_y^2\, dy\,,$$

and, applying the inequality of Ex. 11, § 5, Chap. 1, we conclude that

$$q(x)q''(x) \geqslant \left[\frac{\pi}{\delta(x)}\right]^2 \int_{Y_1(x)}^{Y_2(x)} h^2\, dy = \left[\frac{\pi}{\delta(x)}\right]^2 [q(x)]^2\,, \qquad a < x < b\,.$$

The Carleman differential inequality now follows immediately.

We shall want to take advantage of the situation that occurs when several positive functions satisfy a differential inequality of the Carleman type. Suppose that $w_1,\cdots,w_n$ are each a function of class C'' on $\{a < x < b\}$ and positive, and suppose that λ is a nonnegative function with domain $\{a < x < b\}$ such that $w_k'' \geqslant \lambda w_k$, $k = 1,2,\cdots,n$. Let $W = \left\{\sum_1^n w_k^2\right\}^{1/2}$. Then

$$W'' \geqslant \lambda W\,. \tag{11.6}$$

In fact, proceeding as in the proof of Carleman's lemma, we have

$$WW' = \sum w_k w_k' \tag{11.7}$$

and

$$\begin{aligned}(W')^2 + WW'' &= \sum (w_k')^2 + \sum w_k w_k'' \\ &\geqslant \sum (w_k')^2 + \lambda \sum w_k^2\,.\end{aligned} \tag{11.8}$$

Applying the Cauchy-Schwarz inequality to (11.7), we obtain

$$(W')^2 \leqslant \sum (w_k')^2\,,$$

a result that, applied to (11.8), yields the inequality (11.6).

Application to the Growth Problem Stated at the Beginning of this Section. We consider a nonconstant entire function f meeting the conditions stated above. We suppose that $m = 1$ and that $f'(z) \neq 0$ for all z in the level set $\{|f(z)| = 1\}$. It will be easy to verify that the general case may be reduced to the case where these assumptions hold. We introduce the subharmonic function $u = \overset{+}{\log} |f|$, and

$$Q(r) = \left\{\int_0^{2\pi} [u(re^{i\theta})]^2\, d\theta\right\}^{1/2}, \qquad 0 < r < \infty\,. \tag{11.9}$$

We shall show

THEOREM 11.1. $\lim_{r\to\infty} r^{-1/\alpha} Q(r)$ *exists and is positive.*

Before we turn to the proof, let us consider the implications of this theorem for $M(r;f)$. Since $M(r;f) > 1$ for r sufficiently large, we see that

$$Q(r) \leqslant (2\pi)^{1/2} \log M(r;f)$$

for r sufficiently large. Hence,

$$\liminf_{r\to\infty} r^{-1/\alpha} \log M(r;f) > 0 . \tag{11.10}$$

Also, since u is subharmonic and nonnegative, we have, by the Schwarz inequality,

$$\log M(r;f) \leqslant \max_{|z|=r} \left\{(2\pi)^{-1} \int_0^{2\pi} u(2re^{i\theta})\, K\left(e^{i\theta}, \frac{z}{2r}\right) d\theta\right\}$$

$$\leqslant \frac{3Q(2r)}{\sqrt{2\pi}} . \tag{11.11}$$

Hence, if the left-hand side of (11.10) is *finite*, we have

$$\limsup_{r\to\infty} r^{-1/\alpha} \log M(r;f) < +\infty . \tag{11.12}$$

Taken with (11.10) this says—to use the terminology of Valiron—that f is *of regular growth of order* $1/\alpha$.

[The inequality (11.10) is implicit in the work of A. Hüber, Thesis, Swiss Federal School of Technology 1952.]

EXERCISE

1. Verify that it suffices to consider the reduced case of Theorem 11.1.

PROOF OF THEOREM 11.1: It is well to note that the set $\{|f(z)| = 1\}$ has only a finite number of points in common with each circumference $C(0;r)$. To see this, we observe that

$$g{:}z \to f(z)\overline{f(r^2/\bar{z})}$$

is analytic in $\{0 < |z| < \infty\}$ and that

$$g(z) = |f(z)|^2 , \qquad |z| = r .$$

If $\{|f(z)| = 1\}$ had an infinite number of points in common with $C(0;r)$, then $|f(z)| = 1$ for $|z| = r$ and f would not be a nonconstant entire function.

We shall also want to control the points of the level locus $\{|f(z)| = 1\}$ at which

$$\frac{\partial}{\partial\theta}(\log |f|) = 0 , \tag{11.13}$$

the reference to polar coordinates being obvious from the notation. We assert that *the set of points in question clusters at no point of the finite plane.* To establish this assertion we proceed as follows. We suppose the assertion false and let a denote a finite cluster point of the set. We fix a disk $\Delta(a;r)$ on which f is nonvanishing and univalent and let g now denote an analytic logarithm of the restriction of $f/f(a)$ to $\Delta(a;r)$ satisfying $g(a) = 0$. It is easy to see that the left-hand side of (11.13) is simply $\text{Re}\,[izg'(z)]$. Let h denote the inverse of g. Then $z \to \text{Re}\,[ih(z)g'(h(z))]$ is harmonic at 0 and vanishes on a set of points of the imaginary axis that clusters at 0. It follows that $z \to \text{Re}\,[ih(z)g'(h(z))]$ vanishes on an open interval of the imaginary axis containing 0 and, hence, that the left-hand side of (11.13) vanishes on an arc γ (not containing 0) of the level locus $\{|f(z)| = 1\}$. The gradient of $\log|f|$, namely, $\left(\frac{\partial}{\partial x}\log|f|, \frac{\partial}{\partial y}\log|f|\right)$, is nowhere equal to (0,0) on γ. This fact, taken with the vanishing of $\frac{\partial}{\partial\theta}\log|f|$, implies the nonvanishing of $\frac{\partial}{\partial r}\log|f|$ on γ. On now considering γ in polar form, from the fact that $|f| = 1$ on γ we infer that γ lies on some $C(0;r)$. This is impossible, since only a finite number of points of γ lie on a given $C(0;r)$. Our assertion follows.

To continue, we let $q(s) = Q(e^s)$, $-\infty < s < +\infty$, and notice that q is a nondecreasing continuous function, since u^2 is subharmonic in K. Further, using the results that have been developed up to this point, we shall now see that

$$q''(s) \geqslant \alpha^{-2}q(s) \tag{11.14}$$

for all sufficiently large s save possibly for a set of s not clustering at any finite value. In fact, let r_0 be such that $M(r;f) > 1$ for $r > r_0$. We verify that (11.14) holds for $s > \log r_0$ save when s is the logarithm of the modulus of a point of $\{|f(z)| = 1\}$ satisfying (11.13). Let $v(\sigma) = \log|f(e^\sigma)|$. Let s_1 be an admitted s, and let t_1 be such that $v(s_1 + it_1) < 0$. Then, by the implicit-function theorem, we see that there exists an interval centered at s_1 such that $v(s + it_1) < 0$, $s \in I$, and the level locus $\{(s,t) \mid v(s + it) = 0,\ s \in I,\ t_1 < t < t_1 + 2\pi\}$ is the union of a finite number of C' functions $\gamma_1,\cdots,\gamma_{2m}$, each having domain I and satisfying $\gamma_1 < \cdots < \gamma_{2m}$ ($m \geqslant 1$). It follows that the set

$$\{\sigma \mid v(\sigma) \geqslant 0,\ \text{Re}\,\sigma \in I,\ t_1 < \text{Im}\,\sigma < t_2 + 2\pi\}$$

is representable as the union of m disjoint domains of the type to which reference is made in Carleman's lemma and that for $s \in I$,

$$q(s) = \left\{\int_{t_1}^{t_1+2\pi} [v^+(s + it)]^2\, dt\right\}^{1/2}$$

$$= \left\{\sum_{k=1}^{m} \int_{\gamma_{2k-1}(s)}^{\gamma_{2k}(s)} [v(s + it]^2\, dt\right\}^{1/2}.$$

Let

$$q_k(s) = \left\{ \int_{\gamma_{2k-1}(s)}^{\gamma_{2k}(s)} v^2 \, dt \right\}^{1/2}.$$

Since, by Carleman's lemma,

$$q_k''(s) \geqslant \alpha^{-2} q_k(s), \qquad s \in I, k = 1,2,\cdots,m,$$

we conclude from (11.6) that (11.14) holds in I.

We now wish to conclude that q is convex with respect to the family $\{Ae^{s/\alpha} + Be^{-s/\alpha}\}$, A and B being finite real numbers. Furthermore, we wish to do this without reference to the geometric accidentals of the problem associated with the exceptional s. We note that q^2 is convex and nondecreasing, thanks to the subharmonicity of u^2; hence, for $s > \log r_0$, the left and right derivatives of q at s exist and the left does not exceed the right. Let $\log r_0 < s_1 < s_2 < +\infty$, and let l denote the function of the form $Ae^{s/\alpha} + Be^{-s/\alpha}$ satisfying $q(s_k) = l(s_k)$, $k = 1,2$. We assert that $q(s) \leqslant l(s)$, $s_1 < s < s_2$. Otherwise y, the restriction of $q - l$ to $\{s_1 \leqslant s \leqslant s_2\}$, would attain its absolute maximum (> 0) at a point s_3, $s_1 < s_3 < s_2$. If s_3 were a nonexceptional s, we should have

$$y''(s_3) \geqslant \alpha^{-2} y(s_3) > 0,$$

so that y would have a *strong* relative minimum at s_3. This is impossible. If s_3 were exceptional, at all events the left derivative of y at s would be nonnegative and the right derivative would consequently be nonnegative. Now

$$y''(s) \geqslant \alpha^{-2} y(s) > 0$$

for s greater than but sufficiently near s_3. Consequently, $y'(s) > 0$ for s greater than but sufficiently near s_3, and hence y would not have a maximum at s_3. Our assertion follows.

The proof is now readily concluded. Given $\log r_0 < s_1 < s_2 < s_3 < +\infty$, the convexity property of q implies that

$$q(s_2) \leqslant q(s_1) \frac{\sinh\left(\dfrac{s_3 - s_2}{\alpha}\right)}{\sinh\left(\dfrac{s_3 - s_1}{\alpha}\right)} + q(s_3) \frac{\sinh\left(\dfrac{s_2 - s_1}{\alpha}\right)}{\sinh\left(\dfrac{s_3 - s_1}{\alpha}\right)}. \tag{11.15}$$

Letting $s_3 \to +\infty$, we obtain

$$q(s_2) \leqslant q(s_1) \exp\left(\frac{s_1 - s_2}{\alpha}\right) + 2A \sinh\left(\frac{s_2 - s_1}{\alpha}\right) e^{s_1/\alpha}, \tag{11.16}$$

where $A = \liminf_{s \to +\infty} e^{-s/\alpha} q(s)$. It follows that $A > 0$, for otherwise q would be bounded and f would be constant. From (11.16) we infer

$$\limsup_{s \to +\infty} e^{-s/\alpha} q(s) \leqslant A.$$

Returning to Q, we see that the theorem follows.

EXERCISES

2. Elaborate upon the assertion of the third sentence of the last paragraph but one of the proof of Theorem 11.1. Also upon the last sentence but one of the paragraph immediately preceding this exercise.

3. Let u be positive and harmonic on $\{r_1 < |z| < r_2\}$, and $1 < p < +\infty$. Let $m(r) = \{(2\pi)^{-1} \int_0^{2\pi} [u(re^{i\theta})]^p \, d\theta\}^{1/p}$, $r_1 < r < r_2$. Show that $m''(r) + r^{-1} m'(r) \geqslant 0$, $r_1 < r < r_2$, and conclude that m is convex in $\log r$.

HINT: Obtain the first two derivatives of m^p, and adapt the appropriate steps of the proof of the Carleman lemma to the present situation.

4. Conclude from the preceding exercise the following theorem: If u is nonnegative and subharmonic on $\{r_1 < |z| < r_2\}$ and $1 < p < +\infty$, then $\{(2\pi)^{-1} \int_0^{2\pi} [u(re^{i\theta})]^p \, d\theta\}^{1/p}$, the pth circumferential mean of u, is convex in $\log r$.

There remains the question whether for each α, $0 < \alpha < 2$, there exists an admitted f for which $\lim r^{-1/\alpha} Q(r) < +\infty$. That this is so can be seen with the help of the Mittag-Leffler E_α function, which has the following properties:

(1) $E_\alpha(z) - (1/\alpha)\exp(z^{1/\alpha})$ is bounded in sector $S_\alpha = \{|\operatorname{Arg} z| < \alpha\pi/2\}$;

(2) $E_\alpha(z)$ is bounded on $K - S_\alpha$. By $z^{1/\alpha}$ will be meant the determination $\exp(\alpha^{-1} \operatorname{Log} z)$, where $\operatorname{Log} z$ is the analytic logarithm of z in $\{|\operatorname{Arg} z| < \pi\}$ that vanishes at 1. If the above conditions (1) and (2) are satisfied by two entire functions (replacing E_α), they differ by a constant.

To establish the existence of a function having the stated properties it is convenient to introduce β satisfying $\alpha < \beta < \min\{2\alpha, 2\}$ and the following paths: $C(r)$, defined by $z = re^{i\theta}$, $-\alpha\pi/2 \leqslant \theta \leqslant \alpha\pi/2$; Γ_β, consisting of the ray $\{\operatorname{Arg} z = -\beta\pi/2\}$ traced from ∞ to $e^{-i\beta\pi/2}$, the arc of the unit circle traced in the counterclockwise sense from $e^{-i\beta\pi/2}$ to $e^{i\beta\pi/2}$, and finally the ray $\{\operatorname{Arg} z = \beta\pi/2\}$ traced from $e^{i\beta\pi/2}$ to ∞. We consider

$$f_r(z) = \frac{1}{2\pi i\alpha} \int_{C(r)} \frac{\exp(t^{1/\alpha})}{t - z} \, dt \tag{11.17}$$

and show that the $\lim_{r\to\infty} f_r$ is an entire function satisfying (1) and (2). The function E_α is this limit.

It will be convenient to introduce also the auxiliary function

$$g_\beta(z) = \frac{1}{2\pi i\alpha} \int_{\Gamma_\beta} \frac{\exp(t^{1/\alpha})}{t - z} \, dt \tag{11.18}$$

for z in the component Ω_β of the complement of Γ_β that contains 0. It is an easy consequence of the Cauchy integral theorem that

$$\lim_{r\to\infty} f_r(z) = g_\beta(z)\,, \qquad z \in \Omega_\beta\,.$$

It follows from the Cauchy integral formula applied to $\exp(z^{1/\alpha})$ and the contour consisting of the arc $z = re^{i\theta}$, $-\frac{1}{2}\beta\pi \leqslant \theta \leqslant \frac{1}{2}\beta\pi$, and the part of Γ_β in $\Delta(0;r)$ with sense reversed that

$$\lim_{r\to\infty} f_r(z) = \frac{1}{\alpha}\exp(z^{1/\alpha}) + \frac{1}{2\pi i\alpha}\int_{\Gamma_\beta} \frac{\exp(t^{1/\alpha})}{t-z}\,dt\,, \qquad z \in K - \bar{\Omega}_\beta\,. \tag{11.19}$$

Hence, it is easy to see that $\lim f_r$ is entire. We designate $\lim f_r$ by E_α. From (11.19) we see that if β_1 and β_2 are admitted β, $\beta_1 < \beta_2$, then

$$E_\alpha(z) - (1/\alpha)\exp(z^{1/\alpha})$$

is bounded in $\{|\operatorname{Arg} z| \leqslant \beta_1\pi/2\} \cap \{|z| \geqslant 2\}$, since $|t - z|$ has a positive lower bound when z is in the stated set and $t \in \Gamma_{\beta_2}$. Further, a similar argument shows that $E_\alpha(z)$ is bounded in Ω_{β_2}. It suffices to consider $g_{\beta_1}(z)$ of (11.18). It is now immediate that E_α fulfills the requirements (1) and (2).

EXERCISES

5. Elaborate upon the above exposition, furnishing the details of the limit arguments that were omitted.

6. Show that $f = E_\alpha$ is admitted by Theorem 11.1 and that the associated Q satisfies

$$0 < \lim_{r\to\infty} r^{-1/\alpha}Q(r) < +\infty\,.$$

[6]

The Boundary Behavior of the Riemann Mapping Function for Simply-connected Jordan Regions

1. Some General Observations. In the present chapter our concern will be with a special aspect of the following problem:

Let f denote a univalent meromorphic function with domain $\Delta(0;1)$, let $\Omega(f) = f[\Delta(0;1)]$ and let g denote the inverse of f. What can be said about the behavior of f in the neighborhood of a point of $C(0;1)$ and about the behavior of g in the neighborhood of a point of fr $\Omega(f)$? In particular, what role does the structure of fr $\Omega(f)$ play in determining the boundary properties of f and g?

The particular aspect of this problem that we shall study in this chapter is the characterization of $\Omega(f)$ for which f and g admit univalent continuous extensions to $\overline{\Delta(0;1)}$ and $\overline{\Omega(f)}$, respectively. The answer may be simply stated: *The $\Omega(f)$ for the f that admit univalent continuous extentions to $\overline{\Delta(0;1)}$ are precisely the simply connected Jordan regions*. A region Ω, we recall, is termed a *Jordan region* provided that fr Ω is the union of a finite number of mutually disjoint closed Jordan curves.

The subject by its very nature leads us to expect a confluence of ideas from the theory of functions of a complex variable and the topology of plane sets. The latter discipline is not, however, quite so simple as the low dimensionality of the plane might suggest. To persuade ourselves that this is so, it suffices to think of the sophistication connected with the proofs of the Jordan curve theorem and related results. We shall want to use the Jordan separation theorem, but only a mild form (and only for special kinds of Jordan curves). The chapter will be completed with an account of Beckenbach's proof of the strong form of the Cauchy integral theorem.

The general problem of the boundary behavior of the Riemann mapping function and its inverse has received considerable attention in a series of investigations going back to the beginning of the present century. Special mention should be made of Osgood's conjecture (1903) (see § 3, this chapter), which is really the theme of the present chapter; its independent solution by Osgood and Taylor on the one hand and Carathéodory on the other hand (1913); and the important pioneer work of Carathéodory on the general boundary problem, which introduced the fundamental concept of a prime end. For the reader who wishes to pursue the boundary problem further and who reads German, we warmly recommend pages 3 to 90 of Band IV of Carathéodory, *Gesammelte*

Mathematische Schriften, which contain the paper on prime ends and two papers on the boundary problem. A valuable extensive summary of the work done on the boundary problem is due to Gattegno and Ostrowski, "Représentation conforme à la frontière," *Mémorial des sciences mathématiques*, Fascicules CIX, CX, 1949. These articles contain very comprehensive bibliographies.

Unfortunately, there is a paucity of material on the boundary problem in English in monographs or treatises. Apart from the treatment of Littlewood in his *Lectures on the Theory of Functions*, which was cited in other connections, mention should be made of the treatments in Carathéodory's *Conformal Representation*, in Carathéodory's *Theory of Functions*, vol. 2, and in Courant's *Dirichlet's Principle*. In all these accounts, the topological results employed are regarded as material from another discipline, material whose detailed treatment the reader will find in a treatise of that discipline.

2. An Example. The boundary behavior of the Riemann mapping function is seen to be very special when comparison is made with the boundary behavior of an unrestricted homeomorphism of $\Delta(0;1)$. The Fatou theorem leads to the conclusion that a univalent meromorphic function on $\Delta(0;1)$ possesses a radial limit at almost all points on $C(0;1)$. The following example of a homeomorphism of $\Delta(0;1)$ onto itself shows that one cannot expect anything like the radial property for unrestricted homeomorphisms of $\Delta(0;1)$:

$$f(z) = z \exp\left[(1 - |z|)^{-1} i\right]. \tag{2.1}$$

Each ray is mapped by f into a spiral tending asymptotically to $C(0;1)$; for θ fixed, a continuous determination of $\arg f(re^{i\theta})$, $0 < r < 1$, becomes positively infinite as r tends to 1.

3. The Central Theorem. Suppose that f admits a univalent continuous extension $\bar{f}$ to $\overline{\Delta(0;1)}$ or, equivalently, that g admits a univalent continuous extension $\bar{g}$ to $\overline{\Omega(f)}$. Then $\operatorname{fr} \Omega(f)$ is the image of $C(0;1)$ with respect to f and, hence, is a closed Jordan curve. It follows that *$\Omega(f)$ is a simply connected Jordan region.* Osgood conjectured in 1903 that the converse was true: *If $\Omega(f)$ is a Jordan region, then f and g admit univalent continuous extensions to the closures of their respective domains.*

That Osgood's conjecture is true is the substance of the theorem of Osgood-Taylor and Carathéodory, namely,

THEOREM 3.1. *The Osgood conjecture is valid.*

This is the central theorem of the present chapter. The starting point of our considerations is the following lemma.

LEMMA 3.1. *Let f denote a univalent meromorphic function with domain $\Delta(0;1)$. Let γ denote a univalent continuous map of $\{0 \leqslant t < 1\}$ into $\Delta(0;1)$ such that $\lim_{t\to 1} f \circ \gamma$ exists ($= a$) and belongs to the frontier of $f[\Delta(0;1)]$. Then $\lim_{t\to 1} \gamma$ exists (and, of course, is a point of $C(0;1)$).*

It is immediate that $\lim_{t\to 1} |\gamma| = 1$. We suppose, as we may without loss of generality, that $\gamma(t) \neq 0$, $0 \leqslant t < 1$. Let φ denote a continuous determination of the argument of γ. The lemma will follow at once as soon as we show that φ possesses a finite limit as t tends to 1. If this were not the case, there would exist α, β satisfying $\alpha < \beta < \alpha + 2\pi$ and a sequence $((s_k,t_k))_1^\infty$ satisfying:

(1) $0 < s_1$; $s_k < t_k < s_{k+1}$, all k; $\lim_{k\to\infty} s_k = 1$.

(2) If $\varphi^*(t)$ denotes the determination of the argument of $\gamma(t)$ satisfying $\alpha \leqslant \varphi^*(t) < 2\pi + \alpha$, then $\alpha < \varphi^*(t) < \beta$ for $s_k < t < t_k$ and $\{\varphi^*(s_k), \varphi^*(t_k)\} = \{\alpha,\beta\}$, $k = 1,2,\cdots$.

This assertion is readily established by applying obvious continuity considerations. The details are left to the reader.

Let Ω denote $\{z \mid 0 < |z| < 1,\ \alpha < \arg z < \beta\}$. Then let Ω_0 denote $\{z \mid 0 < |z| < \frac{3}{4},\ \alpha < \arg z < \beta\}$. We suppose that $|\gamma(t)| > \frac{3}{4}$ for all t. We let Γ_k denote the closed Jordan curve consisting of the arc $\{\gamma(t) \mid s_k \leqslant t \leqslant t_k\}$ and the segments joining 0 to $\gamma(s_k)$ and $\gamma(t_k)$. Let Ω_k denote the component of the complement of Γ_k with respect to $\hat{K}$ which contains Ω_0. It is easy to show that $\Omega_k \subset \Omega$, $k = 1,2,\cdots$. For, if $\Omega_k \not\subset \Omega$, then Ω_k would contain $\Delta(\infty;1)$. Hence, if Γ_k is sensed, $O(z;\Gamma_k) = 0$, $z \in \Omega_k$. But, since $|O(z;\Gamma_0)| = 1$, $z \in \Omega_0$, where Γ_0 is a sensed closed Jordan curve (with image $=$ fr Ω_0), we conclude that $|O(z;\Gamma_k)| = 1$, $z \in \Omega_0$. (For details and arguments of this type, cf. Appendix, § 3a.) This is impossible. Hence, $\Omega_k \subset \Omega$. We suppose, as we may without loss of generality, that f is bounded on Ω. It suffices to replace f by $[f - f(z_0)]^{-1}$, where $z_0 \in \Delta(0;1) - \bar{\Omega}$ and $f(z_0) \neq \infty$. Let $\sup_{\Omega} |f - a| = M$, and let ω denote the harmonic measure of the arc $\{e^{i\theta} \mid \alpha < \theta < \beta\}$ with respect to Ω. Let $\mu_k = \max |f \circ \gamma(t) - a|$, $s_k \leqslant t \leqslant t_k$. Then

$$\log \left| \frac{M}{f(z) - a} \right| \geqslant \left(\log \frac{M}{\mu_k}\right) \omega(z)\,, \qquad z \in \Omega_k\,, \tag{3.1}$$

as may be seen by comparing both sides of (3.1) on fr Ω_k. But this would imply that (μ_k) does not tend to zero, as may be seen by considering (3.1) at a point $z \in \Omega_0$. Contradiction. Lemma 3.1 follows. It should be observed that we do not use the fact that fr $\Omega_k = \Gamma_k$ (which will be seen to be the case in Appendix, § 3d), but only the weaker (and trivial) fact that fr $\Omega_k \subset \Gamma_k$.

EXERCISES

1. Establish Lemma 3.1 with the aid of Fatou's theorem for positive harmonic functions.

HINT: Let L denote a rational function of degree 1 satisfying: $L(f(0)) = 0$, $L(a) = \infty$. Let $g = L \circ f$, and apply the Fatou theorem to $h(z) = \log |g(z)/z|$.

2. Lemma 3.1 was formulated with its immediate application to the proof of Theorem 3.1 in mind. In what respects can the hypotheses on f and γ be relaxed?

We now turn to the essential part of the proof of the Osgood-Taylor-Carathéodory theorem. If we knew that $\Omega(f)$ was *locally connected* at each point of fr $\Omega(f)$, the proof could be readily concluded (see Ex. 4, below). To say that $\Omega(f)$ is locally connected at a point $\zeta \in$ fr $\Omega(f)$ means that for each $r > 0$ there exists $s > 0$ such that $\Delta(a;s) \cap \Omega(f)$ is contained in a component of

$$\Delta(a;r) \cap \Omega(f).$$

Since a Jordan region is locally connected at each of its frontier points, $\Omega(f)$ has the stated property. However, the usual proofs of this local-connectedness property of a Jordan region involve an extensive study of questions of plane topology. Here, we employ instead methods made available by the possibility of solving the Dirichlet problem for a Jordan region.

Let Γ denote fr $\Omega(f)$, let a denote a given point of Γ at which we wish to study the limiting behavior of g, and let b denote a point of Γ distinct from a. Now let $\tilde{h}$ denote a function continuous on $\overline{\Omega(f)}$ and harmonic in $\Omega(f)$ which is monotone increasing on the two subarcs γ_1 and γ_2 of Γ determined by a and b and which attains its maximum at a. The existence of such a function $\tilde{h}$ is assured by the developments of Chap. 4. We take b as the initial point of γ_1 and γ_2, so that the meaning of monotoneity of $\tilde{h}$ on γ_k is readily construed. We next introduce $h = \tilde{h} \circ f$ and proceed by studying the level loci $\{h(z) = c\}$, where $\inf h < c < \sup h$. The points where $h_x - ih_y$ vanishes make up a countable set, and for our purposes we may put aside the c for which $\{h(z) = c\}$ contains a zero of $h_x - ih_y$. The remaining c will be termed *admitted*. (Actually all c strictly between inf h and sup h are admitted, but this information is not needed here.) On applying the implicit function theorem and separation arguments, we shall conclude that for admitted c, $\{h(z) = c\}$ is necessarily the homeomorph of the real line defined by a function γ on R which is univalent, regular analytic (that is, $\gamma'(t) \neq 0$, and γ is the restriction to R of a function analytic on a region containing R), and, further, satisfies the condition that

$$\lim_{t\to-\infty} |\gamma(t)| = \lim_{t\to+\infty} |\gamma(t)| = 1.$$

To draw the stated conclusions, we fix a point z_0 satisfying $h(z_0) = c$, and we consider the C' complex-valued functions Z that are of modulus less than 1, have as domain an open connected subset of R containing 0, and satisfy

$$\begin{cases} Z(0) = z_0,\ Z'(0) = \dfrac{h_y(z_0) - ih_x(z_0)}{|h_y(z_0) - ih_x(z_0)|}, \\ |Z'(s)| = 1,\ h \circ Z(s) = c\,. \end{cases} \tag{3.2}$$

Thanks to the implicit-function theorem, it is easy to see that the class of such Z is not empty. Further, their union, Z_c, is a member of the class. This may be established by verifying with the aid of a connectedness argument that two such Z agree on the intersection of their domains. The following two alternatives present themselves: (1) Z_c is not univalent; (2) Z_c is univalent.

(1) Z_c *is not univalent.* That is, there exist σ and $\tau > 0$ such that $Z_c(\sigma) = Z_c(\sigma + \tau)$. Suppose that $Z_c'(\sigma) = -Z_c'(\sigma + \tau)$. Then $s \to Z_c(2\sigma + \tau - s)$ is an admitted Z; in fact, it is Z_c itself. But this would imply that $Z_c'(\sigma + \frac{1}{2}\tau) = 0$. Hence, we must have $Z_c'(\sigma) = Z_c'(\sigma + \tau)$, and we conclude that the domain of Z_c is R and that $Z_c(s + \tau) = Z_c(s)$ for all $s \in R$. We are now assured that there is a least positive τ with the stated property; for convenience we shall denote it by τ. The function Z_c is analytic; further, it is univalent on $\{0 \leqslant t < \tau\}$. The image of Z_c is a closed Jordan curve k in $\Delta(0;1)$. We note that if j is a piecewise regular analytic Jordan curve, then for at least one component ω of the complement of j with respect to the finite plane, $O(z;j) \neq 0$, it being understood that j is sensed (see Appendix, § 3a). Applying this result to k, we see that the closure of such an ω would lie in $\Delta(0;1)$ and that, by the maximum principle, h would be constant in ω (we use only fr $\omega \subset k$, not the equality) and hence constant in $\Delta(0;1)$. This is impossible. Hence,

(2) Z_c *is univalent.* From (3.2) and the implicit-function theorem, we see that $|Z_c(s)|$ tends to 1 as s tends either to α or to β, where α is the infimum of the domain of Z and β is its supremum. Further, using the fact that $\tilde{h} \circ f \circ Z_c(s) = c$ and using also the boundary behavior of $\tilde{h}$, we see that $\lim_{s \to \alpha} f \circ Z_c(s)$ and $\lim_{s \to \beta} f \circ Z_c(s)$ exist. Hence, Lemma 3.1 of the present chapter assures us that $\lim_{s \to \alpha} Z_c(s)$ and $\lim_{s \to \beta} Z_c(s)$ exist. If $\lim_{s \to \alpha} Z_c(s) = \lim_{s \to \beta} Z_c(s)$, then a paraphrase of the argument of the preceding paragraph shows that h would be constant. Here, however, we use the Phragmén-Lindelöf maximum principle, since we lack information on the limiting behavior of h at $\lim_{s \to \alpha} Z_c(s)$. Consequently, $\lim_{s \to \alpha} Z_c(s) \neq \lim_{s \to \beta} Z_c(s)$.

We assert that the image set δ of Z_c is precisely the level set $\{h(z) = c\}$ and that it separates $\Delta(0;1)$. That $\Delta(0;1) - \delta$ is not connected and, in fact, has precisely two components may be seen as follows. Let s_1 and s_2 denote the two subarcs of $C(0;1)$ that have the same endpoints as δ, and let Δ_k denote the component of $\Delta(0;1) - \delta$ that satisfies $s_k \subset \text{fr}\,\Delta_k$. It is easy to see that $\Delta_1 \cap \Delta_2 = \emptyset$. It suffices to consider the order of a point of Δ_1 and of a point of Δ_2 with respect to the closed Jordan curve formed from s_1 and δ and endowed with a sense. [The absolute value of the order is 1 for a point of Δ_1 and 0 for a point of Δ_2; see Appendix, § 3a.] If $\Delta(0;1) - \delta$ had another component, say Δ^*, then fr $\Delta^* \subset \bar{\delta}$ and an application of the Phragmén-Lindelöf maximum principle would force the constancy of h. [We are deliberately working with only the most primitive separation theorems and are not presupposing the theorem concerning the separation of a Jordan region by a cross cut.] It follows that $\Delta(0;1) - \delta$ has precisely two components.

We next consider $f \circ Z_c$ and denote the image set by γ. It is to be observed that $\lim_{s \to \alpha} f \circ Z_c(s) \neq \lim_{s \to \beta} f \circ Z_c(s)$. Otherwise a (the) component G of $\hat{K} - \bar{\gamma}$ not containing the points of Γ distinct from this supposed common limit would lie in $\Omega(f)$. For fr G contains some point of γ. Hence, $G \cap \Omega(f) \neq \emptyset$, and since $G \subset \Omega(f) \cup \text{ext}\, \Omega(f)$, it follows that $G \subset \Omega(f)$. The Phragmén-Lindelöf maximum principle would then force the constancy of $\tilde{h}$.

Let σ_a denote that subarc of Γ with the same endpoints as $\bar{\gamma}$ which contains a, and let σ_b denote that subarc of Γ with the same endpoints as $\bar{\gamma}$ which contains b. Let $d \in \gamma$, and let Ω_a denote a (the) component of $\hat{K} - (\gamma \cup \sigma_a)$ satisfying $d \in \text{fr}\, \Omega_a$, $b \notin \Omega_a$. We note that the proof of Theorem 1, Appendix, § 3(a) assures us that there are precisely two components of $\hat{K} - (\gamma \cup \sigma_a)$ for which d is a frontier point. Now $\Omega_a \subset \Omega(f)$. For otherwise Ω_a would have to contain a point of $\Gamma - \sigma_a$ and, hence, b. Let Ω_b be similarly taken, the roles of a and b above being interchanged. As for the case of Ω_a, we see that $\Omega_b \subset \Omega(f)$. Further, by the minimum principle for harmonic functions, $\tilde{h}(z) \geqslant c$, $z \in \Omega_a$. Hence, since h is not constant, $\tilde{h}(z) > c$, $z \in \Omega_a$. In a similar manner we conclude that $\tilde{h}(z) < c$, $z \in \Omega_b$. It follows that Ω_a and Ω_b are disjoint. It is easily verified that Ω_a and Ω_b are components of $\Omega(f) - \gamma$. Since there are precisely two components of $\Omega(f) - \gamma$, namely, $f(\Delta_1)$ and $f(\Delta_2)$, we conclude that $\delta = \{h(z) = c\}$ and that $\{h(z) > c\}$, which is $g(\Omega_a)$, is connected. It is now immediate that $\{h(z) > c\}$ is connected for arbitrary c satisfying $\inf h < c < \sup h$.

We introduce $A = \bigcap \overline{\{h(z) > c\}}$, $\inf h < c < \sup h$. Clearly, A is a nonempty connected subset of $C(0;1)$. We assert that it reduces to a point. Otherwise there would exist distinct points ζ_1, ζ_2 on $C(0;1)$ and a sequence $(\delta_k)_1^\infty$ of Jordan (that is, univalent) paths in $\Delta(0;1)$ satisfying: $\lim_{k\to\infty} \delta_k(0) = \zeta_1$, $\lim_{k\to\infty} \delta_k(1) = \zeta_2$, $\min h \circ \delta_k > \sup h - (k+1)^{-1}$. A repetition of the argument of Lemma 3.1 of this section shows that f would have to be constant, since $\max_{0\leqslant t\leqslant 1} [f \circ \delta_k(t), a] \to 0$. [We are using the chordal metric.] Since this is impossible, we see that A reduces to a point, say ζ. From this fact and $h = \tilde{h} \circ f$, we see that $\lim_a g = \zeta$, since $\{h(z) > c\}$ lies in a given neighborhood of ζ for c sufficiently near but less than $\sup h$. It follows that g admits a continuous extension $\bar{g}$ to $\overline{\Omega(f)}$.

The proof of the theorem will follow once we show that $\bar{g}$ *is univalent*, for then f admits a continuous univalent extension to $\overline{\Delta(0;1)}$. To this end, we note that since $\{h(z) > c\}$ is connected, there exists a continuous map P of $\{0 \leqslant t < 1\}$ into $\Delta(0;1)$ such that $\lim_{t\to 1} h \circ P(t) = \sup h$ (cf. the proof of Iversen's theorem). We have $\lim_{t\to 1} P(t) = \zeta$ and $\lim_{t\to 1} f \circ P(t) = a$. It follows from Theorem 7.1 of Chap. 5 that $\lim_{r\to 1} f(r\zeta) = a$. [In order to apply Theorem 7.1 of Chap. 5 to a univalent meromorphic function φ on $\Delta(0;1)$, consider $S \circ \varphi - P$, where S is a rational function of degree 1 satisfying $S(\varphi(0)) = \infty$ and P is the principal part of $S \circ \varphi$ at $z = 0$.] We now see that if $\bar{g}(a) = \bar{g}(b)$ for points a and b of $\text{fr}\, \Omega(f)$, then $a = b$. The theorem follows.

EXERCISES

3. Show with the aid of the Osgood-Taylor-Carathéodory theorem that a simply connected Jordan region is locally connected at each of its frontier points.

4. Given f a univalent meromorphic function on $\Delta(0;1)$. Suppose that Ω, the image of f, is locally connected at $a \in \text{fr}\, \Omega$. Let g denote the inverse of f. Show that $\lim_{a} g$ exists. Show that if Ω is locally connected at each point of fr Ω, then Ω is a Jordan region. The latter result is due to A. Schoenflies.

5. Suppose that Ω is a simply connected region in K. Suppose that there exists a univalent analytic function φ with domain $\{0 < \text{Re}\, z < 1;\ |\text{Im}\, z| < h\}$ such that

$$\gamma = \varphi\{0 < \text{Re}\, z < 1;\ \text{Im}\, z = 0\} \subset \text{fr}\, \Omega$$

and

$$\Omega_1 = \varphi\{0 < \text{Re}\, z < 1;\ 0 < \text{Im}\, z < h\} \subset \Omega$$

(under these circumstances γ is called a *free analytic boundary arc of* Ω). Let g denote a univalent analytic function mapping Ω onto $\Delta(0;1)$. Show that the restriction of g to Ω_1 is the restriction to Ω_1 of a univalent meromorphic function on $\varphi\{0 < \text{Re}\, z < 1;\ |\text{Im}\, z| < h\}$. What can be said about the boundary behavior of the inverse of g?

HINT: Consider $g(\varphi(z))$, $z \in \varphi^{-1}(\Omega_1)$, and apply the Schwarz reflexion principle (Ex. 5, § 3, Chap. 4) to $\log |g(\varphi(z))|$.

---

4. The Stronger Form of the Cauchy Integral Theorem. The following theorem, usually called the stronger form of the Cauchy integral theorem, may now be readily established thanks to the Osgood-Taylor-Carathéodory theorem and a very ingenious use of subharmonic functions which is due to Beckenbach (see E. F. Beckenbach, "The Stronger Form of Cauchy's Integral Theorem, *Bull. AMS*, **49**: 615–618, 1943).

THEOREM 4.1. *Let Ω denote a bounded simply connected Jordan region. Let Γ denote a closed path of the form $t \to \psi(e^{2\pi it})$, where ψ is a homeomorphism of* $C(0;1)$ *onto fr Ω. It is assumed that Γ is rectifiable. Let f be continuous on $\overline{\Omega}$ and analytic in Ω. Then*

$$\int_{\Gamma} f(z)\, dz = 0\,. \tag{4.1}$$

COROLLARY 4.1. *Let $a \in \Omega$. Under the hypotheses of Theorem* 4.1, *we have:*

$$2\pi i O(a;\Gamma) f(a) = \int_{\Gamma} \frac{f(z)}{z-a}\, dz\,.$$

PROOF: We introduce φ, the continuous extension to $\overline{\Delta(0;1)}$ of a univalent analytic function mapping $\Delta(0;1)$ onto Ω. Thus φ is a one-to-one continuous map of $\overline{\Delta(0;1)}$ onto $\overline{\Omega}$. We let γ_r denote the closed path defined by

$$\gamma_r(t) = \varphi(re^{2\pi it}), \qquad t \in R\,. \tag{4.2}$$

We may assume without loss of generality that $\Gamma = \gamma_1$. In fact, $\varphi^{-1} \circ \Gamma = \exp \circ (2\pi i \alpha)$, where α is a strictly monotone continuous map of R onto itself satisfying the condition that $| \alpha(t+1) - \alpha(t) | \equiv 1$. Thus $\Gamma = \gamma_1 \circ \alpha$. We make the harmless normalization $\Gamma = \gamma_1$.

Let n denote a positive integer, let $\varepsilon_n = e^{2\pi i/n}$, and let

$$u_n(z) = \sum_{k=0}^{n-1} | \varphi(\varepsilon_n^{k+1} z) - \varphi(\varepsilon_n^k z) | . \tag{4.3}$$

The auxiliary function u_n is the essential tool of Beckenbach's argument. We note that u_n is continuous on $\overline{\Delta(0;1)}$ and subharmonic in $\Delta(0;1)$. We let l_r denote the length of γ_r. By the maximum principle,

$$u_n(z) \leqslant \max_{|\zeta|=1} u_n(\zeta) \leqslant l_1 , \qquad | z | \leqslant 1 . \tag{4.4}$$

Hence, since $\lim_{n\to\infty} u_n(z) = l_{|z|}$, $0 < | z | \leqslant 1$, we conclude that $l_r \leqslant l_1$. [Actually, it is easy to see that l_r is increasing and continuous, although it is not necessary to know this for the proof of Theorem 4.1. It suffices to note that

$$l_r = r \int_0^{2\pi} | \varphi'(re^{i\theta}) | \, d\theta , \qquad 0 < r < 1 ,$$

and to use the subharmonicity of $| \varphi' |$ in $\Delta(0;1)$ and the inequality

$$\lim_{r\to 1} l_r \geqslant \lim_{r\to 1} u_n(r\zeta), \ | \zeta | = 1.]$$

We next note that for $0 < r < 1$,

$$\int_{\gamma_r} f(z) \, dz = \oint_{C(0;r)} [f \circ \varphi(z)]\varphi'(z) \, dz = 0 ,$$

by the analyticity of $(f \circ \varphi)\varphi'$ in $\Delta(0;1)$ and the Cauchy theorem for functions analytic in $\Delta(0;1)$. Hence

$$\left| \int_{\gamma_1} f(z) \, dz \right| = \left| \int_{\gamma_r} f(z) \, dz - \int_{\gamma_1} f(z) \, dz \right|$$

$$\leqslant \left| \int_{\gamma_r} f(z) \, dz - \sigma_{r,n} \right| + | \sigma_{r,n} - \sigma_{1,n} | + \left| \sigma_{1,n} - \int_{\gamma_1} f(z) \, dz \right|, \tag{4.5}$$

where $\sigma_{r,n} = \sum_{k=0}^{n-1} f(\varphi(r\varepsilon_n^k)) \, [\varphi(r\varepsilon_n^{k+1}) - \varphi(r\varepsilon_n^k)]$.

Introducing ω, the modulus of continuity of $(r,t) \to f(\varphi(re^{2\pi i t}))$, $0 \leqslant r, t \leqslant 1$, we obtain, using the standard estimates for Riemann-Stieltjes integrals,

$$\left| \int_{\gamma_1} f(z) \, dz \right| \leqslant l_r \omega\left(\frac{1}{n}\right) + | \sigma_{r,n} - \sigma_{1,n} | + l_1 \omega\left(\frac{1}{n}\right), \qquad 0 < r < 1 . \tag{4.6}$$

Hence, letting $r \to 1$, we obtain

$$\left| \int_{\gamma_1} f(z)\, dz \right| \leqslant 2l_1 \omega\left(\frac{1}{n}\right), \tag{4.7}$$

and letting $n \to \infty$,

$$\int_{\gamma_1} f(z)\, dz = 0 .$$

Theorem 4.1 is established. The corollary is an immediate consequence of thc theorem applied to g defined by

$$\begin{cases} g(z) = \dfrac{f(z) - f(a)}{z - a}, & z(\neq a) \in \overline{\Omega}, \\ g(a) = f'(a) . \end{cases}$$

Theorem 4.1 and its corollary may be extended to the case where Ω is an unrestricted bounded Jordan region with "rectifiable boundary." However, we shall not treat this question (see M. H. A. Newman, *Topology of Plane Sets of Points*, 2nd ed. Cambridge University Press, 1951).

Appendix

1. Riesz Representation Theorem for C

In this article of the appendix we shall give a proof of the Riesz representation theorem for positive additive functionals on **C**:

Given $\lambda \in \Lambda$, *there exists a nondecreasing function* μ *on* R *satisfying* $\mu(x + 2\pi) = \mu(x) + \lambda(1)$ *such that*

$$\lambda(f) = \int_a^{a+2\pi} f\, d\mu\,, \qquad f \in \mathbf{C}\,.$$

The proof given here is applicable to other classes of continuous functions.

PROOF: Given $f \in \mathbf{C}$, it will be convenient to introduce the *norm* of f, $\|f\| = \max_{x \in R} |f(x)|$. For each positive integer n, we introduce first

$$\varphi_n(x) = \max\left\{1 - \frac{n}{2\pi}|x|, 0\right\} \tag{1}$$

and then

$$\psi_n(x) = \sum_{k=-\infty}^{+\infty} \varphi_n(x - 2\pi k)\,. \tag{2}$$

Now $\psi_n \in \mathbf{C}$. Further,

$$\sum_{k=0}^{n-1} \psi_n\left(x - \frac{2\pi k}{n}\right) \equiv 1\,. \tag{3}$$

Given $f \in \mathbf{C}$, we introduce

$$f_n(x) = \sum_{k=0}^{n-1} f\left(\frac{2\pi k}{n}\right) \psi_n\left(x - \frac{2\pi k}{n}\right) \tag{4}$$

and note that

$$|f(x) - f_n(x)| \leqslant \omega_f\left(\frac{2\pi}{n}\right),$$

where ω_f is the modulus of continuity of f. [Consider $f(x) - f_n(x)$ on an interval $\{2\pi k/n \leqslant x \leqslant 2\pi(k+1)/n\}$, and observe that f_n is linear on this interval and takes the same values as f at the endpoints.] Hence

$$\|f - f_n\| \to 0\,. \tag{5}$$

Further,

$$\lambda(f_n) = \sum_{k=0}^{n-1} f\left(\frac{2\pi k}{n}\right) \lambda\left[x \to \psi_n\left(x - \frac{2\pi k}{n}\right)\right]. \tag{6}$$

We define

$$\mu_n(t) = \sum_{0 \leqslant k < nt/2\pi} \lambda\left[x \to \psi_n\left(x - \frac{2\pi k}{n}\right)\right], \qquad 0 \leqslant t \leqslant 2\pi, \tag{7}$$

so that

$$\mu_n(0) = 0,$$

$$\mu_n(t) = \lambda(1), \frac{2\pi(n-1)}{n} < t \leqslant 2\pi.$$

We define μ_n elsewhere by the requirement that, for all x, μ_n is to satisfy

$$\mu_n(x + 2\pi) = \mu_n(x) + \lambda(1).$$

We now see that

$$\lambda(f_n) = \int_a^{a+2\pi} f\, d\mu_n. \tag{8}$$

By the selection principle we are assured of the existence of a subsequence $(\mu_{m(n)})_1^\infty$ of $(\mu_n)_1^\infty$ such that for each rational number q, the sequence $(\mu_{m(n)}(2\pi q))_1^\infty$ possesses a finite limit. We define μ by

$$\mu(x) = \sup\left\{\lim_{n\to\infty} \mu_{m(n)}(2\pi q) \mid 2\pi q \leqslant x,\ q \text{ rational}\right\}. \tag{9}$$

The function μ is a monotone nondecreasing function satisfying

$$\mu(2\pi q) = \lim_{n\to\infty} \mu_{m(n)}(2\pi q), \qquad q \text{ rational},$$

and

$$\mu(x + 2\pi) = \mu(x) + \lambda(1).$$

We assert that μ has the desired property:

$$\lambda(f) = \int_a^{a+2\pi} f\, d\mu, \qquad f \in \mathbf{C}.$$

To see that this is so, we introduce a finite increasing sequence $(t_k)_0^s$, where $t_0 = 0$, $t_s = 2\pi$ and each t_k is a rational multiple of 2π. Let $\delta = \max(t_{k+1} - t_k)$, $k = 0, \cdots, s-1$. From (8) and the standard appraisals relating Riemann-Stieltjes integrals and their approximating sums, we have

$$\lambda(f_{m(n)}) \leqslant \sum_{k=0}^{s-1} f(t_k)\left[\mu_{m(n)}(t_{k+1}) - \mu_{m(n)}(t_k)\right] + \omega_f(\delta)\lambda(1) \tag{10}$$

and

$$\lambda(f_{m(n)}) \geqslant \sum_{k=0}^{s-1} f(t_k)\,[\mu_{m(n)}(t_{k+1}) - \mu_{m(n)}(t_k)] - \omega_f(\delta)\,\lambda(1)\,, \qquad (11)$$

ω_f being the modulus of continuity of f. Hence,

$$\lambda(f) \leqslant \sum_{k=0}^{s-1} f(t_k)\,[\mu(t_{k+1}) - \mu(t_k)] + \omega_f(\delta)\,\lambda(1)\,,$$

and, consequently,

$$\lambda(f) \leqslant \int_0^{2\pi} f\,d\mu\,.$$

Similarly,

$$\lambda(f) \geqslant \int_0^{2\pi} f\,d\mu\,.$$

We conclude that

$$\lambda(f) = \int_0^{2\pi} f\,d\mu\,, \qquad f \in \mathbf{C}\,.$$

The theorem is established.

2. Lebesgue's Theorem

An account of F. Riesz's proof for the continuous case of Lebesgue's theorem is to be found in F. Riesz and B. Sz.-Nagy, *Leçons d'Analyse Fonctionnelle*, Budapest, 1952.

As far as I am aware, Riesz never gave a detailed account of the proof for the general case. He states on several occasions (*ibid.*, p. 9) that it calls only for a few simple modifications of the proof for the continuous case. Since we want to use the Lebesgue theorem unrestrictedly and wish to keep the exposition self-contained, we shall in fact consider the general theorem (cf. J. von Neumann, *Functional Operators*, vol. 1, Princeton, 1950).

The core of Riesz's argument is his celebrated "rising-sun lemma." We consider a function g with domain a bounded closed interval $\{a \leqslant x \leqslant b\}$, $a < b$, which takes values in R and which possesses one-sided finite limits at each point of $\{a \leqslant x \leqslant b\}$. That is, for each c, $a \leqslant c < b$, there exists $r(c) \in R$ such that, for each $\eta > 0$,

$$|\,g(x) - r(c)\,| < \eta$$

for x sufficiently near but greater than c; and, correspondingly, for each c, $a < c \leqslant b$, there exists $l(c) \in R$ such that for each $\eta > 0$,

$$|\,g(x) - l(c)\,| < \eta$$

for x sufficiently near but less than c. The numbers $r(c)$ and $l(c)$ are uniquely specified. They are termed, respectively, the *right-handed limit* and the *left-handed limit* of g at c. We write $g(c^+)$ for $r(c)$ and $g(c^-)$ for $l(c)$. We now associate with g the function G defined by

$$\begin{cases} G(x) = \max\{g(x), g(x^-), g(x^+)\}, & a < x < b\,, \\ G(a) = \max\{g(a), g(a^+)\}\,, \\ G(b) = \max\{g(b), g(b^-)\}\,. \end{cases} \tag{1}$$

It is easy to see that G is upper semicontinuous on $\{a \leqslant x \leqslant b\}$. Riesz's lemma may be stated as follows:

LEMMA. *Let E denote the set of x in $\{a < x < b\}$ for which there exists ξ satisfying $x < \xi \leqslant b$ and*

$$G(x) < g(\xi)\,.$$

Then E is open, and if $E \neq \emptyset$ and if $\{\alpha < x < \beta\}$ is a component of E, then

$$g(\alpha^+) \leqslant G(\beta)\,.$$

PROOF: That E is open follows from the upper semicontinuity of G. Suppose that $\{\alpha < x < \beta\}$ is a component of E and that, contrary to the assertion, $g(\alpha^+) > G(\beta)$. There exists α_1 satisfying $\alpha < \alpha_1 < \beta$ and $G(\alpha_1) > G(\beta)$. Clearly,

$$\mu = \max_{\alpha_1 \leqslant x \leqslant \beta} G(x) > G(\beta)\,,$$

and

$$\gamma = \max\{x \mid \alpha_1 \leqslant x \leqslant \beta, \quad G(x) = \mu\}$$

satisfies $\alpha < \gamma < \beta$. Hence, $\beta < b$, since $G(\gamma) > G(x) \geqslant g(x)$ for $\gamma < x \leqslant \beta$. Since $G(\beta) < G(\gamma)$, $\beta \in E$. This state of affairs is not possible, since $\{\alpha < x < \beta\}$ is a component of E. We conclude that $g(\alpha^+) \leqslant G(\beta)$, and the lemma of F. Riesz follows.

(a) Dini derivates. Given a finite real-valued function f whose domain is a neighborhood of $c \in R$. By the *Dini derivates* of f at c are meant the following:

$$\begin{cases} \bar{D}_r(c;f) = \limsup_{h \downarrow 0} \dfrac{f(c+h) - f(c)}{h}; \quad \underline{D}_r(c;f) = \liminf_{h \downarrow 0} \dfrac{f(c+h) - f(c)}{h}; \\ \bar{D}_l(c;f) = \limsup_{h \uparrow 0} \dfrac{f(c+h) - f(c)}{h}; \quad \underline{D}_l(c;f) = \liminf_{h \uparrow 0} \dfrac{f(c+h) - f(c)}{h}\,. \end{cases} \tag{2}$$

The four elements listed here are termed, respectively, the *upper-right*, the *lower-right*, the *upper-left*, and the *lower-left derivates* of f at c. The notation is intended to bring out the case; we use the bar over or below the "D," and we use the subscript "r" for "right" and "l" for "left." It is to be observed that, as indicated by the notation, the limits superior and inferior pertain to a one-sided approach, positive h being considered in the first two ratios and negative h in the latter two.

It is easy to see that $f'(c)$ exists and is finite if, and only if, the four Dini derivates of f at c have a common finite value.

Suppose f is a monotone-nondecreasing (and finite-valued) function on $\{a \leqslant x \leqslant b\}$. To establish Lebesgue's theorem, it suffices to show that for *each* such f we have:

PROPOSITION I. $\bar{D}_r(x;f) < +\infty$ *for almost all* x *in* $\{a < x < b\}$,

and

PROPOSITION II. $\bar{D}_r(x;f) \leqslant \underline{D}_l(x;f)$ *for almost all* x *in* $\{a < x < b\}$.

For, applying I and II to

$$x \to -f(a+b-x)\,,$$

we infer:

PROPOSITION III. $\bar{D}_l(x;f) < +\infty$ *and* $\bar{D}_l(x;f) \leqslant \underline{D}_r(x;f)$ *for almost all* x *of* $\{a < x < b\}$.

But now we see that

$$0 \leqslant \bar{D}_r(x;f) \leqslant \underline{D}_l(x;f) \leqslant \bar{D}_l(x;f) \leqslant \underline{D}_r(x;f) \leqslant \bar{D}_r(x;f) < +\infty \tag{3}$$

for almost all x of $\{a < x < b\}$. It suffices to note that the set of x, $a < x < b$, for which (3) holds is the intersection of the subsets of $\{a < x < b\}$ on which, $\bar{D}_r(x;f) \leqslant \underline{D}_l(x;f)$, $\bar{D}_l(x;f) \leqslant \underline{D}_r(x;f)$, and $\bar{D}_r(x;f) < +\infty$, and to use II, III, and I.

PROOF OF PROPOSITION I: Let p be a positive number. We define $g(x) = f(x) - px$, $a \leqslant x \leqslant b$, so that g satisfies the hypotheses of the lemma. Let E_1 denote the set of x satisfying $a < x < b$ for which there exists ξ, $x < \xi \leqslant b$, $g(x) < g(\xi)$. We have

$$E \subset E_1 \subset E \cup \{G(x) > g(x);\, a < x < b\}\,, \tag{4}$$

the notation being that of the lemma. Now the set of x at which $G(x) > g(x)$ is countable, since f, being monotone, has only a countable set of discontinuities. For each component interval $\{\alpha < x < \beta\}$ of E, we have

$$g(\alpha^+) \leqslant G(\beta)\,,$$

and, hence, we have

$$f(\beta^+) - f(\alpha^+) \geqslant p(\beta - \alpha)\,,$$

$[f(b^+)$ by convention being simply $f(b)]$. Hence, given $\eta > 0$, there exists a countable family of open intervals whose union contains E_1 and which is such that the sum of the lengths of the intervals is less than

$$\eta + p^{-1} \sum [f(\beta^+) - f(\alpha^+)]$$
$$\leqslant \eta + p^{-1} [f(b) - f(a)]\,.$$

Now $\{\bar{D}_r(x;f) = +\infty;\, a < x < b\} \subset E_1$. Since η and p are arbitrary, I follows.

Proof of Proposition II: We wish to show that

$$\{a < x < b;\, \bar{D}_r(x;f) > \underline{D}_l(x;f)\} \tag{5}$$

is a set of measure zero. Let q, s denote rational numbers satisfying $0 < q < s$, and let $E(q,s)$ denote the intersection of

$$\{a < x < b;\, \underline{D}_l(x;f) < q\} \tag{6}$$

and

$$\{a < x < b;\, \bar{D}_r(x;f) > s\}\,. \tag{7}$$

Then the set (5) is the union of the $E(q,s)$ and, hence, is of measure zero provided that each $E(q,s)$ is of measure zero.

Let $g_q(x) = f(x) - qx$; let G_q correspond to g_q, as G corresponds to g in the Riesz lemma; and let $E(q)$ denote the set of x, $a < x < b$, for which there exists ξ, $a \leqslant \xi < x, g_q(\xi) > G_q(x)$. By the Riesz lemma (with sense reversed), $E(q)$ is open, and if it is not empty and if $\{\alpha < x < \beta\}$ is a component, then

$$g_q(\beta^-) \leqslant G_q(\alpha) = g_q(\alpha^+)\,.$$

Consequently,

$$f(\beta^-) - f(\alpha^+) \leqslant q(\beta - \alpha)\,. \tag{8}$$

The set (6) is contained in

$$E(q) \cup \{a < x < b;\, G_q(x) > g_q(x)\}\,.$$

The second component set of the preceding line is countable.

Returning to the component $\{\alpha < x < \beta\}$ of $E(q)$, we let $\alpha < \alpha_1 < \beta_1 < \beta$ and apply the proof of I to conclude that

$$\{\alpha_1 < x < \beta_1;\, \bar{D}_r(x;f) > s\}$$

is contained in the union of a countable set and an open set O, the sum of the lengths of the components of which, $m(O)$, satisfies

$$m(O) \leqslant \frac{1}{s}\,[f(\beta_1) - f(\alpha_1)]\,.$$

The notation $m(O)$ is to have the same meaning for arbitrary open $O \subset R$. Hence, it is easy to see that

$$\{\alpha < x < \beta;\, \bar{D}_r(x;f) > s\}$$

is contained in the union of a countable set and an open set $O_{\alpha,\beta}$ satisfying

$$m(O_{\alpha,\beta}) \leqslant \frac{1}{s}\,[f(\beta^-) - f(\alpha^+)] \leqslant \frac{q}{s}\,(\beta - \alpha)\,.$$

Hence, $E(q,s)$ is contained in the union of a countable set and an open set $O^{(1)}$ satisfying

$$m(O^{(1)}) \leqslant \frac{q}{s}\,(b - a)\,. \tag{9}$$

We now proceed inductively. Given n a positive integer. Suppose that $E(q,s)$ is contained in the union of a countable set and an open set $O^{(n)}$ satisfying

$$m(O^{(n)}) \leqslant \left(\frac{q}{s}\right)^n (b - a)\,. \tag{10}$$

We show that $E(q,s)$ enjoys the corresponding property with n replaced by $n + 1$. To see this, it suffices to consider the restriction of f to the closure of a component of $O^{(n)}$ if $O^{(n)} \neq \emptyset$ (otherwise the problem is trivial) and to apply the argument culminating in (9). We are led to the conclusion that $E(q,s)$ is contained in the union of a countable set and an open set $O^{(n+1)}$ satisfying

$$m(O^{(n+1)}) \leqslant \frac{q}{s}\,m(O^{(n)}) \leqslant \left(\frac{q}{s}\right)^{n+1} (b - a)\,.$$

Hence, we see that for each positive integer n, $E(q,s)$ is contained in the union of a family of open intervals the sum of whose lengths does not exceed

$$2\left(\frac{q}{s}\right)^n (b - a)\,.$$

Hence, $E(q,s)$ is of zero measure, and II is established.

3. The Jordan Theorem. Simple Connectivity

The only result used in Chap. 6 that awaits accounting is the following weak form of the Jordan curve theorem: *If γ is a closed Jordan curve subject to certain regularity conditions, then the complement of γ is not connected.* This result is easily established with the aid of the notion of the order of a point with respect to a closed curve. Once this theorem is cared for, the debts incurred in the body proper of the present book to results quoted but not proved are settled. However, with the aid of the notion of order, we have at our disposal a thoroughly accessible proof of the Jordan curve theorem which is due to F. Riesz. We shall give an account of that part of the Riesz proof which pertains to the separation property.

It is also desirable to consider certain questions of elementary plane topology—problems concerning Jordan curves and the notion of simple connectivity—which are readily treated at this point, thanks to methods and results already established. The study of these questions culminates in theorems that belong to the thesaurus of the worker in the theory of functions of a complex variable. The treatment given below is subject to the objection (quite justifiable from the point of view of purity of method) that it leans heavily on function-theoretic props. The references of Chap. 6 afford accesses that are more topological in character. However, the approach followed here, appearing as it does at the end of the book, needs no apology when the results obtained are thought of as "a big corollary" (which, indeed, they are, in the true etymological sense).

(a) The Jordan Theorem with Restrictive Hypothesis. The first theorem we treat is

THEOREM 1. *Let Γ denote a closed Jordan curve in K and suppose that γ is a subarc of Γ which admits a representation of the form $\{x + if(x) \mid |x - a| \leqslant h\}$, where f is a real-valued function with domain $\{|x - a| \leqslant h\} \subset R$. Then $K - \Gamma$ is not connected.*

It is to be observed that the theorem obviously persists for arcs $\gamma: g(y) + iy$, $|y - b| \leqslant h$. Also, the function f is clearly continuous on $\{|x - a| \leqslant h\}$. The point $a + if(a)$ is at a positive distance d from the set $\overline{\Gamma - \gamma}$. Let h_1 be so chosen that $0 < h_1 < \min\{h, \frac{1}{2}d\}$ and $|f(x) - f(a)| < \frac{1}{2}d$ for $|x - a| < h_1$. Then $\gamma_1 = \{x + if(x) \mid |x - a| \leqslant h_1\} \subset \gamma$, and, further, the rectangle

$$\{|\operatorname{Re} z - a| \leqslant h_1; |\operatorname{Im} z - f(a)| \leqslant \tfrac{1}{2}d\} \tag{a.1}$$

has no points in common with $\overline{\Gamma - \gamma}$. We assume, as we may, that Γ is so sensed that as γ is traversed, the real part of a point on γ is increasing. [By a *sensed representation* of a closed Jordan curve we understand a map $\sigma: t \to \varphi(e^{2\pi it})$, $t \in R$, where φ is a homeomorphism of $C(0;1)$ onto Γ. Any two sensed representations σ_1 and σ_2 of Γ are connected by a relation of the form $\sigma_2 = \sigma_1 \circ \alpha$, where

α is a strictly continuous map of R onto itself satisfying $|\alpha(t+1) - \alpha(t)| \equiv 1$. Further, if α_1 and α_2 both fulfill the conditions stated that are for α, then $\alpha_2(t) \equiv \alpha_1(t) + m$, $m \in I$. An equivalence relation may be introduced in the class of sensed representations of Γ as follows. We say that σ_2 is *equivalent* to σ_1 provided that $\alpha(1) - \alpha(0) = 1$. A bona fide equivalence relation is defined thereby. There are precisely two equivalence classes. To *sense* a Jordan curve is to assign to it an equivalence class of sensed representations. In the text that follows the language would become burdensome if a mild license of expression were not granted. However, the meaning should be clear from context. In the order relations (a.3), (a.4), (a.5), which follow, Γ and Γ_k are used for sensed representations. A similar remark holds wherever we have spoken of the order of a point with respect to a sensed Jordan curve.] We let Γ_1 denote the sensed closed Jordan curve obtained from Γ by replacing γ_1 with the path:

$$\begin{cases} (a - h_1) + i\{(1-3t)f(a-h_1) + 3t[f(a) - \tfrac{1}{2}d]\}, & 0 \leqslant t \leqslant \tfrac{1}{3}; \\ (2-3t)(a-h_1) + (3t-1)(a+h_1) + i[f(a) - \tfrac{1}{2}d], & \tfrac{1}{3} < t \leqslant \tfrac{2}{3}; \\ (a+h_1) + i\{(3-3t)[f(a) - \tfrac{1}{2}d] + (3t-2)f(a+h_1)\}, & \tfrac{2}{3} < t \leqslant 1. \end{cases} \tag{a.2}$$

In the same manner, we let Γ_2 denote the modification of Γ obtained by replacing γ_1 with the other arc of the frontier of (a.1) with initial point

$$(a - h_1) + if(a - h_1)$$

and terminal point

$$(a + h_1) + if(a + h_1).$$

Let κ denote the sensed periphery of (a.1) taken in the counterclockwise sense. Finally, let b and c be points of $\{\text{Re } z = a\}$ satisfying

$$f(a) - \tfrac{1}{2}d < \text{Im } b < f(a) < \text{Im } c < f(a) + \tfrac{1}{2}d.$$

We observe that

$$O(b;\Gamma) = O(b;\Gamma_2) = O(a + if(a);\, \Gamma_2) \tag{a.3}$$

and

$$O(c;\Gamma) = O(c;\Gamma_1) = O(a + if(a);\, \Gamma_1). \tag{a.4}$$

Hence,

$$\begin{aligned} O(c;\Gamma) - O(b;\Gamma) &= O(a + if(a);\, \Gamma_1) - O(a + if(a);\, \Gamma_2) \\ &= O(a + if(a);\, \kappa) = 1. \end{aligned} \tag{a.5}$$

Hence, b and c belong to distinct components of $K - \Gamma$, and Theorem 1 follows.

(b) Riesz's Proof of the Jordan Separation Theorem (F. Riesz, *Acta Szeged*, 1939). Here the theorem is

THEOREM 2. *If Γ is a closed Jordan curve in K, then $K - \Gamma$ is not connected.*

PROOF: We suppose, as we may, that $\Gamma \subset \{\text{Re}\, z > 0\}$. Let λ, μ, ν denote three distinct lines, each parallel to the real axis, which meet Γ. (We use parallels to the real axis, whereas Riesz uses rays issuing from a point.) Let A, B, C denote their respective points of intersection with the imaginary axis. We suppose that the lines λ, μ, ν have been so labeled that $\text{Im}\, A < \text{Im}\, B < \text{Im}\, C$. Let A_1, B_1, C_1 denote the first points of encounter of λ, μ, and ν respectively with Γ. (When we say that A_1 is the *first point of encounter* of the line λ with Γ, we mean that $A_1 \in \lambda \cap \Gamma$ and $t + A \notin \Gamma$ for $t < \text{Re}\, A_1$; the *last point of encounter* is similarly defined.) Let γ_1 denote that Jordan subarc of Γ with initial point A_1 and terminal point C_1 which contains B_1. Let γ_2 denote the "other" sensed Jordan subarc of Γ with initial point A_1 and terminal point C_1. Let δ denote the sensed piecewise rectilinear Jordan arc C_1CAA_1. Let B_2 denote the last point of encounter of μ and γ_1. Let σ satisfy $B_2 = B + \sigma$, and let $B' = B + \tau$, where $\sigma < \tau$ and $B + t \notin \gamma_2$ for $\sigma \leqslant t \leqslant \tau$. We show that

$$|\, O(B';\Gamma)\, | = 1\,, \tag{b.1}$$

where Γ is taken to have a sensing. Since $O(z;\Gamma) = 0$ for $\text{Re}\, z < 0$, it will follow that $K - \Gamma$ is not connected.

To establish (b.1), we introduce the sensed Jordan curve Γ_1 corresponding to γ_1 followed by δ and the sensed Jordan curve Γ_2 corresponding to γ_2 followed by δ. We sense Γ by taking it as corresponding to γ_2 followed by γ_1 with sense reversed.

Since $B + t \notin \Gamma_1$ for $t \geqslant \tau$, we see that

$$O(B';\Gamma_1) = O(B + t;\Gamma_1) = 0\,, \qquad t \geqslant \tau\,, \tag{b.2}$$

$O(z;\Gamma_1)$ being equal to 0 for z large.

On the other hand, let us consider the path θ obtained by tracing in succession: the sensed line segment with initial point $B - 1$ and terminal point B_1; the sensed subarc of γ_1 with initial point B_1 and terminal point B_2 (possibly degenerating to a point); the sensed line segment with initial point B_2 and terminal point B'. It is easily verified that the only point common to θ and Γ_2 is B and, further, that

$$O(B - 1;\Gamma_2) = 0\,.$$

By use of the argument of Theorem 1 of this article, we see that

$$O(z;\Gamma_2) = 1$$

for $z \neq B$ on the subarc BB' of θ.

Hence,

$$O(B';\Gamma) = O(B';\Gamma_2) - O(B';\Gamma_1) = 1\,. \tag{b.3}$$

The proof is complete.

It is easy to see that a closed Jordan curve in $\hat{K}$ has an empty interior. It suffices to consider the inverse of a univalent continuous map of $C(0;1)$ into $\hat{K}$ and to note that its domain cannot contain a disk (for otherwise the univalence of the inverse map would be violated). Hence, $\hat{K} - \Gamma \neq \emptyset$, and, considering $S(\Gamma)$ where S is a rational function of degree 1 satisfying $S^{-1}(\infty) \notin \Gamma$, we are led to the conclusion that the Jordan separation theorem holds for closed Jordan curves in $\hat{K}$.

THEOREM 3. *If Γ is a closed Jordan curve in $\hat{K}$, then $\hat{K} - \Gamma$ is not connected.*

(c) On the Concept of Simple-connectivity. We have had occasion to discuss various properties of regions that are equivalent to the property of homotopic simple-connectivity. From our preceding work we know that the homotopic simple-connectivity of a region $\subset \hat{K}$ implies that the region has the property (l) and that we have the chain of implications

$$(\mathrm{l}) \to (\mathrm{s}) \to (\mathrm{s}_1)\,.$$

By the Riemann mapping theorem (formulation of § 12, Chap. 2) we see that to say that a region $\Omega \subset \hat{K}$ is homotopically simply connected is equivalent to saying that it enjoys the property (l) [respectively, the property (s), the property (s_1)] as well as to saying that Ω is conformally equivalent to one of the following: $\hat{K}$, K, $\Delta(0;1)$.

We may introduce other equivalent properties. Thus we shall say that Ω has the *property* (h) provided that each harmonic function on Ω is the real part of an analytic function on Ω. That this property is equivalent to homotopic simple-connectivity is easily verified. The details are left to the reader. In the proof it is convenient to observe that (h) $\to$ (l).

Also, we see immediately that for $\Omega \subset K$ each of the properties considered thus far is equivalent to the property of holomorphic simple-connectivity.

We now want to consider two other notions that are important in the present connection. The first pertains to the manner in which a region is imbedded in $\hat{K}$. The second brings to the fore a function-theoretic property.

(k): A region $\Omega \subset \hat{K}$ will be said to have the *property* (k) provided that $\hat{K} - \Omega$ is connected (possibly empty).

(r): A region $\Omega \subset K$ will be said to have the *property* (r) provided that for each function f analytic on Ω, there exists a sequence of polynomials tending to f uniformly in Ω ("r" for "Runge").

The first theorem we shall establish is

THEOREM 1. *A region $\Omega \subset \hat{K}$ has the property* (k) *if, and only if, it is homotopically simply connected.*

PROOF: We first consider a homotopically simply connected region Ω. It suffices to consider the case where $\hat{K} - \Omega$ contains more than one point. Here, if f is a Riemann mapping function for Ω, we see that fr $\Omega = \bigcap_{0<r<1} \overline{f\{r < |z| < 1\}}$. This implies that fr Ω is connected. Further, as is easy to verify, Ω is a component of $\hat{K}$ — fr Ω, and the union of fr Ω with any component of $\hat{K}$ — fr Ω is connected. Hence, $\hat{K} - \Omega$ is connected; that is, Ω has the property (k).

Suppose now that Ω is a region that has the property (k). Since the case where $\Omega = \hat{K}$ is immediate, it suffices to consider the case where $\Omega \subset K$; in fact, we may confine our attention to the case where Ω is a proper subset of K. We shall consider two approaches to the problem. They both yield the holomorphic simple-connectivity for reduced Ω. Therefrom, our earlier results lead to the homotopic simple-connectivity of Ω. The first approach, which will be based on the Jordan curve theorem for Jordan polygons, will be given only in outline. The interested reader will find it a useful undertaking to furnish a detailed account (see Carathéodory, *Theory of Functions*, vol. 1, pt. 3, Chap 1). The second approach, which we shall treat at length, is due to Saks and Zygmund (see their *Analytic Functions*, Chap. 4). It has the merit of being very simple as well as yielding a treatment of the (r) theorem.

The "Jordan" Approach. We start with the theorem:
If γ is a Jordan polygon $\subset K$, the frontier of each component of $\hat{K} - \gamma$ is precisely γ (proof by open-closed argument and elementary geometric facts), *and $\hat{K} - \gamma$ has precisely two components.*

To show the holomorphic simple-connectivity of Ω, it suffices to show that for each f analytic on Ω and each piecewise rectilinear path Γ in Ω with same initial and terminal point,

$$\int_\Gamma f(z)\, dz = 0 .$$

This in turn will be true if

$$\int_\gamma f(z)\, dz = 0 \tag{c.1}$$

for each sensed Jordan polygon γ lying in Ω. (Pedantically: "This will be true if

$$\int_\sigma f(z)\, dz = 0$$

for each sensed representative σ of the Jordan polygons in Ω.") Since $\hat{K} - \Omega$ is connected and contains ∞, the bounded component of $\hat{K} - \gamma$ lies in Ω.

We proceed inductively, basing the induction on the number of sides of n. If γ is a triangle, then the closure of the bounded component of $\hat{K} - \gamma$ is precisely the convex hull of the vertices of γ, and the Cauchy theorem for the triangle applies. We consider the proposition $P(n)$: If γ has at most $n \geqslant 3$

sides, then (c.1) holds, and we seek to show that $P(n)$ implies $P(n+1)$. To that end, it suffices to show that if γ has $n+1$ sides, there exists a segment σ lying in the bounded component of $\hat{K} - \gamma$ save for its endpoints, which are to lie on γ, and having the property that for each subarc $\gamma_k(k = 1,2)$ of γ having the same endpoints as σ, σ taken with γ_k yields a Jordan polygon of at most n sides. For then the left-hand side of (c.1) is representable as the sum of integrals of f taken over sensed Jordan polygons in Ω having at most n sides.

The existence of such a "diagonal" σ for a Jordan polygon γ of $n+1$ sides, $n \geqslant 3$, may be established as follows. The argument is that given by Kerékjártó (*Topologie*, Berlin, pp. 21-22).

Of the most "southern" vertices of γ, let V denote that vertex which is most "western." Let A and B denote, respectively, the vertex immediately preceding V and the vertex immediately succeeding V.

Suppose that the interior $\mathscr{I}$ of the triangle with vertices A, B, V does not contain points of γ. Then either the segment s with endpoints A and B contains no point of γ distinct from A and B, and in this case s is a diagonal σ; or else the segment s contains a vertex V' of γ distinct from A and B, and in this case the segment with endpoints V and V' is a diagonal σ.

There remains to be considered the case where the interior $\mathscr{I}$ of the triangle with vertices A, B, V contains a point of γ. In this case there is a vertex of γ in $\mathscr{I}$. We assert that *at least one vertex P of γ in $\mathscr{I}$ is such that the segment with endpoints V and P is a diagonal σ*. Suppose the contrary. Let P_1 denote a vertex of γ in $\mathscr{I}$ which has the property that the only vertices of γ on the segment VP_1 are V and P_1. There is a point of γ on VP_1 distinct from V and P_1, for otherwise VP_1 would be a diagonal σ. Let Q_1 denote that point of γ on VP_1 distinct from V and P_1 which is nearest V. The segment of γ that contains Q_1 has at least one endpoint in $\mathscr{I}$. Let P_2 be such an endpoint. We are led to the conclusion that there exists a sequence $((p_n,q_n))_1^\infty$ satisfying the following conditions: (1) $p_n,q_n \in \mathscr{I}$, $n = 1,2,\cdots$; (2) p_n is a vertex of γ, and q_n is that point of γ on the segment V_{P_n}, different from V and p_n, which is nearest V, $n = 1,2,\cdots$; (3) p_{n+1} is a vertex of the segment of γ that contains q_n, $n = 1,2,\cdots$; (4) p_{n+2} is contained in the interior of the triangle with vertices q_n, p_{n+1}, V, $n = 1,2,\cdots$; (5) $p_1 = P_1$, $q_1 = Q_1$, $p_2 = P_2$. The existence of such a sequence can readily be established recursively. It is also easy to see that there is only one such sequence $((p_n,q_n))_1^\infty$ meeting the imposed conditions. Now condition (4) implies that $p_m \neq p_n$ for $m \neq n$. This contradicts the fact that the set of vertices of γ is finite. The assertion follows.

The "Runge" Approach. We establish

THEOREM 2. *Let C be a proper closed subset of $\hat{K}$ that contains ∞. Let f be analytic in $\hat{K} - C$, let A denote a compact subset ($\neq \emptyset$) of $\hat{K} - C$, and let ε denote a positive number. Then there exists a rational function g whose poles lie in C, such that*

$$\max_{z \in A} |f(z) - g(z)| < \varepsilon . \qquad \text{(c.2)}$$

From the present Theorem 2 and Lemma 12.1, Chap. 4, we conclude that if Ω has the property (k), then for each closed rectifiable curve γ in Ω and each f analytic on Ω,

$$\int_\gamma f(z)\, dz = 0;$$

that is, Ω is holomorphically simply connected.

PROOF OF THEOREM 2: We fix a finite positive r satisfying $A \subset \Delta(0;r)$. Let j, k denote integers and n a nonnegative integer. Let $\sigma_n^{j,k}$ denote the square cell

$$\{2^{-n}j \leqslant \operatorname{Re} z \leqslant 2^{-n}(j+1);\ 2^{-n}k \leqslant \operatorname{Im} z \leqslant 2^{-n}(k+1)\}.$$

Let G_n denote the union of the $\sigma_n^{j,k}$ contained in $(\hat{K} - C) \cap \Delta(0;r)$ (to be denoted by D, for brevity). We note that $(\operatorname{int} G_n)_0^\infty$ is nondecreasing and that its limit is D. For n sufficiently large, $A \subset \operatorname{int} G_n$. It follows from the definition of G_n that

$$\operatorname{dist}\{\zeta, \operatorname{fr} D\} \leqslant 2^{1/2-n}, \qquad \zeta \in \operatorname{fr} G_n. \tag{c.3}$$

Now fr G_n is the union of those edges of the cells $\sigma_n^{j,k}$ ($\sigma_n^{j,k} \subset D$) which are contained in precisely one of the cells $\sigma_n^{j,k} \subset D$. For $z \in \operatorname{int} \sigma_n^{j_0,k_0} \subset D$, we have

$$2\pi i f(z)\, \delta(j,k) = \int_{\gamma_{j,k}} \frac{f(t)}{t - z}\, dt, \tag{c.4}$$

where $\gamma_{j,k}$ is the path obtained by circulating along fr $\sigma_n^{j,k}$ in the usual counter-clockwise sense and where $\delta(j,k) = 0$ for $(j,k) \neq (j_0,k_0)$ and $\delta(j_0,k_0) = 1$. Summing the terms of each side of (c.4) for (j,k) such that $\sigma_n^{j,k} \subset D$, we obtain

$$2\pi i f(z) = \sum \int_\varepsilon \frac{f(t)}{t - z}\, dt, \tag{c.5}$$

where ε is a sensed edge of fr $\sigma_n^{j,k}$ lying in fr G_n for some (j,k) satisfying $\sigma_n^{j,k} \subset D$. It follows by a continuity argument (also by comparing analytic functions agreeing on a set clustering at a point in the domain of each) that (c.5) holds for $z \in \operatorname{int} G_n$. This is fundamental. We now fix a positive integer m so that $A \subset \operatorname{int} G_m$ and

$$2^{1/2-m} < \frac{1}{2} \operatorname{dist}\{A, \operatorname{fr} G_m\}. \tag{c.6}$$

From (c.5) applied with $n = m$ to $z \in \operatorname{int} G_m$, we infer that f may be uniformly approximated on A by a rational function whose poles are all of the first order and lie on fr G_m. Now, given $t \in \operatorname{fr} G_m$, let $\tau \in \operatorname{fr} D$ satisfy

$$|t - \tau| \leqslant 2^{1/2-m}.$$

Then

$$\frac{1}{z - t} = \sum_{k=0}^{\infty} \frac{(t - \tau)^k}{(z - \tau)^{k+1}}, \qquad z \in A,$$

the convergence being uniform with respect to $z \in A$, as is easily seen with the aid of (c.6). Hence, f may be approximated uniformly on A by a rational function each of whose poles lies either on C or on $C(0;r)$. If $|t| = r$, $z \to (z - t)^{-1}$ may be approximated uniformly on A by a polynomial. Hence, Theorem 2 is readily concluded.

Let us now consider the property (r). Here we show

THEOREM 3. *A region $\Omega \subset K$ has the property* (r) *if, and only if, it has the property* (k).

PROOF: If Ω has the property (r), then given f analytic on Ω and γ a closed rectifiable curve in Ω, there exists a sequence of polynomials $(p_n)_1^{\infty}$ tending uniformly to f on γ. Hence,

$$\int_{\gamma} f(z)\, dz = \lim_{n\to\infty} \int_{\gamma} p_n(z)\, dz = 0 .$$

Hence, Ω is holomorphically simply connected and, consequently, has the property (k).

Suppose that Ω has the property (k). (This part of the theorem is just the Runge theorem on polynomial approximation.) Given A compact $(\neq \emptyset) \subset \Omega$, we let E denote the set of $t \in \hat{K} - \Omega$ for which $z \to (z - t)^{-1}$ admits uniform approximation on A by a polynomial. We shall show that E is both open and closed in the sense of the relative topology of $\hat{K} - \Omega$, and, hence, since $E \neq \emptyset$, we have $E = \hat{K} - \Omega$.

Given τ satisfying $\infty > |\tau| > \max \{|z| \mid z \in A\}$, then $z \to (z - \tau)^{-1}$ admits uniform approximation on A by a polynomial. Given t finite in E, then for τ satisfying $\tau \in \hat{K} - \Omega$ and $|\tau - t| < 2^{-1} \operatorname{dist} \{t,A\}$, we have

$$(z - \tau)^{-1} = \sum_{k=0}^{\infty} \frac{(\tau - t)^k}{(z - t)^{k+1}}, \qquad z \in A, \tag{c.7}$$

the convergence being uniform on A. It follows, since $t \in E$, that $\tau \in E$ also. Hence, E is *open* in the sense of the relative topology of E. To show that E is closed, let τ (finite) $\in \bar{E} \subset \hat{K} - \Omega$. There exists $t \in E$ satisfying $|t - \tau| < 2^{-1} \operatorname{dist} \{\tau,A\}$. Again (c.7) holds for $z \in A$, the convergence being uniform on A. We conclude that $\tau \in E$. Hence $E = \hat{K} - \Omega$.

Taking Theorem 2 of the present section into account, we see that if f is analytic on Ω, then f admits uniform approximation on A by a polynomial. Theorem 3 follows. It is to be remarked that we may conclude that Ω is holomorphically simply connected if Ω has the property (k) via the reasoning of the present theorem: (k) $\rightarrow$ (r) $\rightarrow$ holomorphic simple-connectivity. This is the procedure followed by Saks and Zygmund in their *Analytic Functions.*

(d) The Components of the Complement of a Closed Jordan Curve. The Jordan curve theorem may be supplemented in several important respects, as we shall now see. We first show

THEOREM 1. *Let γ denote a closed Jordan curve $\subset \hat{K}$. Then each component of $\hat{K} - \gamma$ is a simply connected region whose frontier is γ.*

PROOF: Let Ω denote a component of $\hat{K} - \gamma$. Then at least we are assured that fr $\Omega \subset \gamma$. Since $\hat{K} - \Omega$ is the union of γ with the components of $\hat{K} - \gamma$ distinct from Ω, we see that $\hat{K} - \Omega$ is connected and, hence, that Ω is (homotopically) simply connected. Further, fr Ω cannot reduce to a point. For if fr Ω did reduce to a point a, then $\Omega = \hat{K} - \{a\}$. This is impossible, since $\gamma \subset \hat{K} - \Omega$. At all events, fr Ω is connected. If it is a proper part of γ, it is a Jordan arc $\alpha \subset \gamma$. Suppose that this is the case. By considerations based on the possibility of solving the Dirichlet problem for Ω, we see that there exists a finite real-valued continuous function $\tilde{h}$ on $\overline{\Omega}$, harmonic in Ω, which has the property that the restriction of $\tilde{h}$ to α attains its minimum at a point $c \neq$ the endpoints a, b of α and at no other point of α, while it attains its maximum at a and b and nowhere else, and, finally, is univalent on the subarc with endpoints a, c and on the subarc with endpoints b, c. We paraphrase the proof of Theorem 3.1 of Chap. 6, with the present $\tilde{h}$ taking over the role of $\tilde{h}$ of that proof. The set A of the paraphrased proof must reduce to a point $\zeta \in C(0;1)$. The cluster set at ζ of the Riemann mapping function f must contain a and b and, hence, is α. But then it would not be the case that $\tilde{h} \circ f$ possesses the limit max $\tilde{h}$ at ζ. Contradiction. Theorem 1 follows.

We shall want to make use of a very important property of a univalent continuous map f of an open set O of $\hat{K}$ into $\hat{K}$. A map that carries open sets into open sets is called an *open* map. We shall show

THEOREM 2. *A univalent continuous map f of an open set $O \subset \hat{K}$ into $\hat{K}$ is an open map of O into $\hat{K}$.*

This assertion follows at once from

LEMMA 1. *Let f be a univalent continuous map of $\overline{\Delta(0;1)}$ into K. Then $f[\Delta(0;1)]$ is a component of $K - f[C(0;1)]$.*

PROOF: Let $\gamma(t) = f(e^{2\pi it})$, $t \in R$. Let Ω denote a component of $K - f[C(0;1)]$ for which $O(a;\gamma) \neq 0$ $a \in \Omega$. Then $\Omega \subset f[\Delta(0;1)]$. For if $a \in \Omega$ satisfied $a \in K - f[\Delta(0;1)], f - a$ would have a continuous logarithm, and, consequently, $O(a;\gamma)$ would vanish. On the other hand, since $f[\Delta(0;1)]$ is connected and is contained in $K - f[C(0;1)]$, $\Omega = f[\Delta(0;1)]$. We see concomitantly that there is precisely one component Ω of $K - f[C(0;1)]$ such that $O(a;\gamma) \neq 0$, $a \in \Omega$.

We are now in a position to show that the complement of a Jordan curve has precisely two components. This result and more are contained in

THEOREM 3. *Let Γ denote a closed Jordan curve in $\hat{K}$. There exists a homeomorphism of $\hat{K}$ onto itself that maps $C(0;1)$ onto Γ.*

PROOF: Let Ω_1 and Ω_2 denote distinct components of $\hat{K} - \Gamma$. Each is a simply connected Jordan region whose frontier is Γ. By the Osgood-Taylor-Carathéodory theorem, there exists a univalent continuous map φ_1 of $\overline{\Delta(0;1)}$ onto $\bar{\Omega}_1$ that maps $C(0;1)$ onto Γ, and there exists a univalent continuous map φ_2 of $\overline{\Delta(\infty;1)}$ onto $\bar{\Omega}_2$ that maps $C(0;1)$ onto Γ. Now let ψ denote the univalent continuous map of $C(0;1)$ onto itself that satisfies $\varphi_2(z) = \varphi_1(\psi(z))$, $|z| = 1$. Let φ be defined by

$$\begin{cases} \varphi(0) = \varphi_1(0) , \\ \varphi(z) = \varphi_1\left[|z|\psi\left(\frac{z}{|z|}\right)\right] \quad \text{for } 0 < |z| \leqslant 1 , \\ \varphi(z) = \varphi_2(z) \quad \text{for } 1 < |z| \leqslant +\infty . \end{cases} \tag{d.1}$$

Now φ is a univalent continuous map of $\hat{K}$ into itself. Since $\hat{K}$ is compact, $\varphi(\hat{K})$ is compact. By our present Theorem 2, $\varphi(\hat{K})$ is open. Hence, since $\hat{K}$ is connected, $\varphi(\hat{K}) = \hat{K}$. The theorem is established. Since $\Omega_1 \cup \Omega_2 = \hat{K} - \Gamma$, we see that $\hat{K} - \Gamma$ has precisely two components.

(e) The Complement of a Jordan Arc. Among the classical theorems associated with the Jordan curve theorem is the theorem that asserts that a *Jordan arc does not separate the plane*, a result now rapidly established. We treat the reduced case where the endpoints of the arc are 0 and ∞, as we may without loss of generality.

Let α denote a continuous univalent map of $\{0 \leqslant t \leqslant 1\}$ into $\hat{K}$ satisfying $\alpha(0) = 0$, $\alpha(1) = \infty$. We wish to show that ω, the complement of the image set of $\{0 \leqslant t \leqslant 1\}$ with respect to α, is connected. Let β_1 denote a continuous map of $\{0 \leqslant t \leqslant 1\}$ into $\hat{K}$ satisfying $\alpha = \beta_1^2$, and let $\beta_2 = -\beta_1$. Let Γ denote the union of the images of $\{0 \leqslant t \leqslant 1\}$ with respect to β_1 and β_2. Clearly, Γ is a closed Jordan curve. Let Ω_1 and Ω_2 denote the two components of $\hat{K} - \Gamma$, and let S_k denote the restriction of $z \to z^2$ to Ω_k ($k = 1,2$). We see that S_k is a boundary-preserving map of Ω_k onto a component ω_k of ω. Further, ω_k is simply connected [for it has the property (k)], and $0 \notin \omega_k$. Hence, the identity map of ω_k has an analytic square root, say s_k. Now $s_k \circ S_k(z) = z$, for all $z \in \Omega_k$, or $s_k \circ S_k(z) = -z$, for all $z \in \Omega_k$. Hence, S_k is univalent. It follows that $S_1(\Omega_1) = S_2(\Omega_2) = \omega$. Hence, ω is connected. There exists a Jordan arc γ with endpoints 0, ∞ which lies in Ω_1, save for its endpoints, and which avoids a given point of Ω_1. The union C of $S_1(\gamma)$ and the image of $\{0 \leqslant t \leqslant 1\}$ with respect to α is a *closed Jordan curve*. By suitable choice of γ we are assured that C omits a given point of ω. Thus we see that a Jordan arc may be imbedded in a closed Jordan curve that omits a given point of the plane not on the arc.

Notes

[1] To be exact, it should be noted that Littlewood considers f that are given by power series expansions with radius of convergence > 1, the domain of f being taken as $\overline{\Delta(0; 1)}$, $f(0) = 0$, $\max_{|z|=\frac{1}{2}} |f(z)| = 1$; further $k(f)$ is in terms of his formulation the maximum r such that $C(0; r) \subset f[\overline{\Delta(0; 1)}]$. The infimum of the set of these $k(f)$ is precisely κ. A corresponding gloss is to be made for the second sentence of the Remark.

[2] The theorem of the second paragraph, Ex. 10.

Index